Optics Made Clear

The nature of light and how we use it

Optics Made Clear

The nature of light and how we use it

William L. Wolfe

SPIE PRESS

Bellingham, Washington USA

Library of Congress Cataloging-in-Publication Data

Wolfe, William L.
  Optics made clear : the nature of light and how we use it / William L. Wolfe.
    p. cm. -- (Press monograph)
  Includes bibliographical references.
  ISBN 0-8194-6307-8
  1. Optics--Popular works. 2. Light--Popular works. I. Title.

QC358.5.W65 2006
535--dc22

                                                                2006023057

Published by

SPIE—The International Society for Optical Engineering
P.O. Box 10
Bellingham, Washington 98227-0010 USA
Phone: +1 360 676 3290
Fax: +1 360 647 1445
Email: spie@spie.org
Web: http://spie.org

The International Society
for Optical Engineering

To my grandchildren:

Grego and Melissa Moore and Garrett, Elise, Erin and Colleen Wolfe. May they have as much pleasure and satisfaction in their careers as I have had in mine.

Contents

Preface

I have spent fifty years of my professional life up to my eyeballs in optics. It has been de**light**ful. It has been en**light**ening. It has **bright**ened my life. The phenomena are interesting, important, varied, and often beautiful. The evidence of natural occurrences and examples of optical instruments and gadgets are plentiful. So it has been fascinating to learn about how things around us work and develop some of the many things that improve our lives and understanding. I recall one church service in which one of my artistic friends gave thanks for the beauty of the morning's rainbow. I silently added, "and for understanding how it occurs." This book is my attempt to describe many of these natural phenomena and devices in terms that everyone can understand. I want to share the fun and wonder and beauty and insights. You, too, will know how the rainbow is formed, and your appreciation for natural wonders and human creations should improve greatly.

Have you wondered why the sky is blue? Why the sunset is red? How hummingbirds show us their many colors? Why the road ahead sometimes seems to have water on it when it does not? Is global warming real? Is it a natural cycle or do we cause it? I have attempted to describe these and other natural phenomena in a simple, understandable way, devoid of the "language of the trade."

We now use optics to assemble automobiles and airplanes with incredible precision. We flush toilets automatically using optical beams. We turn on garage lights, open doors, spot speeders, provide night vision for cars, improve agriculture, inspect meats and orange groves, analyze distant planets and galaxies, all with light. Optical instruments are used to an incredible degree in medicine. We now have much-improved endoscopes that probe our intestines and other interior parts. We even have one that is a pill. We can perform surgery at great distances from the patient, and do the same with diagnoses using telemedicine. Dentists can find tooth decay and operate with optics. This is truly painless dentistry. We can make injections without injecting. I have collected a host of such applications and gadgets that appear in our daily life, be it in medicine, communications, aerospace, manufacturing, or agriculture, and explained them in a way everyone should be able to understand.

Have you wondered how telescopes give a magnified image of distant objects? How do microscopes provide a magnified image of close objects? How do spectroscopes, eyeglasses, cameras, binoculars, and similar instruments work? How do the simple rear-view mirrors in cars dim and provide wide fields of view? Explanations of these are included.

An added delight in the study of optics is that the field has been right in the thick of it for most of the major advances in physics, astronomy, and our understanding of the world around us. Galileo, with his telescope, proved that the Earth went around the sun rather than the other way around, and he was declared a heretic for that. Max Planck's study of optical radiation created the origin of quantum mechanics. The study of the detection and emission of light from a phototube led Einstein to the concept of the photon. Spectroscopy was essential for Bohr and others to uncover the structure of the atom. The theory of relativity has as one of its cornerstones the tenet that nothing travels faster than light. Recent experiments by John Mather measured the temperature of the celestial background with optics, and thereby helped to verify the Big Bang theory of the origin of the universe. Numerous other experiments have pinned down its age—at least to within a few billion years. Light is important in the many instruments we use in daily life, in nature around us, and in much of the development of physics.

For this book, it has been my attempt to keep the math to an absolute minimum. In each section, I have started with the simplest of concepts and gradually increased the degree of difficulty. For instance, in the section on telescopes, the simplest of two-mirror telescopes, invented by Isaac Newton, are first described. Gradually the descriptions cover more complicated designs, including the Palomar telescope, ending with the complicated Webb telescope that has a thinned, adaptive mirror and will be placed in space at a Lagrange orbital point (a stable location in space). The section on mirrors starts with a simple plane mirror and ends with the most complicated of adaptive, liquid and light-weighted, aspherical examples. The section on cameras starts with a pinhole camera and ends with the new digital varieties.

This book is divided into five major sections. The first is a description of the basic phenomena of optics; the second includes basic optical components and instruments; the third is all about natural optical phenomena; and the fourth part is a collection of applications. The fifth contains descriptions of the above-mentioned great steps in our understanding of the world around us that are directly related to optics.

The phenomena of optics, as described in the first chapter, can be listed broadly as the emission and absorption of light, polarization, refraction, reflection, interference, diffraction, and scatter. But of course a major question is, "What is light?" That subject is the last one in the first chapter, but unfortunately the answer is not straightforward. The bottom line is that we really do not **know** what light is. We can describe everything it does, and we can say many things that it is like, but we still cannot say what it is. That should not deter the reading of this book. The descriptions here apply to all the gadgets and phenomena. We do not need to know what light is, just how it behaves.

The applications, the use of optics in gadgets in our everyday world, have been taken mostly from several "throw-away" magazines that describe advances and use of optics, but are not very technical nor instructive. I appreciate the fact that the publishers have given me permission to include many photographs from the articles. I have tried very hard to give complete credit for each of them. This also allows the reader to contact any of them for further information. Complete addresses are given for these publications in Appendix B. I have also listed some of the more technical books in Appendix B for those who choose to pursue much more detailed descriptions of the basic principles and the instruments than I give here. Appendix A contains some information about numbers and sizes that may be useful in understanding both the astronomical and the microscopic sizes in optics. You need to have a sense of the sizes of nanometers (billionth of a meter) and light years (a distance of almost 6 trillion miles; it is the distance that light goes in a year).

There are several ways to read this book. Of course, you can go straight through from the front cover to the back, but this is not a novel (although in one sense, it is a mystery). I do not recommend that approach. You can choose a subject, like mirrors, and start at the front, reading further to get more complex information. In this mode it may be necessary to page back to the earlier chapters to refer to a concept that is used in the descriptions about mirrors. You can also choose any of the applications and approach it the same way. Another approach is to read through the basic chapters and then pick and choose the applications of interest.

An interesting pamphlet on optics has been published by the National Research Council. It covers many of these applications and discusses the role of optics in our lives in only 28 pages.[1]

Whatever your reason for getting this book, I hope you find it enjoyable, en-**light**ening, and just plain fun. As you read what I have written, I hope you get the message that I continue to enjoy this subject, and that I feel blessed for having had the opportunity to study the subject and get paid for it!

I would like to acknowledge the assistance of several people. The first is the technical reviewer Nancy Swanson who kept me honest and straight. The second is Merry Schnell, the happy, speedy, and very competent project editor. Then too, Sharon Streams the person who read it as a lay person. Finally, my wife (of more than 50 years), who every once in a while asked what I was typing now. She was very supportive—and even critical!

---

1   National Research Council, *Harnessing Light, Optical Science and Engineering for the 21ˢᵗ Century*, National Academy Press, 1998.

Chapter 1

The Basics

In this chapter, the nature of light is described, as are the main characteristics of light observed and used in various applications. These include refraction and reflection, diffraction, interference, scattering, and the interaction of light with matter—emission and absorption.

Light is described in terms of waves, rays, and photons. Each is a model of light, and each has its advantages and limitations.

Waves

Light travels in waves. Several examples of waves are those in the ocean and the ripples on a quiet pond when a trout rises, as shown in Fig. 1. The ripples (waves) start as the nose of the trout breaks water, probably to snare a fly. Then, they spread outward as a pattern of highs and lows in the water. We can represent these ripples approximately by a series of circles, as shown in Fig. 2. Each solid line

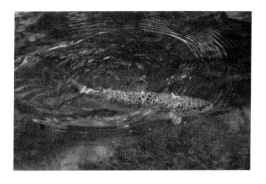

Figure 1 Trout waves.[1]

represents a maximum in the circular wave. Each dashed line represents a minimum. We have to imagine the slopes in between. If we take a cut through these circular waves, the profile, shown in Fig. 3, looks like a series of maxima and minima. One can generate waves by tying a rope to a tree or other solid object and holding the other end. The waves are generated by moving your hand up and down fairly rapidly, or by moving it side to side. The frequency of the wave is a measure of the

---

1   Marinaro, V., *In the Ring of the Rise*, Nick Lyons Books, 1976. (Image courtesy of Random House/Crown Publishing, copyright 1976.)

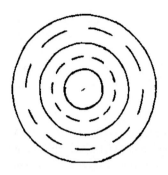

Figure 2 Representation of circular waves.

rapidity with which you move your hand. The wavelength is a measure of the distance between the peaks in the wave. The direction of the wave, often called the *polarization*, is determined by whether you move your hand vertically or horizontally, or in some other direction. It could be at any angle or even in a circular or elliptical motion.

The profile of an idealized wave is shown in Fig. 3. This is a wave of five cycles. A *cycle* is the distance from one part of the wave to the next identical part; for instance, from one peak to the next peak, or one trough to the next trough. This is also called a *period*.

The *frequency* is the number of cycles per second, the unit for which is hertz, named after the famous physicist Heinrich Hertz. The *amplitude* is the height of the wave above zero. Figure 4 shows two waves, one of which has twice the frequency of the other, shown as the weaker line.

Figure 5 shows two waves of the same frequency but with different amplitudes. The wave shown as the heavy line has twice the amplitude of the other. The amplitude is one-half the peak-to-peak value.

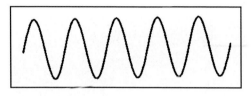

Figure 3 Wave Profile.

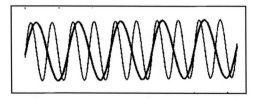

Figure 4 Frequencies.

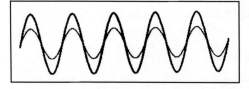

Figure 5 Amplitudes.

Another characteristic of a wave is its *phase*. Phase refers to a particular position in the period of the wave. It could be a point right at the beginning (zero phase), halfway through (half phase), or any other position that can be described as a fraction or a percentage of full phase. Two waves can start in phase if their starting points are the same, or they can be out of phase by some amount if they start at different times or in different places.

Light is called an *electromagnetic wave*, and is part of a continuum of such waves, which are generated by the periodic motion of a charge, much like the motion with the rope. Some other waves with which you may be familiar are radio and television waves that provide us information and entertainment. In both cases, as electrons oscillate in the antenna of the transmitter, they set up electric fields that cause electrons to oscillate in the receivers at our houses. They have the same sort of oscillations and therefore represent the signals we receive.

The electromagnetic spectrum runs from the very high frequency (VHF) gamma and x rays through ultraviolet, blue, orange, and red to infrared, millimeter waves, microwaves, television, radio, very low frequency (VLF), and ultra low frequency (ULF). Figure 6 shows how these all are arranged by frequency; Fig. 7 by wavelength. AM radio ranges from about 600 kilocycles per second (kilohertz or kHz) to 1600 kHz. FM radio is at higher frequency, from about 90 to 110 megahertz (MHz), which is about 150 times higher in frequency and shorter in wavelength. AM radio is relatively unaffected by hills and mountains, while they can block FM radio waves. The AM waves are much larger, about 1000 feet long. The longest waves used for communications are the VLF or very low frequency waves. They are used by submarines, which trail wire antennas on the surface for secure communications. Figures 6 and 7 show the regions

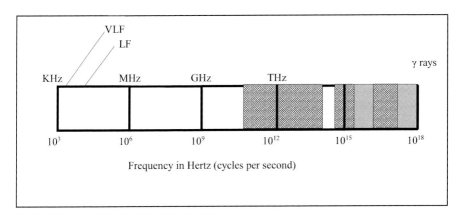

Figure 6 The electromagnetic spectrum on a frequency scale.

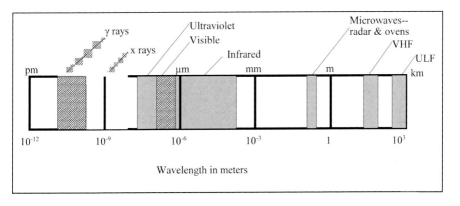

Figure 7 The electromagnetic spectrum on a wavelength scale.

approximately to give an idea of the entire range of the electromagnetic spectrum. I have intentionally given frequencies in several different ways.

Coherence

Laser light is coherent, and the coherence is especially important in communication by light waves. The word *coherence* means "go together," just as *cooperate* means "operate together." It means that the waves continue to travel together. The two waves with the same frequency shown in Fig. 5 (the amplitude example), go together. The peaks of both occur at the same place and so do the troughs and the zeroes. The only difference is the height.

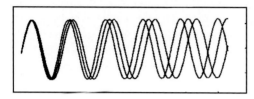

Figure 8 Incoherence from different frequencies.

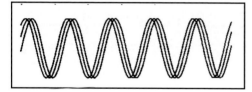

Figure 9 Incoherence from different timing.

There are two ways in which two or more waves do not go together, that is, are not coherent. One is if the waves start at different times, and the other is if they are of different frequencies. Figure 8 shows how the waves gradually get out of synchrony if they start at the same time, but are of slightly different frequencies. Notice that they start in synch, but in about five cycles the maximum of one is about where the minimum of the other occurs. They are out of synch. So one requirement for light to be coherent is that it must be essentially monochromatic (the same color) and the same frequency. The distance over which they are still in reasonably good synchronization is called the coherence length. If the waves are monochromatic but do not all have the same time of generation, their combination will not be coherent. Figure 9 shows how this is with a few waves. As more and more waves are added, starting at different times, there will be peaks at all points and troughs at all points, and the concept of a monochromatic wave is completely blurred. The waves do not become increasingly out of phase as they go to the right as do the waves that consist of several frequencies; they are incoherent from the beginning.

Rays

Rays are straight lines that represent the direction of waves. They are a simpler model than either waves or particles. Figure 10 shows that rays are just lines perpendicular to a wavefront. The wavefront, naturally enough, is just the front of the expanding wave. It is so much easier to design lenses and mirrors and other instruments using straight rays rather than invoking all the characteristics of either waves or photons. When these circular waves expand enough, the wavefronts become straight lines. In three dimensions, the spherical wavefronts become planes. Spherical waves are related to object and image points at finite distances. Plane waves relate to infinite objects and images.

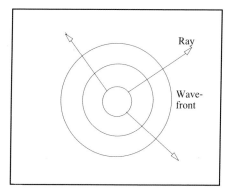

Figure 10 Waves and rays.

Beams

Perhaps the most intuitive description of light propagation is in terms of beams. Turn a flashlight on and a beam of light emanates from it. This is a *divergent beam*, as shown in Fig. 11. The farther it goes, the wider it gets. If you look at it from the other end, it is a *convergent beam*. In a convergent beam the light converges to the point of the cone it makes. Lenses usually generate convergent beams. Divergent beams of light radiate from a point. These are also called pencils of light, in analogy to the point of a wooden pencil. The third type of beam is *collimated*, one that neither diverges nor converges but has the same diameter throughout its entire length. One can never attain a truly collimated beam, but it is a useful approximation and fiction.

These beams can be thought of as consisting of many rays. In particular, the marginal rays would be the outside lines that bound the beams. Ray optics is most useful in the design of lenses, mirrors, prisms, and other such optical components.

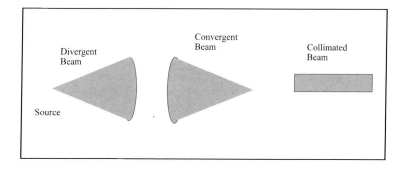

Figure 11 Beams.

Photons

Photons may be regarded as small bundles, clumps, or particles of light. The existence of photons started with the work of Max Planck, who explained the spectrum of blackbody (idealized) radiation by assuming the energy in the material was quantized. There was not a continuum of different energies, but there were jumps. In today's world we would say *digitized*. Planck refused to believe that the light was quantized, that it came in specific, separate clumps of energy. It was Albert Einstein who determined this by his explanation of the photoelectric effect. By the way, it was for this, not his monumental work on relativity, that he was awarded the Nobel Prize.

Duality

So light is described either as a wave motion or as a conglomeration of particles. Light has both properties. Remarkably, so do other particles. Electrons have wavelike properties. In fact, everything has both particulate and wavelike properties. The bigger the particle, the less wavelike it is. That is why we do not think of a baseball as a wave (although some poor hitters may). Some of the ways in which light reacts with matter are best described in terms of photons, and some should be described in terms of waves.

The Conundrum

A number of experiments have been carried out to learn just what a photon really is. One of these uses two slits. Light is shined on the slits, and the pattern behind them is observed. Classically, assuming that light is a wave motion, the pattern should be sinusoidal (like the waves in the illustrations above). The photon explanation then is that the photons follow a probability that sends them into a pattern that is the same as that predicted by the wave theory.

But then the conceptualizing gets more and more difficult. Shine one photon on the double slit. It must go through one slit and not the other. Now shine another after a considerable time has elapsed. It has to go through one of the two slits. The remarkable thing about this is that after many photons have been sent, with considerable time between them, the pattern will be the same!

When a photon goes through one slit, how does it "know" the other one is there? We do not know. But we do know that a photon is not a small clump of localized energy; it is spread out. If we know that a photon is of a particular wavelength, then by the uncertainty principle, we do not know at all where it is.

If this sounds a little weird and a little too complicated for my promised simple explanations, I apologize, but I wanted to make the point that there is great uncertainty in knowing exactly what light is. A fascinating publication[2] at a very ad-

---

2   Roychoudhuri, C., and R. Roy, "The nature of light: what is a photon," *OPN Trends*, OSA, 3, October 2003.

vanced level addressed this question. Several of today's foremost theoretical optical physicists addressed the question: "What is a photon?" I will not give you their full answers, but I will give some snippets that capsulize their answers.

"We will probably never be able to visualize a photon, but we may soon be able to choreograph one; to describe the process rather than the object." This was stated by David Finkelstein of Georgia Tech.

"The particulate nature of the photon is evident in its tendency to be absorbed and emitted by matter in discrete units leading to quantization of light energy." That was expressed by my friend Marlon Scully and his colleagues at the University of Texas (he is now at Princeton University).

In sum, all of these authors describe how the photon behaves as both a wave and a particle, but no one can say what it is.

My favorite description, coming from long-time colleague Stan Ballard, is to think of it as a corrugated hot dog. It has the localization and particality of a hot dog, but it has the wavelike nature of the corrugations. In a letter to the editor following the above-mentioned articles, R. C. Millikan, University of California, Santa Barbara, describes the photon as "a quantum harmonic oscillator with a twist," and even gives his "speculative but serious" picture, as shown in Fig. 12. The photon is traveling in the direction of the arrow and "vibrates up and down and side to side in a spiral sort of motion. It is somewhat localized, but it also has wave properties."

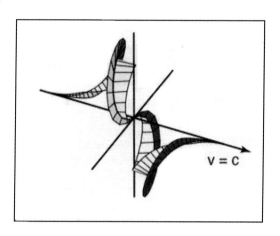

Figure 12 The Photon?[3]

The Practical Solution

Although it is fascinating to read the treatments of these theoreticians in terms of quantum electrodynamics, we do not need to understand it to understand how optical gadgets and optical phenomena work. For understanding almost all instruments, rays are sufficient. For most of the natural phenomena and many instruments, waves provide enough information to understand the interference, diffraction, and scattering effects. Finally, for some of the emission and detection instruments and applications, the particle model is satisfactory.

---

3   Millikan, R. C., *Optics and Photonics News*, November 2003. (Image courtesy of OSA, copyright 2003.)

Refraction and Reflection

Understanding refraction requires an understanding of the speed of light in air and in various other materials. The speed of light has been measured with increasing accuracy over hundreds of years. The earliest measurements were made with people on mountains using various shutters on lights. Light travels so fast that these measurements were doomed to failure; they ended up measuring the response times of the experimenters! Modern measurements have determined this speed with considerable accuracy. In fact, the value is quoted as 299,792,458 meters per second, stated with nine significant figures.

The Speed of Light

Light is the fastest thing in the world. Part of the famous law of relativity, authored by Albert Einstein, is the fact that nothing travels faster than light. In a vacuum it travels at approximately 186,000 miles per second. In metric measure, that is almost 300,000,000 meters (m) per second. In a medium like water, glass, or even air, it travels at a slower rate. It is only a little slower in air, about 0.01%, but it is about 30% slower in water and 50% slower in glass. The ratio of the speed of light in a vacuum to that in a medium is called the *refractive index*. The refractive indices of water and glass, respectively, are about 1.3 and 1.5.

Reflection, Refraction, and Transmission

When light is incident upon a surface, like that shown in Fig. 13, part of it is reflected, part is refracted into the material, where often some is absorbed, and finally it emerges from the other side. The ratio of the amount of light that is reflected to that which is incident is called the *reflectance* or the *reflectivity*. The ratio of that which is transmitted all the way through to the incident amount is the *transmittance* or *transmissivity*. The ratio of that absorbed is called the *absorptivity* or *absorptance*.

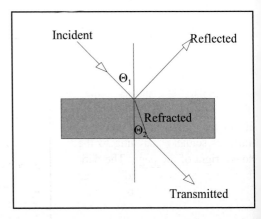

Figure 13 Reflected and refracted rays.

Refraction

Generally, we think of the refractive index of transparent materials like glass, water, and air. It is usually true that the denser (mass per unit volume) a material is, the slower the speed of light in it and the higher the refractive index. It seems reasonable that the speed is lower in a denser material; this is consistent with our observation about other things like running in air and running in water, although the reasons may be different.

As a result of the fact that light travels slower in a medium like glass, it *refracts* or bends. That is, if it is incident on a surface at an angle, the direction the light travels is changed. The change in direction can be calculated by the law of refraction that is usually attributed to Willebrord Snell in Holland in 1621. It states that the angle of refraction is related to the angle of incidence by the product of their sines and the refractive indices.

One reasonable way to understand this refraction is by considering the incidence of plane waves upon a medium of higher density. Figure 14 shows a wavefront first at position A, then at B, then CDE, a little after it first strikes the denser medium. The part of the wavefront in the medium goes slower than the other part because the refractive index is higher (light travels more slowly in a denser medium). It continues this way into wavefront FGH and eventually gets all the way into the medium and then out, where it emerges parallel to its entry direction. An interesting analogy is to assume that the waves represent lines of soldiers marching to the lower right of the page. The dark bar is water. As each soldier enters the water he moves more slowly because it is harder to move through water.

When light travels from a dense medium to a rare one, that is, from a medium of higher index to one of lower index, there are limits on the angles. If the an-

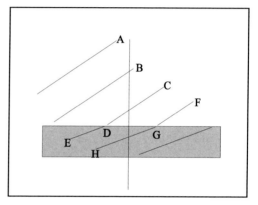

Figure 14 Refraction of waves.

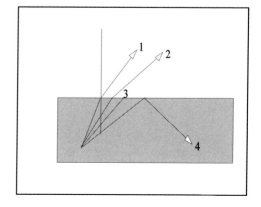

Figure 15 Total internal reflection.

gle of incidence is too large, the light is completely reflected back into the medium of higher index. This is called *total internal reflection*. It can be observed in two simple ways. One is to submerge yourself in a pool and look up and out at increasing angles of incidence. At a sufficiently large angle, the surface of the pool will look silvery, like a mirror.

The angle at which this happens is called the *critical angle*. For water and air, the angle is approximately 37 degrees. In Fig. 15, rays 1 and 2 are refracted as described above; they bend away from the perpendicular to the surface. Ray 3 is at exactly the angle of total internal reflection and travels along the surface. Ray 4 is reflected back into the material. This total internal reflection is an important aspect of fiber optics.

Reflection, Transmission, and Absorption

Light that is reflected from the front surface is not bent, as it is in refraction, but it does change direction. The angle of reflection is equal to the angle of incidence with respect to a perpendicular surface, called the *surface normal*. It is interesting that, for this plane parallel plate, the light that is refracted into the material and reflects off the back face is reflected in the same direction as the initial reflected ray, as shown in Fig. 16. It bends as it is refracted in, and it bends an equal but opposite direction as it exits the front surface. The transmitted ray is deviated in the material, but

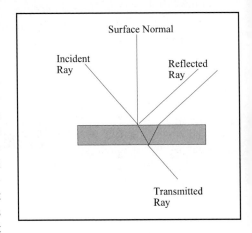

Figure 16 Reflection.

exits parallel to and in the same plane as the incident beam. The light that is absorbed is transformed into heat or some other form of energy. The reflected ray is in the same plane as the incident ray, and the angle of reflection is equal to the angle of incidence. This is *specular transmission and reflection*. If the material has a rough surface, the light gets scattered in both the forward and the backward directions.

It is possible to calculate the reflection of both transparent and opaque materials. Glass, for example, reflects about 4% of the light incident upon it, while metals like aluminum reflect approximately 90%.

Interference

When waves combine, they can interfere with each other. These interference patterns take on many shapes, depending upon the nature of the waves and the geometry of their overlap. For instance, if two waves of the same frequency overlap in line and in phase, the pattern will be essentially the same, but with higher crests, as

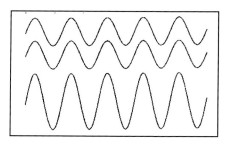

Figure 17 Constructive interference.

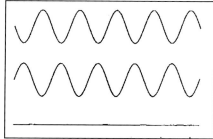

Figure 18 Destructive interference.

shown in Fig. 17. The two waves are shown on top; the combination is below them. This is called *constructive interference.*

If the same two waves are offset by one half cycle, the crests of one will fall on the troughs of the other, and they will interfere. The figure shows interference with two identical waves offset by one half cycle, exactly out of phase, in the same order. The result is nullification of the two waves. This is called *destructive interference* (Fig. 18).

Waves of different frequencies can also interfere. Figure 19 shows an example. Sometimes an effect like this is called *modulation.* The high-frequency wave carries the low-frequency wave, as a radio signal carries the waves that represent the music. It should not be hard to imagine all sorts of other interference patterns generated by waves of different frequencies and amplitudes, and combined in different phases.

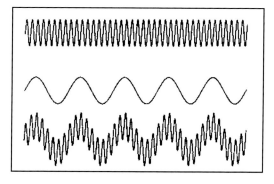

Figure 19 Modulation.

Diffraction

When a light wave impinges upon an obstacle, it is diffracted. The nature of the wave changes. The obstacle may be something like a shield that blocks a part of the wave, or it can be an aperture, an opening that limits the lateral extent of the wave. These ideas can be made more concrete by assuming a plane wave of light that travels from left to right and encounters an opening like the aperture of a camera. This is shown diagrammatically in Fig. 20. By a principle enunciated by Christian Huygens, the wavefront is divided into a series of *daughter waves* that emanate from all the points in the aperture. (The gender is unimportant; perhaps he had a

slew of daughters.) It can be seen
by this construction that at some
distance from the aperture, the
wave is again essentially plane, but
at its edges, it is curved. As the
waves travel further from the aperture, the central portion remains
flat, but the waves expand further
to the sides as semispherical waves.

An analogous thing happens
when the obstacle is, for instance, a
circular disk. The central part of the
wave is now blocked, but the edges
are composed of the combined
daughter waves. This is shown in
Fig. 21. Notice that in the region
behind the obscuration there are no
waves, but to the side and further
along the daughter waves again exist. I have shown the waves at two
different times, as they expand behind the obstacle.

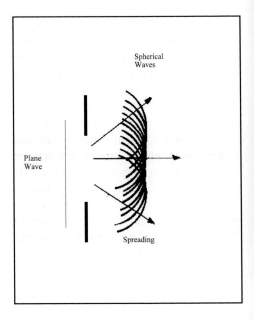

Figure 20 Diffraction.

The Doppler Effect

The speed of light is a constant in vacuum. It is
always the same value, about 2.9975×10^8 m per
second. It is also true that the frequency of light is
determined by the frequency of the vibration; it too
is a constant. So what happens when one observes
light coming from a moving object? If the object is
moving toward the observer, the apparent frequency
is increased, and it is decreased if the object is moving away. This is not easy to observe, since the shift
is small for all but extremely high velocities. The
relative shift in frequency is given by the ratio of the
velocity to the speed of light, v/c. For a Corvette do-

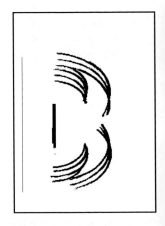

Figure 21 Obstacle diffraction.

ing its best in Montana, this is about 0.0000015%. For a commercial aircraft, it's
about 0.0000075%. For the most part, this is an astronomical phenomenon, the
so-called red shift that reveals how fast some stars are receding from us. It can be
used in some sophisticated laser systems in which such small changes can be measured.

Figure 22 shows how this works, although the reader needs to use a little imagination. A wave is shown, and it is assumed that it is traveling from left to right. A

person on the right traveling from right to left will experience the successive crests of the wave at a higher frequency than a person on the left, moving in the direction of the wave—or even standing still.

    The Doppler effect also occurs with sound waves. Almost everyone is familiar with the sound of a train approaching and then receding into the sunset. The whistle seems to be at a higher frequency as the train approaches, and turns to a deep bass as the train departs. The equivalents in optics would be a blue shift (higher frequency) upon approach and a red shift (lower frequency) in recession.

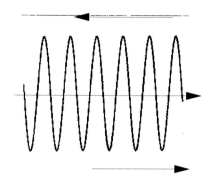

Figure 22 The Doppler effect.

Emission and Absorption

This section describes the processes of the emission and absorption of light that are closely related to the topics of lasers and detectors. It starts with the description of the Bohr atom, which can be visualized much more easily than the more modern quantum mechanical model. It is sufficiently accurate for the descriptions in this book. Real materials are gases that may consist of atoms or molecules, liquids and solids that may consist of a single material or may be compositions. The materials may be metals, insulators, or semiconductors. Each of these has a somewhat different mechanism of both emission and absorption.

    Emission and absorption are intimately related. It is almost always true that a particular mechanism for absorption can be reversed to create a similar emission.

Nature of the Atom

Physicists are still studying atoms, and there are about 100 of them. There have been a number of descriptions, that is, models of the atom. The most recent of these is the esoteric quantum-mechanical model involving statistics and wave functions. A simpler model, the Bohr model, is sufficient to describe the phenomena in this book. In it, the atom consists of a nucleus and surrounding electrons. The nucleus, which consists of protons, has a positive electrical charge; it is surrounded by electrons that circle in orbits at different distances from the nucleus. Hydrogen has one proton in the nucleus and one electron in the first orbit. Helium has two of each and both electrons are also in the first orbit. Because of a variety of rules, the next element has three electrons, but two orbit in the first orbit, and one in the second. The number of electrons in the outermost orbit determines the valence of the material (a

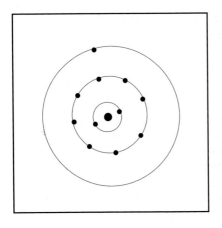

Figure 23 The Bohr atom.

measure of the way the atom will join with other atoms to create molecules). Nature has ruled that stable orbits are those with either two (in the innermost) or eight electrons in the outer orbit. Sodium has two electrons in the first orbit, a filled second orbit with eight, and one in the third, outermost orbit. It is therefore a potential electron donor, and is said to have a valence of +1. Chlorine has the same configuration in its first two orbits, but it has seven electrons in its outer orbit, one less than eight, so it has a valence of –1. It would like to join with an atom that has one electron in its outer orbit to make the stable configuration of eight.

Sodium would be a good choice. When such a union is consummated, the two atoms join to make a molecule, in this case sodium chloride—common salt. Similar unions occur between atoms that have two electrons and those with six electrons and so on.

The electrons in the outer orbits have more potential energy, by analogy with a rock that is farther off the ground than one that is closer to it. It takes energy to move electrons to outer orbits, while energy is released when electrons drop from an outer to a lower orbit. These are often described as *energy levels*. Figure 23 shows the correspondence between electron orbits and electron energy levels. The outer orbit, 3, has the highest energy, E_3. The bottom line is called the ground state, when the atom is stable.

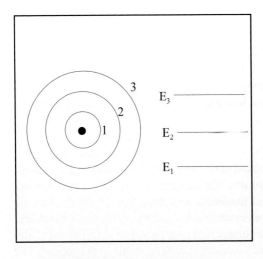

Figure 24 Orbits and energy levels.

One way for an electron to give up its energy when it falls from a higher to a lower energy level is for the atom to emit a photon of light of a specific wavelength or frequency. The relationship is that the energy difference between the two levels equals Planck's constant, h times the frequency of the light. Planck's constant is a small number, $h = 6.626 \times 10^{-34}$, so it takes very little energy to generate a visible photon. The frequency of a yellow photon is approximately 6×10^{14} cycles per second, so the energy required to generate such a photon is approximately 40×10^{-20} joules (J). It would take 10^{24} such photons to equal the caloric energy of one Big Mac!

A Crystal

A well-ordered crystal may be considered a collection of atoms or molecules in a regular pattern. The simplest is cubic. Common table salt, which has the chemical makeup of one sodium atom and one chlorine atom repeated millions of times, is such a cubic crystal. Figure 25 shows a typical cubic crystal, like salt. Of course, there are many, many sites for both the sodium, shown as black, and the chlorine, shown as white. Other crystal arrangements exist, but they need not be considered here. Each site is an atom, with both its nucleus and its surrounding electrons, as represented in the close-up in Fig. 26.

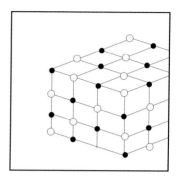

Figure 25 Cubic crystal.

An Insulator (Nonconductor)

Salt is a typical insulator; it does not conduct an electrical current (unless an enormous voltage is applied). The electron orbits are shown in Fig. 26, which represents a portion of the lattice with alternating sodium and chlorine atoms sharing the eight orbital electrons, and the electrons are bound to these sites in the crystal lattice. The only way in which these electrons can participate in current flow is if there is some (fairly large) external source of energy that lets them break

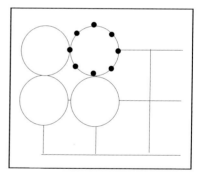

Figure 26 Close-up of crystal.

free from their home site, either sodium or chlorine. (This is called *ionic conductivity*, in which the sodium and chlorine ions move in the lattice to produce current).

A Metal (Conductor)

In a metal, not all the electrons are bound to the atomic or molecular sites; many are free to move in the crystal from site to site. Thus, when a voltage difference like that from the leads of a battery is applied, the electrons flow, making an electrical current. This can be visualized as the electrons moving from site to site through the metal in the direction of the applied voltage.

Semiconductors

A semiconductor is really an insulator in which the energy that binds the electrons to local sites is relatively small. In that case, small additions of energy can free them so that they can participate in electrical conduction, as with a metal. Such energy sources may be thermal agitation of the crystal or the absorption of a photon. Semiconductors are of tremendous importance in technology, partly because they can change their electrical characteristics when light shines upon them.

Energy States in Conductors, Insulators, and Semiconductors

When atoms come together, as they do in a salt crystal, the different individual electronic levels spread, because in such a system no two electrons may have the exact same set of levels (another one of those atomic selection rules). The energy-level diagram then looks something like that shown in Fig. 27. The top level is called the *conduction band*; the next one (down) is the *valence band*. The region between them is called the *forbidden energy gap*. Electrons are not allowed in this region. Electrons can go anywhere from either band to anywhere in the other band. In absorption, the electrons take on energy and go up; in emission, the opposite is true. Electrons in the lower bands stay put. The conduction band contains electrons that are free to move through the crystal lattice and participate in an electrical current.

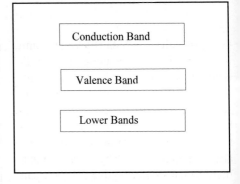

Figure 27 Bands in solids.

If the conduction band has electrons in its stable state, the material is a metal. The imposition of a small electrical voltage generates a current. If there are no electrons in the conduction band, the material is an insulator, a nonconductor. Only a large voltage difference produces an (ionic) current, moving ions. If the energy-band gap is small, then the provision of some energy to the crystal moves electrons from the valence band to the conduction band and provides the possibility of a current. This is a semiconductor; it is an insulator with a small forbidden energy gap.

PN Junctions

Silicon has a valence of four; there are four electrons in its outer orbit. A silicon crystal is a collection of the atoms, which share the outer four electrons to achieve the stable configuration of eight. This is the configuration of pure silicon, but some structures incorporate impurities (dopants) in the pure crystal. These dopants are elements that have either three or five electrons in their outer orbits. Thus, they are either positive (with three electrons) or negative impurities (with five). The impurities are introduced as part of the process of making transistors and chips, sometimes by introducing the dopant in its gaseous form. Then, the chip has both positive and negative regions, and the interface is called a *PN junction*, or *positive-negative junction*. When photons are absorbed at such a junction, a voltage difference is generated across the junction, and this is a way of controlling electronic processes in the crystals. Conversely, if a voltage is applied to the junction, photons may be emitted. These junctions are therefore the basis of some photodetectors and some light-emitting diodes (LEDs).

Gases

Gas molecules can both absorb and emit light. Imagine a molecule of carbon dioxide, CO_2 (Fig. 28). It has a straight-line structure of carbon-oxygen-carbon, somewhat like a bar bell with an extra bell. The molecules of carbon are oppositely charged from those of oxygen, and any vibration (caused by thermal agitation) is then an accelerating dipole (a pair of opposite charges). This gives rise to emission at a specific frequency, the frequency that is dictated by the masses of the atoms and the binding force. There is a similar an energy-level diagram that relates to the different motions—the two oxygen atoms moving in and out, the

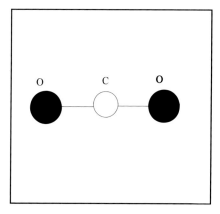

Figure 28 Carbon dioxide.

carbon moving left and right, etc. Other gases consisting of other molecules can have such vibrations and rotations. The combinations of different vibrations and rotations dictate the frequencies of light that are emitted or absorbed by these gases. Each and every gas has a spectral signature, a map of the amount of emission or absorption as a function of frequency. It has a one-to-one relationship with an energy-level diagram.

Liquids

Liquids behave much like gases, but in general the spectra are muddier. The mechanical motions of the molecules in gases may be vibrations, rotations, and combinations, but liquids have only vibrations. And the frequencies are influenced by the many neighboring molecules so that they have less-well-defined frequencies; they are muddier. But the principles are the same; there are vibrating dipoles.

Incandescence

The free electrons in the metal filament of a light bulb move back and forth as a result of the application of an electric current. The electricity gives its energy to the electrons. The electrons accelerate and give up their energy to the photons in the light stream. The spectrum of the light, its variation of intensity with wavelength, is a function of the temperature of the metal filament, and the temperature is a measure of the amount of motion.

Fluorescence

Sometimes when light is incident upon certain materials, the light is absorbed and the energy is transferred to the electrons. These electrons can then give up their energy to photons, but photons of a different wavelength. They rise to a high energy level, give up some of their energy to thermal processes, and then drop down to a lower state. Thus they take up photon energy of short wavelength and give back the energy in photons of lower energy (longer wavelengths). One interesting example of this is white shirts laundered in modern detergents. These detergents have luminescent dyes in them to enhance the whiteness. Try shining an ultraviolet light on them in the dark, and see them glow. The ultraviolet light is the short-wavelength activator, and the glow is white in the visible spectrum at longer wavelengths.

Phosphorescence

Similar to fluorescence, phosphors glow when they are struck by electrons. Just as there are different types of fluorescent materials (both in terms of excitation and radiation), there are phosphors that glow in different colors. The cathode-ray tubes of traditional televisions and computer monitors use such phosphors. They are struck by the electron beam, which is the cathode ray of the cathode-ray tube.

Luminescence

Very similar to both fluorescence and phophorescence, this form of light generation starts with electrical activation, causing electrons to rise to higher energies. Then, when they give up their energy and fall to lower levels, the material emits photons. It is like fluorescence, but with electrical activation. It is like phosphorescence but with internal electrical activation rather than activation from an electron beam.

Raman Effect

This effect, discovered by C. V. Raman, is similar to fluorescence. It is different, however, in that the incoming light must not be at an absorption band, and the emitted light is very weak. A photon is absorbed, giving its energy to an electron, which moves to a higher energy level. The electron then yields some energy to another form, perhaps heat. It then drops to a lower level, emitting a photon of less energy and longer wavelength. It can also yield photons of higher energy if energy is supplied. This is called *stimulated Raman emission*. This effect is of value in certain types of spectroscopy.

Scattering

Although somewhat similar to diffraction, scattering is generally considered to be the change in direction of light rays caused by particulates—particles in the air or water that range from smaller than the wavelength of light to many times larger. Scattering is responsible for the blue sky, red sunsets, and other observable phenomena in nature. Scattering also causes the diffuse look of materials like white paper and cloth.

When a wave of light impinges upon a particle, it is sent in a different direction. The direction is a function of the ratio of the wavelength of light to the diameter of the particle. In this discussion (and most optical texts) the particles are assumed to be spherical, but real ones are not. The differences in the results are usually not great. Figure 29 shows a lightwave approaching the particle from the left. If the wavelength is much larger than the particle, there is some scatter, as shown in the figure. That is, the direction is not altered very much.

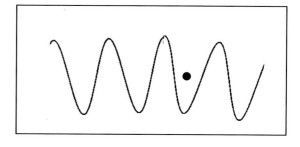

Figure 29 Scatter.

However, if the particle is closer to or smaller than the wavelength of the light, the light is redirected much more, as in Fig. 30. Thus, for a particle of a particular size, but smaller than the wavelength, blue light (which has a higher frequency) is scattered much more than red (which has a lower frequency), about 16 times as much.

When the particle is much larger than the wavelength of the light, the scatter is essentially just reflec-

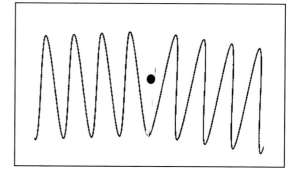

Figure 30 Scatter at a higher frequency.

tion. That is, all wavelengths of light are sent off in the same direction to the same degree.

There are two regimes of particulate scattering. If the particles are small compared to the wavelengths of light, the scattering is called Rayleigh, after the famous Lord Rayleigh, who contributed so much to wave theory. If the opposite is true, that is, if the wavelengths of light are small compared with the particles, the scattering is called Mie scattering after Gustav Mie, who developed the theory for this situation.

Although the two types of scattering arise from the same interactions, these two regions are generally distinguished by the two names. Rayleigh scattering is proportional to the inverse fourth power of the wavelength. This means, for instance, that blue light at about 0.4 micrometers (μm) is scattered 16 times more than red light at about 0.8 μm. The situation is much less dramatic for Mie scattering, for which there is a more modest spectral effect. When the particles are much bigger than the wavelength of the light, then the scattering is not spectrally selective.

Surface scattering is similar. The spectral factor also the reciprocal fourth power for small surface irregularities. There is a geometrical factor involving the angles of incidence and reflection, and a surface factor related to the surface topography. This factor, not incidentally, can be used to calculate the performance of a sinusoidal or other types of diffraction gratings. It has been used to design monochromatic beamsplitters.

Chapter 2

Components and Instruments

Most people are familiar with very basic optical components like mirrors, lenses and prisms. However, some of their characteristics may not be so familiar, and certainly the operation of more complicated instruments like telescopes, microscopes, and spectroscopes is not as well known. Even more exotic are such devices as interferometers, lasers, detectors, and fiber optics. These are all described here, along with a few more.

Mirrors

Mirrors reflect light. They are often a blank, a plate of solid material that is covered with a highly reflecting film, as shown in Fig. 1. The blanks are made of glass, sometimes metal and even plastics or composites. They can have the reflecting coating on either the front or the back surface if the blank is transparent. They can be plane (flat) or curved.

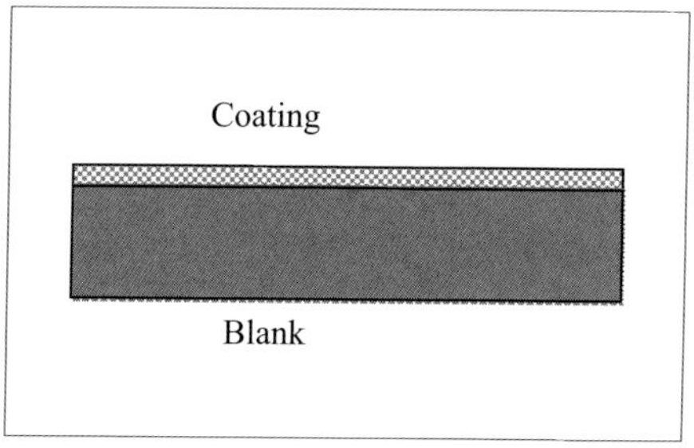

Figure 1 A typical mirror.

Mirrors have been used for a very long time. There is evidence that obsidian mirrors were used in Turkey about 7500 years ago. Mirrors were first *reflectorized* (commonly called silvered) by Justus von Liebig. The modern practice uses tin, silver, gold, or aluminum. Any metal, including copper, can provide the reflection, although certain metals will produce a colored reflection.

Plane Mirrors

These have smooth, even, planar surfaces, and are most often used as vanity mirrors. We use them to shave and apply cosmetics. They seem to reverse images from left to right but not from top to bottom. Full-length mirrors are useful to make sure your slip is not showing and that your shoes are shiny. Ask yourself how big a mir-

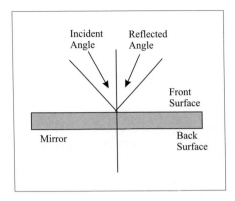

Figure 2 Plane mirror geometry.

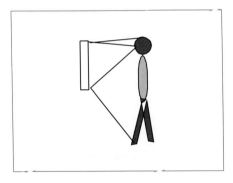

Figure 3 A full-length mirror needs to be only half of the observer's height.

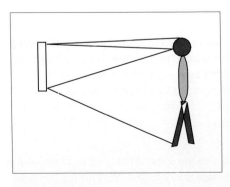

Figure 4 The distance makes no difference.

ror has to be to give a full-length image. Does it depend upon how far you are from the mirror? Think about it before you read on.

Before we answer that question, let us review the basic law of reflection. A plane mirror reflects light according to the law of reflection: the angle a reflected beam or ray makes with the surface is the same as the incident angle it makes on the surface. This is shown in Fig. 2.

A mirror that is only half your height is tall enough to provide you with a full-length image of yourself, no matter how far away you are from it. The geometry shown in Fig. 3 shows that a "full-length" mirror need be only half your height. It can also be used to show that the distance you are from the mirror makes no difference.

The figure shows a person standing in front of a mirror. The top of the mirror is halfway between his eyes and the top of his head. A ray from the top of the head to the top of the mirror determines the angle of incidence. The ray will be reflected back to the eye at an angle equal to this. It is this doubling that allows the mirror to be only half the height of the person using it. The bottom is halfway between his eyes and his feet. The next figure shows the same person about twice as far from the mirror. The mirror is the same size; the angles are smaller. Reflections are shown from the front surfaces for simplicity.

An interesting application for a plane mirror is to view a baby placed rearward in a car seat in the rear seat of the car. Hindsight, by Blue Ridge International Products, is a gaily decorated, large mirror that attaches to the top of the back seat of a vehicle's upholstery and allows the driver to view the baby.[1] Other variations include a wide-angle mirror placed above the windshield on the inside of the car.

"One-Way" Mirrors

Plane mirrors are also used as so-called one-way mirrors in police line-ups and for observing children or psychiatric patients. These mirrors may be simple plates of glass or may be lightly coated with metal. They do not completely reflect the light; they only partially reflect it. The observed room is brightly lit, while the room with the observers is dark. Sit in your own house some night with all the lights on. Look out at your dark yard. You will not be able to see much of anything. Now go outside and look in. You see everything. (Keep your drapes drawn at night!) That is a one-way mirror: the reflection of the glass surface performs the function. During the day, when the light outside is brighter than that in the house, the mirror works the other way.

Richard Axelbaum invented a very interesting application of the one-way mirror.[2] Orthodox Jewish law requires that men and women be separated during synagogue services so that (the male) worshippers can focus on prayer. I saw the separation of the sexes at the Wailing Wall in Jerusalem. In fact, the law requires that men not view women, but women may view men. This has led to the use of one-way mirrors, called *mehitza,* in some synagogues.

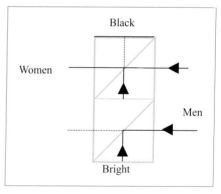

Figure 5 Mehitza.

However, the women had to be in relative darkness in order for this to work. Professor Axelbaum devised a mirror system with the mirror at an angle, strategically placed black plates, and lighted wallpaper. This is illustrated in Fig. 5, which shows a vertical section of the wall that consists of a set of partially reflecting and transmitting mirrors set at 45 deg to the vertical (or horizontal) with a black surface above the mirror and a decorated (wallpapered) surface below. The women see the sum of the men's side of the synagogue and the black surface. So they see mostly the men, who are more brightly lit than the black surface. The men see the combination of the women and the decorative surface. Since the decorative surface

1   The Arizona Daily Star *Startech*, 2. September 22, 1997.
2   Robinson, K. "Window design creates controllable one-way viewing," *Photonics Spectra*, August 1998, Anon., *Optics and Photonics News*, 45, July 1998.

is brightly lit, and the women not so well lit, the men see mostly the decorative surface masking the women. It is clear that there are other applications for this improved but more bulky "one-way" mirror. This is more "one-way" than the simple partially reflective plate.

Rearview Flip Mirrors

We all have these useful rearview mirrors in our cars that reduce the brightness of the light from headlights behind us. These combine the functions of a partially and a fully reflecting surface. The surface that flips is a fully reflecting surface, and provides the proper image of the roadway behind you during the day. The partially reflecting surface always reflects the image from straight behind, as shown by the dotted line at the top in Fig. 6. The fixed mirror adds to this, as shown by the solid line just below it.

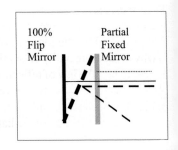

Figure 6 Automobile flip mirror.

At night, however, when oncoming headlights tend to blind you, the mirror can be flipped (shown in the figure by the dashed line, angled to the right, with the headlights coming from the right). The partially reflecting surface now reflects the headlights dimly, while the fully reflecting surface reflects the dark insides of your car, as shown by the dashed line at the bottom. Test this by flipping the mirror in the daytime to see the inside of your car—preferably while parked.

The Old Left-to-Right and Top-and-Bottom Conundrum

In a popular lecture series at MIT years ago they raised the question, "Why do mirrors reverse things left to right, but not top to bottom?" This is a lovely come-on, and many people think that this is true, but it is just not so. Plane mirrors obey the law of reflection in all directions, as described above. When you look in a mirror at your left side, it stays on the left. If you raise your left hand, its image moves up. It does appear that the person looking at you, raises his right hand and has everything reversed, but you are looking at an image. It is also true that your feet are down. If you have trouble with this, tip yourself on your side, and you will see that there is no reversal in either direction. You can also do this with a strip of text held horizontally and vertically.

Convex Mirrors

Mirrors can be curved rather than plane. They can be curved inward, like a soup bowl, or outward, like the surface of a ball. The soup-bowl mirrors are called concave, while the others are called convex. A common example of a convex mirror is the side-view mirror on a car, the one by the passenger that says, "Objects are closer than they appear." Another is a shaving mirror that provides magnification. Figure 7 shows the high-resolution field of view of the eye. The convex mirror widens the field so more can be seen. Then the object is a smaller fraction of the field, and the image is smaller than that produced by the plane mirror. That is why objects are really closer than they appear to be. The law of reflection is still obeyed (or someone would have to get a ticket), but because the mirror is not flat, the image is formed somewhat differently.

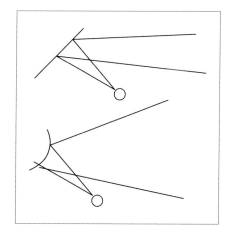

Figure 7 Wide-field mirror.

Concave Mirrors

These have found great use in telescopes. The simplest concave mirrors are made in a spherical form; the soup bowl spherical. Unfortunately, these simple, spherical mirrors suffer from *spherical aberration*. This is shown in Fig. 8. The rays are assumed to come into the mirror from a very distant source, thereby making them parallel to the axis of the mirror. The outer rays come to a focus on the axis at a distance further from the inner rays. This is spherical aberration, a blurring of the image. The so-

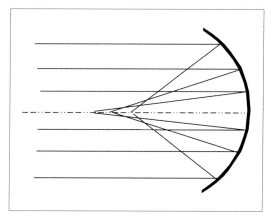

Figure 8 Concave mirror.

lution to this is to change the shape of the mirror as in Fig. 9. In a sense, the outer portions of the mirror are bent toward the axis. The mathematical treatment for this concludes that the proper shape is a paraboloid, a parabola of revolution. In Fig. 9, a spherical mirror is shown with dashed lines; the corresponding paraboloid is indicated with a solid line.

Another interesting concave mirror is the ellipsoid, a 3D ellipse that is like an elliptical bowl. It has two foci. Every ray that goes through one focus of the ellipsoid passes through the other focus. This is useful in relaying images. (An interesting acoustical analogy is in the U.S. Capitol. The dome is an ellipse. If you stand at one focus and whisper, a friend at the other focus can hear you, but those in between

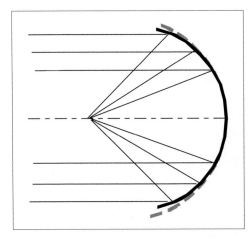

Figure 9 Spherical aberration.

cannot.) A hyperboloid has the same property, but uses convex surfaces. These figures are the so-called conics: sphere, paraboloid, ellipsoid, and hyperboloid. They are all described by second-order equations; that is, the expression involves the square of the radius of curvature of the figure.

Mirror designers, however, are not limited to these figures. They can, in theory, specify any shape. The mathematical expressions for these other figures involve equations that use the fourth, sixth, and higher powers for the radius. Since some of the conics are not spherical surfaces, they are called aspherics, and the surfaces that are not even conics are called higher-order aspheres (higher than the square of the radius). They are almost always circularly symmetric.

Other convex and concave mirrors, and even combinations, are evident in some of the halls of mirrors in "fun houses." They make us look fat, slim, skewed, and otherwise peculiar (or maybe more peculiar). Demonstrations of some of these properties can be made with a nice, silvery, compact disk (CD).[3] The flat CD can be used to demonstrate that the angle of reflection equals the angle of incidence. The CD can be bent between the thumb and forefinger to show both the convex and concave properties, and it can be bent like a potato chip to emulate fun-house mirrors.

Mirror Fabrication

Mirror fabrication can be a very exacting procedure. For technical applications, the figures (shapes) described above must be produced with errors that are less than a billionth of a meter! The figures themselves generally vary from spherical by about the same amount. The surface roughness often must be less than 10 billionths of a meter as well. Solid mirrors are generally made on large turntables. The solid blank is laid horizontally on the turntable and is rotated slowly while different tools are used to grind and polish the mirror. Spherical mirrors are easy. A relatively large tool is rested against the blank with a little weight on it; a slurry of abrasive is sloshed on the mirror; and the mirror turns and turns. Every so often the mirror is tested for its radius of curvature. My team at the University of Arizona made a 2-m-diameter spherical mirror like the one shown in Fig. 10 in about a month.

---

3   Turner-Valle, J., "Fun with CDs," *Optics and Photonics News*, 72, February 1998.

Aspheric mirrors are more difficult, but the process is the same. Usually the first step is to grind the best-fit spherical surface. Then tools are applied at different radial positions to generate the desired figure on the mirror. The conic surfaces—paraboloid, ellipsoid, hyperboloid—are harder, but they are not as

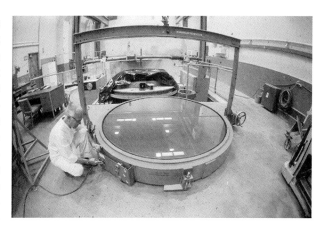

Figure 10 Mirror manufacture.

hard as the general aspheric surface. We generated 2-m-diameter mirrors with higher-order aspherics as well, but they took about six months to complete.

The mirror material has, if you will, a material influence on the process. The Mount Palomar mirror was made of ordinary glass that has relatively high thermal expansion, therefore its shape changes as a result of the heat of grinding or polishing. So only a little grinding or polishing at a time could take place before the mirror would have to cool and be tested. This can be a tedious process, and it was. Other glass-like materials, such as Cervit and Zerodur, have a very low thermal expansion and do not suffer this problem.

Metal mirrors have certain advantages that are most useful in the aerospace field. They can be made with flanges that have appropriate fittings for mounting—just screw on a bolt and nut. I call them "ears." Glass mirrors usually have some kind of straps that hold them in place. Metal mirrors have high thermal conductivity, so the heat does not build up but dissipates. Sometimes they can be used without a coating since the reflectivity of metals like aluminum is quite high. However, they have a major drawback: they cannot be tested for residual strain as can glass-like mirror blanks (see the section on mirror testing).

One of the preferred metals for space applications is beryllium, because it has a high strength-to-weight ratio, meaning a certain size mirror can be rather light. For military applications, it has the advantage that it is impervious to energetic radiation, the kind that would come from an atomic blast. It is transparent to the rays generated by the blast.

Beryllium has two major disadvantages. Since it is made by hot-pressing the material into shape, there are enough imperfections that it is difficult to get a really smooth polish. It is also very toxic as a dust. Machining must be done with vacuum attachments so that the dust that is created by the tool is immediately removed.

Mirror blanks are sometimes made from composite materials incorporating some kind of epoxy. They can be graphite-epoxy, aluminum-epoxy, etc. They can have the advantage of an adjustable thermal expansion, are lightweight, and can be formed in all sorts of ways. They have a major disadvantage for some space applications; they outgas (exude gases) in the vacuum of space and heat of the sun. The gases that escape from the blank can deposit on the surface and ruin the reflectivity. Silicon carbide has been one of the promising materials in this group. One version is made by creating a block of chopped carbon fibers that are embedded in a phenolic resin. The block is machined to shape and then fired until the resin turns to carbon. Then, at higher temperatures, silicon is added, and it turns to silicon carbide. This takes a much better polish than beryllium.

There has been some use of liquid mirrors, but applications are limited. A spinning liquid, if the rotation rate is right and the axis is vertical, takes on the shape of a perfect parabola and therefore has the properties of a parabolic mirror, notably lacking spherical aberration. So the imagery can be very good on axis.

However, the mirror must remain vertical and spinning if it stays liquid. One approach is to spin a resin and then let it harden, and use a thin layer of mercury as the reflecting surface. Another is a mercury mirror. Although you might recoil from the use of mercury, which is a poisonous gas in air, it has a low vapor pressure and tends to seal itself off from the air with an oxide layer. One such mirror, with a 3-m diameter, is in NASA's Orbiting Debris Observatory in Sunspot, New Mexico. Another, 2.7-m version, is at the University of Western Ontario. UCLA operates a similar mirror near Fairbanks, Alaska, and NASA has a 3-meter version in operation in Houston, Texas.[4]

Mirror Testing

This is a complicated subject that requires excruciating care. The easy part is testing the glass blanks for any residual strain, or strain that remains in the blank caused by imperfections. Such strain can relieve itself at the worst times and change the figure of the mirror. It will not change for the better! The test is to view the mirror blank in polarized light. Any regions of stress will show up as part of the polarization pattern, due to the phenomenon known as *stress birefringence*, a change in refractive index caused by stress on the material. Such a test cannot be done with (opaque) metal and composite mirror blanks. They must be extensively heat treated. There is a "catch 22" in this situation. If the heat treatment is done after the final figure is

Figure 11 Mirror testing.

obtained, the figure may change a little, but enough to be trouble. If the mirror receives a final polish after the last heat treatment, the polishing itself may introduce some stress.

---

4   "Liquid Mirrors: a high-quality, low-cost alternative to glass," *Photonics Spectra,* November 1998.

The more difficult task is measuring the figure (shape) of the mirror. This is done in at least two stages. The spherical shape can be tested with a spherometer: the lengths of three legs from a plane are measured, and the sphere is calculated. As the figure is refined, more sophisticated techniques are required. The main one is *interferometry*. One of the interferometers described elsewhere in this book is used to generate a 2D interference pattern. The fringes represent the contour of the mirror similar to contour lines on topographic maps that indicate the heights of the terrain. There is a catch: the shape must be quite good in order for the interferometer to work. If it is more than a few wavelengths in error, it will be out of the coherence length of the interferometer. Thus, part of the process is the design and construction of a so-called null lens to make the adaptation. Then the shape can be measured to within a fraction of the wavelength of the light.

Some applications also require the measurement of scattering. This can be done with a profilometer—a stylus that is drawn across the surface, recording the detailed profile of the surface. Then calculations relating the surface roughness to the degree of scatter are performed. A better method is the use of a *scatterometer*. Several of us could use a microscope light and an eyeball to make this measurement. Our extensive experience allowed us to do this with sufficient accuracy, but there are also meters that measure how much of the incident light goes into which angles. That is a scatterometer.

Lightweight Mirrors

In astronomy and many other space applications, the weight of the mirror is critical. The lighter the better. Several techniques have been developed to make mirror blanks lighter than solid blanks. It is easy to imagine simply coring out sections from the back of the mirror, as shown in Fig. 12. The amount that can be cored and still maintain the structural rigidity, and therefore the shape, is critical. Other methods can make this egg-crate-like structure. One is to make a thin plate and an egg crate and fuse the plate to the crate, as shown Fig. 13. In this case, care must be

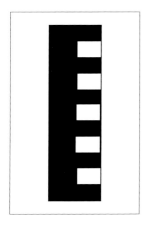

Figure 12 An egg-crated mirror.

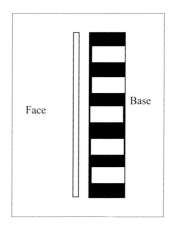

Figure 13 Face-plate mirror.

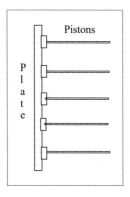

Figure 14 Adaptive mirror.

taken to avoid any stress where the struts of the crate meet the face plate. Such stress causes distortion in the mirror.

Another form of lightweight mirror is the adaptive structure. The thin plate is backed by a series of pistons that determine the shape of the mirror. The comparison between this and the egg-crate structure is the weight of the egg crate compared to the piston structure. However, the adaptive mirror has the advantage that its shape can be dynamically controlled. This allows the possibility of constructing adaptive optics telescopes, which are described in the section on telescopes.

Cryogenic Mirrors

Most infrared spaceborne telescopes are operated at very low temperatures, and this causes some very interesting manufacturing and test problems. The mirror figure is different at the operating temperature than it is at the manufacturing temperature. One could try to make the mirror at the operating temperature, but that is just about impossible. Instead, some workers form the mirror at room temperature based on what it should be at the cold temperature by way of modeling. Others use actuators that adjust the figure at operating temperature.

One nice way to handle this is to make the mirror and its support structure (the optical bench) out of the same material. The contraction of the bench largely compensates for the change in figure of the mirror. Some examples are the IRAS (Infrared Astronomical Satellite), the COBE (COsmic Background Experiment), and SIRTIF (Space InfraRed Telescope Facility). COBE was cooled to just a few degrees above absolute zero, about 450° F below zero; the others to only about 400° F below zero!

John Mather, the principal investigator on COBE, did find that the temperature of the cosmic background was indeed 3 Kelvin (K), that is, three degrees above absolute zero. This is the value predicted from the expansion of the universe from the time of the Big Bang. A related microwave experiment has further confirmed this and provided information that the subatomic size of the initial universe exploded so violently that it created a universe that is essentially flat.[5] But the Earth is still round!

An Electronic Mirror

A mirror proposed for use in space uses a piezoelectric material (one that changes its dimensions when a voltage is applied to it) and an electron beam to refine its shape. The mirror itself is a thin piece of piezoelectric material that can be folded

---

5   "Imaging the early universe," *Optics and Photonics News*, July 2000.

before launch. Upon deployment, it unfolds and approximates the final figure. A figure (shape) sensor is used to determine what changes need to be made, and the changes are accomplished by the ablation caused by bombardment with electrons. The resultant charge distribution maintains the desired shape for several hours to a few days, when it must be refreshed.[6]

The Hubble Telescope Primary Mirror

The Hubble telescope was a very long and expensive development that pushed the frontiers of telescope manufacture. The primary mirror was the driver. The telescope was designed as a Richey-Chretien: the concave primary mirror was an asphere, as was the convex secondary; the form was Cassegrainian (see p. 65). The *areal density* (weight of the mirror divided by its area) is 180 kilograms per square meter. The problems with this mirror and the Hubble Telescope are discussed in more detail in the section on telescopes.

Mirrors for the Next-Generation Space Telescope, NGST, the Successor to the Hubble Space Telescope.

Large lightweight mirrors are being developed at the University of Arizona Mirror Lab for the NGST.[7] Small models, only 2 m in diameter, are being formed as precursors. Ultimately these lightweight mirrors will be used in space at a temperature of 35 K. A thin membrane is laid on an egg-crate structure and the figure is controlled by many pistons on its back. Two mirrors with 0.5- and 1-m diameters with 2-millimeter (mm) face plates have passed critical tests. Whereas the Hubble primary was 180 kilograms (kg) per square meter, the NGST mirror is hoped to be 15 kg per square meter. Even lower values using the techniques described here are anticipated.[8]

Mirror Coatings for the National Ignition Facility (NIF)

The National Ignition Facility is a large laboratory in California that is devoted to the generation of power by fusion. The technique is to use many high-power lasers that all concentrate their output on a hydrogen pellet that is to provide the fusion and the energy. The laser beams are directed to that point by a series of convex and plane mirrors. In order to provide the most power, each mirror has a high-reflectance coating. While most mirrors are coated with aluminum, investigators at the NIF have developed higher-reflectivity, more expensive mirror coatings. They are

---

6   Krups, T. J. "A different type of space mirror," *Optics and Photonics News*, July 2000.
7   "Lightweight mirror technology," *Oscillations*, The University of Arizona, July 1998.
8   Bilbro, J., "Optics in orbit," *OE Magazine*, August 2001.

sputtered silver with silicon nitride. The silver provides a reflectivity of greater than 95% from 400 to 1000 nm.[9] Bare silver, of course, tarnishes, just like dining-room silverware.

Magnificent Mirror

The *Multiple-Mirror Telescope* atop Mount Hopkins in southern Arizona has recently been replaced by a single large mirror 6.5 m in diameter. This is a paraboloid made in the Mirror Lab at The University of Arizona. It is made of Pyrex and was spun slowly on a very large turntable while being held at a temperature a little above its softening point. This spinning motion combined with gravity results in the paraboloidal shape. The mirror is backed by many refractory bricks to form an egg-crate structure at the rear of the mirror to make it considerably lighter than a solid paraboloid, with sufficient thickness to keep it from sagging.

Aristotle and the Mirror Weapon

It has been reported, and it has been argued about. Did Aristotle really use mirrors as a weapon against an attacking fleet? Those who say yes argue that he lined up many of his soldiers with concave mirrors and they reflected the light from the sun onto the ships in the harbor, thereby setting them on fire. Some pictures show the soldiers apparently using their shield for this, but shields are convex, not concave, as they are used. They would have to be reversed and have shiny backs. Those who doubt this story claim that the technology did not exist to build such mirrors. I don't think it would have been too hard to do a reasonable job of shaping and polishing what amounts to the back of the shields. After all, a perfect figure is not needed.[10]

Lenses

These simple devices have had widespread use in cameras, eyeglasses, periscopes, microscopes, and more. They are based on the bending or refraction of light. Probably the first use of a lens was by the emperor Nero.[11] While watching one of the many entertainments in the arena, Christians and lions for instance, he peered through one of his emerald baubles. It just happened to be the right size and shape to provide a good, enlarged image of the arena. Spectacles were probably first invented by the Arabian optics pioneer, Alhazen, in the 900s.

---

9   Hand, A., "Silver coatings maintain reflectance," *Photonics Spectra*, September 1998.
10   Dickey, F. "Laser beam shaping," *Optics and Photonics News*, April 2003.
11   D. Macaulay, *The Way Things Work*, Houghton Mifflin, 1988.

Descriptions

Lenses are described by the number of elements in them, the materials of which they are made, the location of the elements and stops, their focal lengths and diameters, f and D, and their focal ratio, f/D, called the F-number, or speed. These are illustrated in Fig. 15. The term "lens" has two meanings. It may mean a single element or a collection of lens elements.

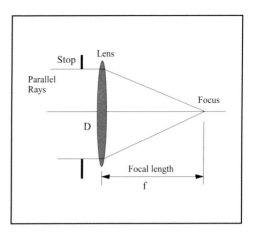

Figure 15 A simple lens.

Single-element Lenses

A simple, one-element lens has two surfaces that can be concave, convex, or plane. These are shown in Fig. 16. Although the first and last of these may look the same, just reversed in direction, they do have different focusing properties.

The operation of a single-element lens for focusing light from the sun is shown in Fig. 17: parallel rays come from the sun and are bent by the curved surfaces, all coming to a single spot called the focus of the lens. It is simple to show how this works by taking a magnifying glass and focusing the sun onto a piece of paper. In fact, in a short time, the paper will begin to burn as a result of the focused heat from the sun. Be careful when you try this (outdoors). This is a simple and effective way to measure the focal length of a lens. Find the position of the lens that gives the smallest spot and measure the distance from the lens to the piece of paper.

We almost had a fire this way. When I retired, I received a very nice optical sculpture, a sphere mounted on a wooden platform (Fig. 18). I proudly placed it in our living room. As the sun came beaming through the window, it impinged upon

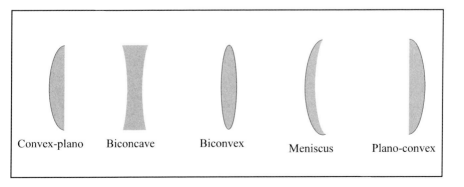

Figure 16 Single-element lens shapes.

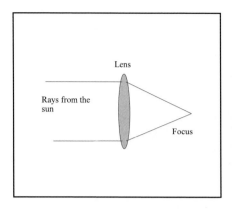

Figure 17 Focusing the sun.

Figure 18 Retirement ball.

the sphere, and the sphere, a kind of lens, focused the light to a point on the wood. Fortunately, the sun moved in the sky (so to speak) fast enough that there was only a seared spot and not a flame. This happens with fish bowls, too, but the water absorbs some of the energy.

Lens Aberrations[12]

Usually, single-element lenses do not provide sufficiently good performance. They suffer *aberrations*, deviations from ideal performance. Simple aberrations are called Seidel or third-order aberrations, and are classified as spherical aberration, coma, astigmatism, curvature of field, distortion, and color or chromatic aberration.

Spherical aberration is illustrated in Figure 19. The spherical shape of a lens is just not quite right to form a perfect image of a spot on the optical axis (the center line) or a full image

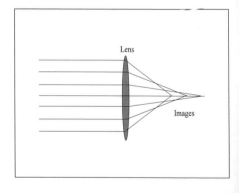

Figure 19 Spherical aberration (exaggerated).

for that matter. Spherical aberration occurs on the optical axis as well as at other

---

12 Many texts exist on this subject. Some are Jenkins, F.A., and H. E. White, *Fundamentals of Optics*, Third Edition, McGraw Hill, 1957; Born, M., and E. Wolf, *Principles of Optics*, First Edition, Pergamon, 1959; and Smith, W., *Modern Optical Engineering*, Second Edition, McGraw Hill, 1990.

points in the field of view. The figure
shows the aberration for a nonaxis point
source an infinite distance away. Some
more sophisticated lenses use surfaces
that are not spherical, but are especially
configured to eliminate spherical aberration. They are called aspherical surfaces.
The first excursion from sphericity involves the so-called conic surfaces: ellip-
soids, paraboloids, and hyperboloids.
The next involves more complicated
surfaces that are called higher-order
aspherics.

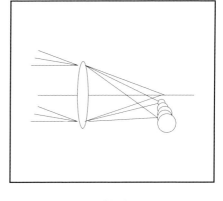

Figure 20 Coma.

Lenses show a complete parallel
with mirrors. They both have all the
same aberrations (except mirrors do not have color aberrations), and they come as
spherical, conic surfaces, and higher-order aspheres.

Comatic aberration, or coma, occurs only for points that are not on axis. It results from the fact that different portions of the lens have different magnification.
Coma is illustrated in Fig. 20. As you can see, the image blur has the general shape
of a comet. Thus, it is called coma or comatic aberration. I did not show all of the
rays that generate the spots that make up the coma patch. The greater the angles that
the rays make with the optical axis, the larger the blur circle.

When the object point is still further off axis, the situation is aggravated, and
there occur two points of focus. This is a result of the magnification being different
in the vertical direction from the horizontal. This is shown in Fig. 21, and is called

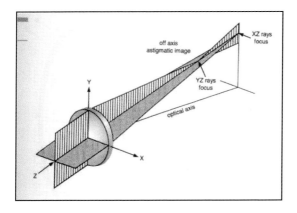

Figure 21 Astigmatism.[13]

---

13 Adapted from Fischer, R. E., and B. Tadic-Galeb, *Optical System Design*,
McGraw-Hill, 2000. (Image courtesy of McGraw-Hill, copyright 2000.)

astigmatism, the appearance of imagery that does not come from a single point. It is interesting that a stigma is a bad thing in common parlance, but if a lens is stigmatic, it is a good thing. It means the light comes to a point.

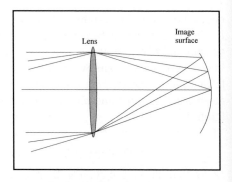

An image formed by a single lens is curved, as shown in Fig. 22. Since film and other extended-area sensors are almost always flat, field curvature is considered an aberration. In some systems the image sensor can be curved and this aberration is not important. Usually,

Figure 22 Image curvature.

however, curvature of the field is a detriment to obtaining good, crisp images. This occurs because the distance from the center of the lens to the image surface is the same if the image surface is curved.

A single lens also suffers from distortion. Visualize this by considering the image of a perfect rectangle. In general, it will be imaged as a set of curved lines that resemble either a pincushion or a barrel, and, logically enough, these are called pincushion and barrel distortion.

The final Seidel aberration is color or chromatic aberration. The refractive index changes with wavelength; it is different for different colors. Therefore, the focal points are slightly different for different colors of light. This is illustrated in the next figure. Both axial and lateral chromatism, chromatic aberration, are considered in lens design procedures.

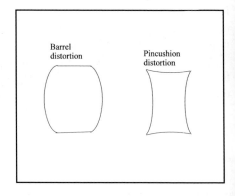

Figure 23 Distortions.

If all aberrations are completely corrected (an extremely unlikely situation), the lens will still not be perfect. It is limited by diffraction. Assume a plane wave is incident upon the lens. The surfaces, thicknesses, and refractive indices are all designed to bring this wave to a focus, a perfect point.

The section on diffraction showed that as the daughter waves propagate from an aperture, the center of their collection is a good plane wave. At the

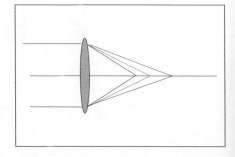

Figure 24 Chromatic aberration, chromatism.

edges, however, the resultant wave is no longer plane but sort of spherical. The lens is not designed to take care of this geometry; so the point becomes blurred as a result of diffraction. It is not surprising that a larger aperture has smaller diffraction—more of the plane wave is generated. It is not so obvious that diffraction limitations are smaller with shorter wavelengths. These shorter wavelengths fit more easily into the aperture and, in effect, have a greater plane wave after diffraction.

Correction of Aberrations

Aberrations are corrected, or at least reduced, by careful design and the addition of other lens elements to make the complete lens perform satisfactorily. In a real sense, the business of correcting aberrations is the business of lens design after the initial calculations have been made.

The first step in reducing aberrations in a single lens is to adjust the radii of curvature, or the curvature of the front and back surfaces of the lens. The focal length calculated by the lensmaker's equation is established by the refractive index and the two radii, but there are many choices of the two radii that give the same result. Thus the lens may be bent. That is, the two radii are chosen in such a way that spherical aberration is eliminated and coma is minimized. The ratio of radii depends upon the refractive index, and well-established formulas are available for this. That is all that can be done with a single lens.

Figure 25 shows several lenses that have been bent differently; they have different shape factors. Each of these lenses has the same focal length, or power, but different amounts of spherical and comatic aberration.

The next step is to add another element so that the lens becomes a doublet. The doublets can be of the same material or two different materials and they can be in contact or spaced apart. So-called air-spaced doublets are generally superior because the spacing is a design variable and four different surfaces are available. The

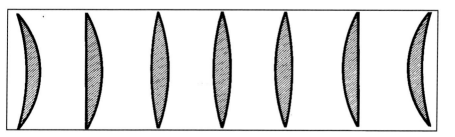

Figure 25 Differently shaped lenses.[14]

14 Jenkins, F., and H. White, *Fundamentals of Optics*, McGraw Hill, 1957. (Image courtesy of McGraw-Hill, copyright 1957.)

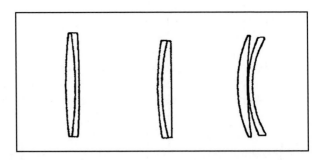

Figure 26 Three doublets: Fraunhofer, Gauss, and Steinheil.[15]

contact doublet must have the rear surface of the first element match the front surface of the rear element. The broken-contact doublet has no appreciable spacing between the two elements, but the two mating surfaces do not have to match.

A very early doublet was designed by Chevalier for Daguerre's early photography systems in the early 1800s. It was a lens that consisted of a planoconvex element and a biconvex lens in contact. This lens can be used with either element facing forward, but the performance is different. With the convex surface forward, the lens provides good on-axis imagery but has rather large curvature of field. When turned around, the on-axis imagery suffers some, but the field curvature is almost nullified. This latter form is what was used by Daguerre. The aperture placed in front of the lens masked some of coma. Such an aperture is called a stop. The two elements were made of different materials, and in this way the lens was partly corrected for chromatic aberrations, i.e. it was *achromatized*. Three other contact doublets are those of Fraunhofer, Gauss, and Steinheil, shown in Fig. 26 from left to right.

Johnson[16] describes these in more detail, enumerating design procedures and typical results. Two interesting designs are the Dialyte, which is an air-spaced doublet, and the Periskop, which consists of two facing menisci. The stop position and lens shapes corrected curvature of field and the symmetry took care of coma and astigmatism. This design type, now called periscopic, has been used in several Kodak cameras.

Many other designs exist. The patent literature is a good source for descriptions of more than 1000 different lenses. Many good computer programs used today for lens design include the full prescriptions in the software.

An excellent description of the history of the photographic lens has been given by Kingslake.[17]

15 Smith, W., Chapter 14, "Camera Lenses," *The Optical Engineer's Desk Reference*, W. L. Wolfe, ed., Optical Society of America, 2004. (Image courtesy of OSA, copyright 2004.)
16 Johnson, R. B., Chapter 1, *Handbook of Optics*, Bass, M., E. Van Stryland, D Williams, and W. L. Wolfe, McGraw Hill, 1995.
17 Kingslake, R., *A History of the Photographic Lens*, Academic Press, 1989. (Images courtesy Academic Press, copyright 1989.)

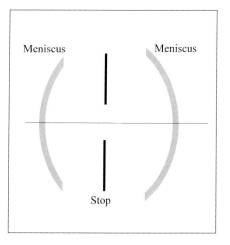

Figure 27 Periskop lens.

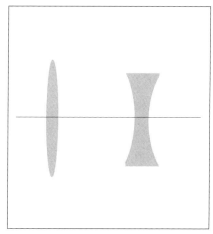

Figure 28 Dialyte lens.

Triplet Lenses

The first and classical triplet, shown in Fig. 28, was designed by H. Dennis Taylor. It has six surfaces, two separations, and even three different materials as design variables to correct for aberrations. This is a fairly powerful configuration, and has had many variations. Some designers place a stop between either the first and second or second and third lenses, and some make one or more of the elements contact doublets. The Tessar lens, a very popular photographic lens invented by Paul Rudolph of Zeiss, is one of these variations. It is shown in Fig. 30. The Leitz version (Fig. 31) has three contact doublets. The Brendel has a doublet for the first lens, but singlets for the others. Interestingly, the Zeiss Tessar seems to be better than the more complicated Leitz version.

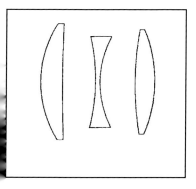

Figure 29 Cooke triplet.[17]

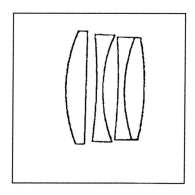

Figure 30 Tessar.[17]

Double-Gauss Lenses

Friedrich Gauss in the early 1800s described a lens with a pair of menisci, and the design was doubled and later patented. It has been used in many 35-mm camera systems: the Zeiss Biotar and the Leica Sumitar, for instance. It is shown in Fig. 30. Notice that it started with a meniscus lens in front and one behind the stop, shown at the center. Then a second meniscus was added to both the front and back, keeping the lens symmetrical. Then, for good measure, a cemented doublet was added to both sides—thus, the Leitz double Gauss. Those by Angenieux and Fujioka look similar, with the Fujioka perhaps having the best performance. Best must be defined, as better on axis or average over some specified field of view.

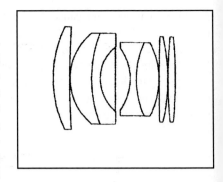

Figure 31 Leitz double Gauss.[17]

Petzval Lenses

Petzval invented the lens named after him in 1839. Shown in Fig. 32, it has an objective lens followed by an airspaced doublet followed by an achromatic airspaced doublet consisting of a contact doublet and a meniscus. It is useful for projectors and portrait lenses, partly because it has an intermediate image where a slide can be placed.

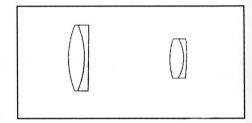

Figure 32 Petzval lens.[17]

Telephoto Lenses

A telephoto lens is one in which the focal length is longer than the lens itself. This is accomplished by the use of a positive front lens group widely separated from a negative lens group in the rear. This principle is illustrated in Figure 33.[18] The EFL is the effective

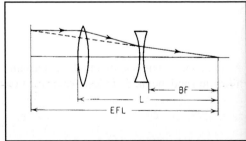

Figure 33 Telephoto lens.[18]

18 Smith, W. J., *Modern Optical Engineering*, McGraw-Hill, 1990. (Image courtesy of McGraw-Hill, copyright 1990.)

focal length, usually just called the focal length. BF is the back focal length, the distance from the last surface to the focus. L is the length of the lens, from front surface to focus. These lenses are often used with cameras for long distance applications. The large focal length is required for magnification; the telephoto principle keeps the lens from getting too long. Reverse telephoto or retrofocus lenses have a negative front lens group and a positive rear group. They are often used for wide-angle applications with single-lens reflex cameras.

Fisheye Lenses

This lens, by definition, covers a field of view of at least 180 deg. It may be thought of as a retrofocus lens carried to the extreme. The aperture stop is different for each angular field position, so the lens is much bigger than its aperture. One example is that of Kenro Miyamoto. The rays at the bottom of the figure show light coming from one part of the field that is much smaller than the lens. Note the small beam coming in from below.

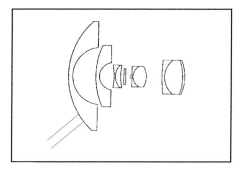

Figure 34 Miyamoto fisheye lens.

Telecentric Lenses

Telecentric lenses have either the entrance pupil or exit pupil at infinity. This means that the aperture stop is located at a focal point of the system. These systems are often used in sighting systems in which a crosshair is focused at infinity to minimize parallax and position error.

Zoom Lenses

A zoom lens is one that maintains a constant focal length while changing the magnification and the field of view. There are two different types of zoom lens systems: optically compensated and mechanically compensated. In an optically compensated three-element system, two lenses are moved with respect to a third, but the two lenses that move remain a fixed distance from each other. In Fig. 35, lenses A and C move. Note that the system has two different focal lengths for the two different positions. The distance from the last element to the focal point is larger for the top system than for the bottom.

In a mechanically compensated system, one lens is used to change the magnification, that is, the focal length, while another refocuses the system. It may seem that these are both mechanically compensated since in both cases lenses have to be

moved. However, optical com-
pensation is simpler to imple-
ment mechanically. They had
to be called something!

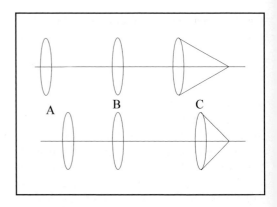

There are several different
types and more than 100 individual designs for both the visible and the infrared.[19]

Aspheric Lenses

The simplest lenses, both to design and to make, are spherical.
That is, the shape of the lens is
spherical. For some applications,

Figure 35 Simple optical compensated zoom system.

it is better to make the shape nonspherical, or aspherical. This provides an additional
design variable so that such lenses can be better than their spherical counterparts.
The simplest of the aspherical lenses are those with elliptical, parabolic, or hyper-
bolic curves. Higher-order aspheric surfaces can provide even more flexibility in
design. Such figures are harder to generate. Therefore, the elements are more expensive to make. I had our shop make a 2-m-diameter spherical mirror. It took
about one month to get it done properly. They also made a 2-m higher-order
aspheric mirror. It took 6 months.

Microlens Arrays[20]

A microlens is generally understood to have a critical dimension of less than 1 mm,
but some people consider them to be as large as 1 cm. Arrays of these microlenses can
be used over a charge-coupled device (CCD) array (discussed on p. 54) to improve
the quality of the imagery, or they can be used over arrays of lasers to improve the
beam quality of each laser. They have to be economical and reasonably precise.
Other examples include optical testing using Shack-Hartmann screens, which can be
refractive or diffractive lenses, Fresnel zone plates, and even holographic lenses. One
realization is a plastic sheet with a host of these small lenses. Another is an array of
cylindrical elements, and even crossed arrays of cylinders. The diffractive lenses
have the potential of economy, but have less efficiency than refractive elements. The
crossed cylinders can be used nicely as anamorphic correctors (correctors that have

19 Mann, A., *Infrared Optics and Zoom Lenses*, SPIE Press, 1990.
20 Milster, T. D., "Miniature and micro-optics," *Handbook of Optics*, Chapter 7, Vol. 2,
    M. Bass, E. Van Stryland, D. R. Williams, and W. L. Wolfe, eds., 1995.

optical power in different directions) to properly shape asymmetrical laser outputs into circularly symmetrical beams.[21]

Fresnel Lenses

These are named after the French physicist Augustin Fresnel (with a silent ess). They are used on most lighthouses, and have found application as stamped sheets of plastic that are placed in the rear of some large vehicles for better views of the road behind. Figure 36 shows a normal lens with a set of lines indicated. If the lens is cut on these lines, and the back parts are cut off and the pieces reassembled, one has the Fresnel version of the lens. It is thinner, which is the main reason for doing it. It does not work quite as well as the original lens, partly because the diffraction limit has been reduced to that determined by an individual facet size.

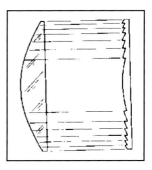

Figure 36 Fresnel lens.[22]

Diffractive Lenses[23]

These lenses, also called binary optics, work on the principle of diffraction rather than refraction. Chapter 1 shows how a series of parallel grooves can diffract light of different colors into different angles, according to well-known laws. So you can form grooves by some technique on a piece of optical glass and bend the rays. It is almost impossible to design a diffractive element to cover a wide spectral band because of the high degree of chromatic aberration. Fortunately, the aberration is opposite to that of refractive elements so that hybrid lenses are the rule. Part of the image formation is done by refraction and the other part by diffraction.

Prisms

Almost everyone is familiar with the simple prism. However, prisms are used for two different purposes. One is the separation of light into its component colors; the other is the redirection of light, somewhat like a mirror. The first type of prism is

21 Morey, J., "Microlens arrays sharpen the details," *Photonics Spectra*, December 1997.
22 Smith, W. J., *Modern Optical Engineering*, McGraw Hill, 1990. (Image courtesy of McGraw-Hill, copyright 1990.)
23 Sweat, W., "Diffractive optics" *The Optical Engineer's Desk Reference*, W. L. Wolfe, ed., OSA and SPIE Press, 2003.

called dispersive. Logically enough, but not completely accurate, the second kind is called nondispersive.

Dispersive Prisms

When light is incident upon a simple prism, as shown in Fig. 37, it leaves the opposite side in different directions as a set of different colors. This is because the amount of bending, which results from the refractive index, varies with color. A plot of the refractive index of various materials is shown in Fig. 38. This points out that the index is higher for shorter wavelengths and lower for longer ones. Therefore, the blues will be bent more than the reds. If you know both the refractive index and the prism angle, you can calculate the amount of bending. A

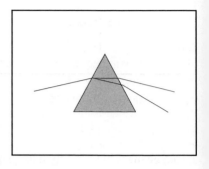

Figure 37 Dispersive prism.

prism with larger differences in refractive index is said to be more dispersive, and is usually a better prism for use in a spectrometer, which is meant to separate the colors. The regions where the refractive index changes precipitously also have high absorption. Thus, only the middle portion of the curve is useful for prism spectrometers.

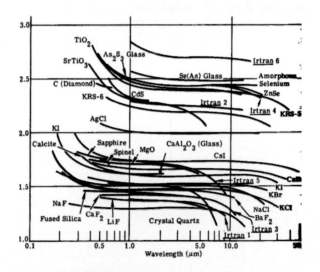

Figure 38 Material dispersion.[24]

24   Wolfe, W., G. Zissis, eds., *The Infrared Handbook*, SPIE, 1989.

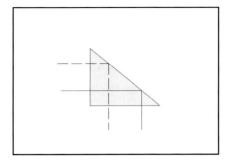

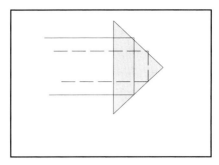

Figure 39 Right angle.   **Figure 40** Porro.

Nondispersive Prisms

Although the name nondispersive prisms implies that these do not separate the colors of light, it really means that they are not intended to do so. Attention must be paid to dispersion, and designs may have to account for it. There do exist achromatic prism designs, those that minimize the separation of colors. One of their main uses is in binoculars, where they invert and reverse the images made by the lenses. Of course, they are used in a variety of other optical instruments for many of the same purposes.

Several of the more popular prisms are shown below. Many more are described in the *Handbook of Optics*.[25] As the figures show, the right-angle prism bends the light beam in a right angle. Since the light enters and exits perpendicular to the surfaces, there is no dispersion. The Porro prism sends the light back upon itself, and for the same reason, there is no dispersion. The image is inverted. The Dove, or in-

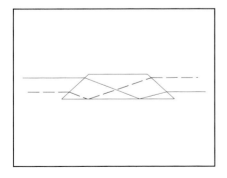

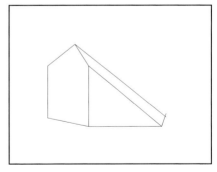

Figure 41 Dove, or inverting.   **Figure 42** Amici, or roof.

25 Wolfe, W. L., Chapter 4 in *Handbook of Optics*, M. Bass, E. Van Stryland, D. Williams, and W. Wolfe, eds., Optical Society of America, 1995.

verting prism, sends the light on in the same direction but inverts the image. The dispersion from the front surface is offset by that of the rear. The Amici or roof prism is more complicated, but it accomplishes the same thing as the right-angle prism with an additional reversion from left to right.

The Cube Corner

This is a kissin' cousin to the prisms discussed in this section. It is the corner of a cube that is either hollow or solid. Light that enters it from any direction (within a large range) will be returned upon itself, retroreflected. Corner cubes, as they are sometimes inaccurately called, have been placed on the moon to reflect laser signals back to Earth to measure distances. The cube corner is shown in two dimensions to illustrate how light is retroreflected.

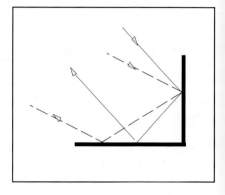

Figure 43 Cube corner.

Fibers

Fiber optics are long, thin, solid or hollow tubes that guide light along their length. They depend on multiple reflections of the light along the inside of the tube. The solid ones generate this reflection by total internal reflection (discussed in Chapter 1); hollow ones use ordinary metallic or dielectric reflections from the inside surface. The solid ones are by far the most frequently used; the hollow ones are primarily used for infrared applications, where useful materials are rare.

In Fig. 44, a ray is shown entering the fiber. It is refracted at the front face, and totally reflected at the outer surface. That is repeated many times, depending upon the length of the fiber, and the ray exits at the right end, also by refraction. Rays incident

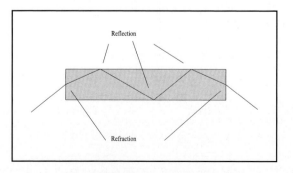

Figure 44 Rays in a single fiber.

more obliquely on the front surface will not be totally reflected, and the entering cone (the tapered end of an optic fiber) is determined by that limit. The geometry also dictates that the exiting cone is the same as the entering cone of light.

Optical fibers have a variety of uses.[26] Some just redirect light, some scramble and unscramble images, and the most recent, and maybe most useful application, is transmitting information in the form of television signals and data. You might use a single fiber to redirect the light by simply bending it, but the bend must not be too sharp or the condition for total internal reflection will be violated. Most single fibers consist of a low refractive-index core covered by an outer high-index material (Fig. 45). Some communication devices have a graded index, low in the center and gradually increasing with distance from the center.

Fiber optic bundles are considered either coherent or incoherent, depending upon whether the strands are packed together in an organized or random manner. Figure 46 shows a coherent bundle on top. All of the fibers are arranged in exactly the same way at both the input and output ends. The incoherent bundle may be arranged randomly (I have shown only some of the individual fibers). This could be used for encoding and decoding. Fiber bundles like this might also be tapered—in the shape of a cone—and used instead of a lens to concentrate light. Some fibers used for geometric applications may be large, approaching a millimeter in diameter, but most are about the size of a human hair.

The fibers used for communication are designed to support a number of electromagnetic modes. This means that there are different patterns of the electromagnetic

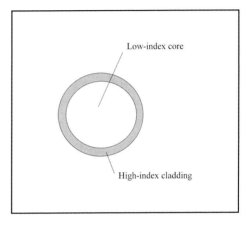

Figure 45 Clad fiber.

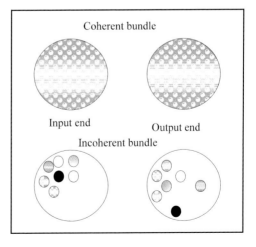

Figure 46 Fiber bundles.

---

26   Lerner, E., "Optical fibers carry information of the age," *Laser Focus World*, March 1997.

(optical) fields in the fiber. These might be a single maximum of the field in the middle of the fiber or a pair of equally spaced maxima at the sides, or any number of combinations of distributions of the field. The graded-index fibers can support about 1000 of these modes.

Design considerations include both attenuation and dispersion as well as sizing to establish the mode patterns. Attenuations are caused by absorption in the material and scattering. The scattering is of the Rayleigh type and therefore decreases rapidly with increasing wavelength. The material absorption depends upon the material, but the two dictate that the best spectral regions are around 1300 and 1500 nanometers in the near-infrared region of the spectrum. Dispersion is dictated largely by the change with wavelength in the refractive index of the core material. Again, the spectral regions of lowest dispersion coincide with those of lowest attenuation. Some things work advantageously, but the spectral region is where sources have been more difficult to obtain.

Cameras

By camera, I mean an optical device that records an image. The simplest is the pinhole camera; more complicated versions are the single-lens reflex or SLR, the instant camera, and modern digital cameras. Even more complicated devices include reconnaissance cameras and stroboscopic systems.

The essential elements of a camera are an aperture stop, a means for forming an image, a shutter, and a recording medium. The different types of cameras have these elements in varying degrees of complexity and price. These essentials are shown in the Fig. 47. The aperture is usually determined by an adjustable iris near the front of the lens system. It controls how much light can enter the system. The lens forms an image on the film. When a picture is taken, the user presses the button and the shutter opens. It should stay open long enough for enough photons to impinge on the film to expose it sufficiently for a good picture. That number is determined by the length of time the shutter is open, the size of the cone of light impinging on the film, and the sensitivity of the film. A larger cone is a fatter one. The figure illustrates the imaging of an object at infinity so that the image is formed at the focal point.

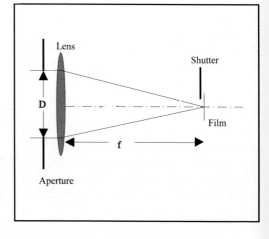

Figure 47 Geometry of the camera.

Cameras are described in terms of their optical speed, exposure time, resolution and secondarily by versatility, size, weight, and price. The optical speed is specified as an F number (also called the focal ratio) and relative aperture, and is the ratio of the focal length, f, divided by the aperture diameter, D. The exposure time is usually expressed in terms of the shutter speed, and this ranges from about 1/1000 second to "bulb." Only the more expensive cameras have shutter speeds faster than about 1/250 sec. "Bulb" means that the shutter is triggered open, sometimes by squeezing a bulb, sometimes by pushing a plunger. The shutter stays open until the "bulb" is released. The focal ratio is an inverse measure; that is, the higher the speed, the lower the F number. The optical speed is really the size of the cone of light that impinges on the image plane, and that determines the number of photons that get to it. The cone of light is inversely proportional to the square of the F number, and that is the reason you see such strange sequences of F number settings on cameras.

Camera users and designers require a certain resolution over the usable field. That is one of the reasons that resolution is usually not described in the specifications. It has to be good enough. The resolution, however, is inversely related to the F number. The section on aberrations gives more detail, but the aberration blur varies from being inversely related to the F number to being inversely related to the cube of the F number. This means that to obtain a faster speed (smaller F number) and retain the required resolution, the camera lens must be of higher quality. That is why an $F/1.2$ camera is more expensive than an $F/2$ camera.

Apertures

These are usually irises that are placed somewhere in the optical train. They must be placed at an aperture stop or a pupil of the system. They limit the area of the cone of light that can enter the camera.

The relative aperture is a measure of the speed and is specified as the F number. The amount of light on the film is proportional to the square of the F number. That is why the typical numbers are 1.2, 2.8, 4, 5.6, 8, 11, 16, and 22. Each stop down (from 4 to 2.8 for instance) provides about twice as much light to the film. Try it. The squares of these numbers approximately double for each successive value. For instance, the square of 5.6 is 31.36 and the square of 8 is 64. (The square root of 32 is 5.657).

Shutters

The shutter is an opaque material that is placed somewhere in the optical train, where it is switched out by the trigger to allow light to reach the film and take a picture. There are two main types of shutters: a between-the-lens shutter, and an image-plane shutter. The designations are apt; that is where they are located. Between-the-lens shutters are usually larger and not quite as fast.

Lenses

This is a very large subject about which many books have been written. It is treated in more detail in the section on lenses. Briefly, there are designs for medium fields of view (about 45 deg), wide angles, up to about 90 deg, and so-called landscape or fisheye lenses that cover a full 180 deg. These all have to have photographic-quality resolution, although some of the landscape lenses show considerable distortion. The higher the speed (smaller F number), the harder it is to design them, and generally the more complicated and expensive they get.

Rangefinders

Although they are not essential components of cameras, means for bringing the subject into focus are highly desirable elements. These vary from presentation of the scene to the eye for subjective evaluation to active rangefinders.

In a single-lens reflex camera, the actual scene is reflected to the viewer's eye by means of the flip mirror. The operator then adjusts the focus by moving the lens until the sharpest image possible is obtained. When the shutter is tripped, the mirror flips out of the way, and the image goes to the film, which must be exactly the same distance from the mirror as is the viewing screen.

A second version is the split-image rangefinder. The operator sees in the viewer a chopped-up image of the object unless it is in focus. This is generated by obtaining two or more images from different angles, and combining them. When out of focus, the images do not correspond and "break up." When in focus, they join nicely.

Active rangefinders usually use small light-emitting diodes (LEDs) or other miniature light sources. The light is flashed on, and the time it takes to reach the object and return is counted by a microchip. The return is sensed by a small light detector. Light travels at about one foot for every nanosecond (a billionth of a second), so a typical distance, say 10 feet, will result in a delay of about 20 nanoseconds (and the range is half that). These are reasonable measurements, and the ranging is essentially instantaneous.

Light Meters

In the days when I first used a camera, you also had to have a light meter. A light meter consists of a light detector calibrated to measure the amount of light incident upon it. Some collect the light from an entire hemisphere; others, so-called spot meters, are more directional. In both cases, they give information about how much light is available, and therefore what combinations of F number and shutter speed should be used for proper exposure. Shutter speeds slower than about 1/30th to 1/50th of a second tend to result in blurring due to camera motion. Unless there is motion in the scene, you should use as slow a shutter speed as possible so the F number can be as large as possible, and the aberrations will be smaller while the range of distances for which the image is in focus is maximized.

Modern single-lens reflex cameras have built-in light meters. Some provide the information in terms of allowable speeds, and some set them automatically, usually with a manual override. Point-and-shoot cameras set the speeds according to the advice given above.

The Pinhole Camera

As shown in Fig. 48, a pinhole camera is nothing more than a box with a hole in it that is small compared to the dimensions of the box. I had the pleasure of demonstrating this to a sixth-grade glass. We closed all the shades except for one high window, where I inserted a piece of cardboard with a hole that was about six inches in diameter. A few kids went outside and danced around. Those inside could then watch their images dancing upside down on the top of the opposite wall.

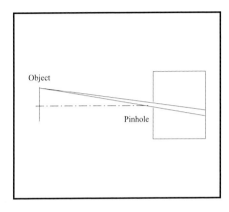

Figure 48 Pinhole camera.

The pinhole is both the aperture stop and the means for forming an image. The beam is limited by the hole's size, and it forms the image by limiting the rays directionally. You can put a piece of film at the image plane, but it is fun to use it as a camera obscura as I did in the classroom. It can be seen in Figure 49 that rays from the top of the object are close together at the back of the box, where a low-quality image is formed. The image has higher resolution when the hole is

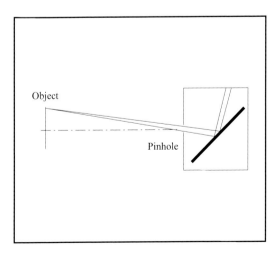

Figure 49 Folded pinhole camera.

smaller or the distance from the hole to the back surface is shorter. That is why Kodak introduced its box camera with a lens that focuses the rays on the back wall. The pinhole camera in the form of the camera obscura is said to have been used by many artists to trace landscapes and other objects. They typically used a folding flat mirror to put the image on a glass plate on the top of the box, where the tracing could be made. A pinhole camera is also called a *stenopic camera*. Several books and articles have been written about the pinhole camera,[27] and there is an ongoing argument about its use by Renaissance artists. That is discussed in the section on art in Chapter 4.

The Kodak Box Camera

This ugly old camera was an improvement over the pinhole camera. It was a black cube about six inches on a side with the simplest of lenses in it instead of the simple pinhole. The film moved across the back of the box, and, of course, the image was upside down on the film. It was the standard personal camera for years, and Kodak made tons of money on the film it sold. That's what I call the Kodak effect: give the camera away and make money on the film.

Figure 50 Kodak box camera.[28]

One reason that George Eastman was initially successful was that he invented the dry film process that eliminated the need for an on-site photo lab. In addition to the simple box camera, Kodak had the very famous Brownies. These were not little girls in tan uniforms, or elves that make cookies; they were an array of different cameras all designed by Frank Brownell. There is also a nice treatment of this subject in book form.[28]

Figure 51 Discs.[28]

27   Shull, J., *The Hole Thing*, Morgan and Morgan 1974; Oakes, J. W., *Minimal Aperture Photography Using Pinhole Cameras*, University Press of America, 1986. *Optics and Photonics News*, November 2001.
28   Coe, B., *Kodak Cameras, the First Hundred Years*, Hove Foto Books, 1988. (Images courtesy of Hove Books, copyright 1988.)

Kodak had other cameras as well: Retinas, Retinettes, Instamatics, Discs and Pocket 110s, and folding cameras. The folding cameras usually had a folding front side and a lens that moved on bars with a bellows.

Kodak's true 35-mm cameras were those that used 35-mm film in rolls with perforations on the side, a format that is well known today, and originated by W. K. L. Dickson, Thomas Edison's assistant. They came in a variety of shapes and forms, but most were fold-out, fixed-lens devices.

The Kodak cartridge cameras came in three versions: Instamatic 126, Pocket 110, and disc. These are cameras into which you drop a film cassette. It does not need to be threaded and started on the rollers. The number "126" is an arbitrary designation; the format is 28 × 28 mm. To add to the confusion, many models were designated with other numbers, none of which was 126! They came in fixed-focus, reflex, and other forms. The distinction was the form of cassette. The Pockets were smaller cameras with 16-mm film—an image of 13 × 17 mm. These "spy" cameras were, out of necessity, simple. The disc cameras substituted a relatively rigid, rotary disc of film segments for the film cassettes.

The Retinas and Retinettes were typically 35 mm, fixed-lens cameras that folded the lenses out with a hinged part of the body. A few models were reflex cameras.

Figure 52 Folding (bellows) camera.[28]

The Single-Lens Reflex (SLR) Camera

This upscale camera has a detachable lens with an aperture in the front, a flip mirror in the body, and film that rolled by in the rear, the film plane. It is shown in Fig. 53. The two main advantages of this design are that the lenses can be interchanged and the viewer shows exactly what will show up on the film. That is because the mirror in the rear is in one position, shown by the solid line, when the picture is being lined up and in the other position, the dashed line, when the picture is taken. This also provides a subjective measure of whether the object is in focus. Does it look good in the viewer? It flips in the process of taking the picture. The lenses you can choose range from wide-angle versions (60 deg or so) to high-magnification telephoto lenses that give a magnification of about 500 and need a heavy tripod to support them!

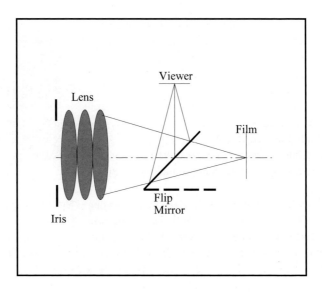

Figure 53 Single-lens reflex camera.

The Polaroid Instant Camera

The main thing that differentiates this camera from noninstant cameras is the film, at least in principle. Whereas Eastman invented the dry-film process, Edwin (Din) Land, who founded Polaroid,[29] invented instant-development film. By the way, Polaroid was started as a company that made polarizing films of oriented plastic, another invention of Land. We now know it as Polaroid, the material, not the company.

The Point-and-Shoot Camera

These "cameras for dummies" have a rangefinder that sets the focal position, a simple lens (usually about F/4), and a light meter that sets the shutter speed. So all you have to do is point it and shoot it. If there is not enough light, the electronic chip will send a signal to the flash system to activate that. What makes all this possible? First, the advent of very fast film; second, the advent of microchips that can translate the light measurement and range data into the settings; last, efficient optical rangefinders.

Digital Cameras

These are the most modern of personal cameras. The principal difference in principle is that they do not use film, but rather an array of solid-state-light sensors, or CCDs. These arrays are little silicon detectors that transform incident photons to

---

29   Wensberg, P. C., *Land's Polaroid*, Houghton Mifflin, 1987.

electrons in the chip. Whereas the resolution of film is usually better than that of a camera and depends some on the film, the format of these arrays varies and is a function of the cost. Each individual silicon sensor, called a pixel, is about 5–10 µm on a side. The format is specified in the number of megapixels (millions of pixels). The cameras range generally from a little less than one megapixel to about six. A one megapixel chip is about 15 mm or a half inch on a side. The sensors are at least as sensitive as high-speed film, so the tricks of the point-and-shoot cameras can apply. In addition, the picture can be shown on an LED screen before it is taken, and it can be erased later. The pictures are saved in electronic form, so that they can be transferred to a computer and manipulated with respect to size, contrast, hue, color, etc.

There is an important trade-off between the number of pixels and their performance. It is not advisable just to make the array larger in cross section. A larger chip is more expensive and requires that the rest of the camera be larger in proportion, making it costlier and more awkward. So the approach is to make the individual pixels smaller. But, in analogy to buckets, a smaller pixel can hold fewer electrons at maximum. This reduces both sensitivity and range of light conditions over which the camera can operate.[30]

These cameras may have optical zoom and/or electronic zoom. This latter technique entails combining the outputs of two or more pixels to make the image seem larger at the expense of resolution.

Little Cameras

The digital cameras just described are meant for consumer use and are about the size of the point-and-shoot cameras. However, very small versions are available that do not have all the features but have very different uses. They can be made the size of a lipstick or a pen. (A typical pixel is about 15 µm. A fairly large format is 500×500 pixels. Such a chip is then 7.5 mm, 0.3 inch on a side). The applications are mind bending. They can be mounted on phone poles and traffic lights to monitor anyone traveling and especially those who run red lights. Some, the size of a quarter, are used in remote-control cars, to watch babysitters, to find and nab philanderers, to watch for the Loch Ness monster, and watch for traffic jams.[31] James Bond can use one as well! As with many advances in technology, the uses can be good and bad, beneficial and detrimental. It is up to society to determine how this wonderful new imaging technology will be used.

30 Theuwissen, A., "For pixels, size matters," *Photonics Spectra*, August 2000.
31 *The Denver Post*, July 26, 1999.

Film

This is another subject that could take a book—and has taken several! Films come in different sizes, in black and white, color, and in different speeds (sensitivities) and granularities. Film is generally an acetate backing with an emulsion laid on top of it. The emulsion generally consists of silver halides and other materials.

The sizes include the ubiquitous 35-mm film, and this indicates that the long dimension of a single exposure is 35 mm. Another is 24 mm. A variant is the half-frame 35-mm film, which portrays two images on one 35-mm frame, each 24-mm long and 18-mm wide. The APS film has an image area of 16.7×30.2 mm. These have been used in some so-called spy cameras. Size 120, used in larger cameras, is 6 cm wide, and is often specified as 6×6 film. Variants include 6×7 and 6×9, all indicating the size of the film in centimeters. Large-format cameras use film that is approximately 10×13 and 20×25 cm, but these are restricted to professional use because they are very expensive and hard to handle.

Films come with different speeds and resolutions, and, generally, we trade speed for resolution. That is, the high-speed films have somewhat lower resolution, because they have larger grains that collect more photons. Films have historically been rated by either an American Standard Association (ASA) or Deutsche Industrial Norm (DIN) number. The 35-mm color film I used with my first camera was ASA 35, and that was as fast as you could get. Today, ratings are by International Standards Organization (ISO) numbers. The ISO is a modern standardization agency. In a sense, it copped out with its new numbers, but it does make it easy to compare. The ISO number is a combination of the ASA and DIN numbers. For instance, a film with an ASA of 32 and a corresponding DIN of 16 has an ISO of 32/16. See, they used them both! Current films range from 25/15 to 3200/36, a far cry from some years back. These are all arbitrary ratings, just like the scores in a diving competition, but they are less subjective!

Telescopes

Most modern telescopes are made of front-surface mirrors, with the reflective coating on the front surface. They come in a variety of shapes, sizes, and combinations. Their design is a part of the more general discipline of optical design, which includes the design of lenses, mirrors, prisms, gratings, and other optical elements.

Astronomical and Terrestrial Telescopes

These two types differ according to whether the object is at infinity and whether an erect image is available to the eye. If the object is at infinity and the image is inverted, the telescope is said to be astronomical. These are the types used in observatories. Sighting telescopes, used by the military and hunters, are terrestrial.

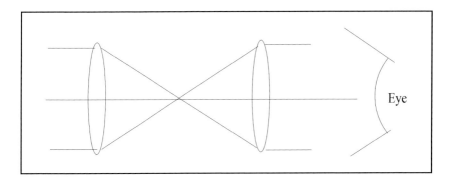

Figure 54 Terrestrial Keplerian telescope.

Terrestrial Telescopes

These devices provide an image directly to the eye and therefore need some mechanism to make the image erect rather than inverted. Two classical versions of this are the Keplerian and Galilean telescopes. The Keplerian telescope uses a simple, positive objective lens followed by a simple, positive eyepiece, as shown in Fig. 54. There is a primary image between the lenses. The secondary lens, called an eyepiece, collimates the beam and sends it to the eye. The image is therefore erect and appears to be at infinity—or at least far away.

The version devised by Galileo uses a negative eyepiece, as shown in Fig. 55. It still erects and collimates, but is somewhat shorter. The diameter of the exit pupil, which is the size of the beam that exits the telescope, is normally set at 3 mm in order to "match" the entrance pupil of the eye, which varies from about 3 mm in bright light to 8 mm in dim illumination. The telescopes are assumed to operate during the day. Night vision devices have larger exit pupils. Binoculars and rifle scopes usually have pupils of about 5 mm to allow easier viewing by the eye.

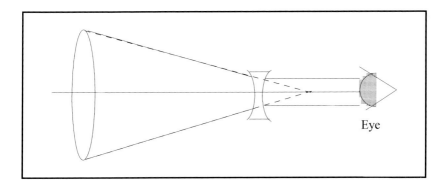

Figure 55 Terrestrial Galilean telescope.

Single-Mirror Astronomical Telescopes

As indicated in the title, only one mirror is used to collect the light. The simplest of these is the spherical mirror. Spheres are the easiest surfaces to make. If you rub two surfaces together long enough with a little grit between them, they will both end up being spheres. Unfortunately, spherical mirrors suffer from spherical aberration. This is discussed in the section on mirrors.

Another difficulty with these mirrors is that they fold the light back on itself, so that some means must be established to make the focal plane, or image, accessible. One technique for doing this was created by Sir Isaac Newton. He put a folding flat in place, as illustrated in Fig. 56.

Many years later, A. H. Pfund, of Johns Hopkins University, modified this technique by using the folding flat before reflection from the paraboloidal mirror. It provides much less obscuration of the beam.

Herschel used a different technique; he just tipped the mirror. This eliminates all obscuration, but it introduces comatic aberration. This is an off-axis aberration, and the geometric theorem about parallel rays coming to a focus applies only to on-axis rays.

A modern version is to use an *eccentric pupil* system (Fig. 59). Approximately half of the full mirror is used. The rays are then on axis, and there is no obscuration. Obviously, the bottom half of the mirror is not used. The mirror for the eccen-

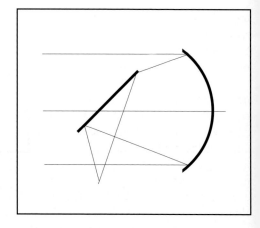

Figure 56 Newtonian telescope.

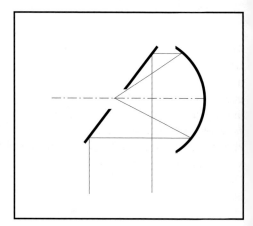

Figure 57 Pfund telescope.

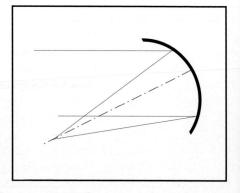

Figure 58 Herschellian mirror.

tric pupil system is then more difficult to make than one of the same size for the Herschellian telescope. One way is to make a mirror that is as large as the full mirror and cut it in half. The cutting can be done carefully on the lap with a special tool that resembles a hole saw. Another way is to make just the smaller mirror using modern numerically controlled grinding machines. The choice depends upon such things as the tolerances and the availability of the machines.

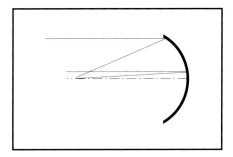

Figure 59 Eccentric pupil mirror.

Two-Mirror Astronomical Telescopes

The use of two mirrors provides two advantages. The first is that the direction of the light is not reversed (actually, it is reversed twice); the second is that the imagery is better. The most common of the two-mirror systems is probably the Cassegrain. It consists of a paraboloidal primary and hyperboloidal secondary. Again, plane geometry teaches that any ray directed toward the one focus of a hyperbola will go to the focus of the other sheet.

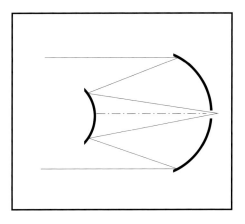

Figure 60 Cassegrain telescope.

This is illustrated in Fig. 60. Thus, the rays of light that enter parallel to the axis of the paraboloid are directed to the focus of the paraboloid and then to the hyperboloid, where they are reflected to its other focus.

There have been two modifications of the Cassegrain design. One employs a spherical secondary, and is therefore easier to fabricate, but has a somewhat poorer performance. The other employs two general aspherical surfaces, and is both harder to make and performs better. The first is called a Dall-Kirkham; the second a Ritchey-Chretien. The latter was the design used for the Hubble telescope.

Many other designs have been conjured up using three and more mirrors. An excellent description is given in two publications by the Optical Society of America.[32]

---

32 Turner, M., "Reflecting and catadioptric objectives," *The Optical Engineer's Desk Reference*, W. L. Wolfe, ed., Optical Society of America, 2003; Jones, L., "Reflective and catadioptric objectives," *Handbook of Optics*, Bass, M., E. Van Strylen, W. L. Wolfe, eds., the Optical Society of America and SPIE, 1999.

The Palomar Telescope

One goal of astronomy in its search for knowledge about our universe has always been larger telescopes. The "classic" approach has been to make larger and larger monolithic chunks of glass. The Hale telescope on Mount Palomar has been the most famous of these. It is a large piece of silicate glass that is mounted on top of a mountain in Southern California, near San Diego. I consider it the first of the really large telescopes, but I guess many were considered large as they grew from 10 inches to 20 to 30 to 60 to 100 to 200 inches. Certainly the Mount Wilson telescope at 100 inches (2.54 m) and the Hale have to be considered large. They are bigger in diameter than I am tall (or short). The Hale took about ten years; it was finished in 1938. There were monumental difficulties in casting such a disk in quartz, and finally the effort was ceased in favor of Pyrex glass. Pyrex has a much larger thermal expansion, so that final figuring took a long time. The grinding and polishing of the Hale primary, in fact, took more than two years. At the end, when extreme precision was required, they could polish no more than an hour at a time before they had to stop to measure the figure. Although the glass did not get hot, it heated enough that thermal expansion affected the instantaneous figure of the mirror.

Two other technical advances contributed to the success of the Hale telescope. John Strong developed an evaporative process for depositing a highly reflective aluminum surface on the mirror. Heretofore such surfaces were silver, which tarnishes like any silver—it becomes covered with silver sulfide. Aluminum oxidizes, but it then becomes a sapphire, transparent, hard overcoat. In conjunction with the Mount Wilson telescope, Frank Ross developed a refracting corrector for use near the focus that greatly extended the useful field of view.

The telescope has a parabolic primary and two different secondaries. One is the hyperbola for the Cassegrain configuration, the other is flat for the Newtonian. Still another, the coudé (pronounced coo-day), essentially an extended Newtonian, is shown in Fig. 61.

Additional descriptions of the Palomar project, including politics, funding, structures, and more, are in the literature.[33]

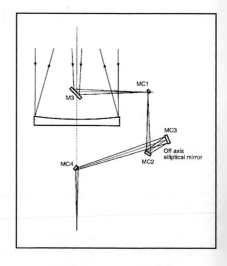

Figure 61 Coudé focus.

---

33   Wright, H., *Palomar, The World's Largest Telescope*, Macmillan, 1952, and Woodbury, D. O., *Glass Giant of Palomar*, Dodd, 1939.

The Multiple-Mirror Telescope

An alternative technique for the construction of large telescopes was proposed and implemented by Aden Meinel and Frank Low. They thought that if they used several mirrors to collect the light and then combined the individual outputs to a single focus, it would be more efficient. The telescope they constructed was called the Multiple-Mirror Telescope or MMT. The six 1.8-m mirrors of the 'scope were made in the Optical Sciences Center optical shop at the University of Arizona, and the entire telescope was mounted in a dome on Mount Hopkins in southern Arizona in 1979. This was the first telescope that did not use a monolithic primary mirror. Two comparisons can be made with the Hale telescope: the first is the collecting area, the second is the resolution. The Hale primary, with a 200-inch diameter, and an area of 31,416 square inches (20.26 square meters), is 1.286 times larger in collecting area than the MMT. The resolution is also determined by the diameter, but this is more complicated. The Hale diameter is 200 inches (5.08 meters). The MMT, when used in the ordinary mode, has a diameter of 72 inches for each mirror. But when two mirrors are used coherently, that is, the light from the two mirrors is combined in exactly the right way, the effective diameter is somewhat larger than 220 inches, a little better than the Hale. Exactly the right way, coherently, means that the distance from each of the mirrors to the focal point is exactly the same, to within a fraction of the wavelength of the light. The MMT was constructed in about three years from its beginning to first light (the first look at the sky), and cost much less in equivalent dollars. I had the pleasure of providing a little assistance to Jacques Beckers in determining thermal gradients in the housing for this telescope.

The Adaptive Optics Telescope

Adaptive optics mirrors are described in the section on mirrors. In short, they are mirrors the shapes of which can be varied enough to compensate for distorted incoming wavefronts. For the system to work, however, the amount and type of distortion must be measured in order for the mirror to be properly adjusted. This is done in one of two ways, either by the use of a real star or the generation of a fake star (a known source above the atmosphere). That source has been created in two ways. One is to shine a laser at air molecules about 15 kilometers above Earth; the other is to use a laser to excite sodium molecules that have been placed 95 kilometers (km) high.[34]

---

34   Hardin, R., "Laser helps take twinkle out of stargazing," *Photonics Spectra*, December 1997.

Modern Ground-Based Telescopes

Several telescopes that are really
large have come from recent developments. One such is the idea
of multiple mirrors; the other is
the use of large, spun Pyrex mirrors.

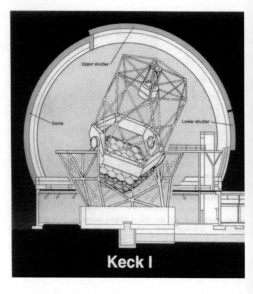

The Keck telescope on Mauna
Kea in Hawaii is a 10-m diameter
telescope accomplished by con-
tacting many 0.9-m octagonal
mirrors. The MMT is considered a
dilute multiple-aperture primary,
since the individual mirrors are
not in contact. The Keck is called
a filled aperture. A drawing is
shown in Fig. 62.

The Large Binocular Tele-
scope (LBT) atop Mount Graham
in Arizona uses two 8-m primaries
in a double Cassegrain configuration shown in Figs. 63 and 64 be-

Figure 62 The Keck telescope. (Image courtesy of Keck Observatory.)

ing trucked up the mountain. They are combined coherently. The collection area is
200 square meters; the effective diameter for resolution is about 24 m. The mirrors
were made by the spun Pyrex technique in the University of Arizona Mirror Lab.

Pennsylvania State University designed an 8-m telescope that is considered partially filled, for which many circular mirrors are placed in contact. So there does exist

Figure 63 Mirror Box.[35]   **Figure 64** One binocular mirror cell.[35]

35   Photos courtesy John Hill, Jim Slagle, and John Little.

Figure 65 Large Binocular Telescope Observatory at sunset.[35]

some nonmirror areas in the overall primary, but the mirrors are not separated. The European Space Organization has erected a telescope in La Silla, Chile, high in the Andes. It has a 3.5-m, thin monolithic primary, with active correction by way of pistons. They have planned a larger version that incorporates many individual telescopes.

The Hubble Space Telescope (HST)

This may be the most widely known telescope in existence! A Ritchey-Chretien design with a 2.4-m primary mirror diameter, it has an extremely lightweight egg-crate blank of ultra-low expansion fused quartz. It was designed to be diffraction limited at about 0.6 μm wavelength. However, as was widely chronicled, it had serious spherical aberration. This arose from an error in the testing process. As discussed in the section on testing mirrors, one of the most precise methods is interferometry. However, interferometric tests can only be performed when the imagery is sufficiently good. To get to this point, a correcting lens is used, although the lens can be a mirror, and the mirror must be in the right place. The workers had a very nice method of placing the mirror correctly which involved using a beam of light to see where it was. Unfortunately, there was a reflecting spot on the surround that gave a spurious reflection that imitated the fiducial mark they were using. The mirror displaced axially about 1.3 mm from where it should have been. They measured wrong; so they ground and polished to the wrong figure (shape). A second check was made with a different Offner compensator, and it showed the discrepancy. The corrector or compensator design is not significant, but they were both designed by Abe Offner of Perkin Elmer, who made the telescope. Unfortunately, the workers had more faith in the first-described measurement than the latter, and they failed to make another check. They were way over budget and time! One other criticism can be leveled: there was no end-to-end check.

The in-space fix has worked beautifully. After the problem was analyzed, a program was established to correct the telescope. Appropriate correctors were used in each of the instruments near the focus of the HST in 1993. Since then, as stated by R. N. Wilson, "...the HST has been converted from a public debacle to a public and astronomical triumph." I can claim a very small contribution to the fix when I was on sabbatical at Ball Brothers, Inc.

The Next-Generation Space Telescope

The Hubble Space Telescope, after its ignominious start, has performed some astronomical feats of imaging our galaxy and beyond. The Next-Generation Space Telescope (NGT), later known as NNTT (National New Technology Telescope), and then known as the James Webb Telescope, is an even more ambitious undertaking.[36] It will (probably) be an 8-m diameter mirror that operates in the infrared portion of the spectrum (about 1 to 25 μm), providing an angular resolution of about 0.06 seconds of arc (0.29 μrad) at 2 μm that covers a field of view of about 4×4 arc minutes over a

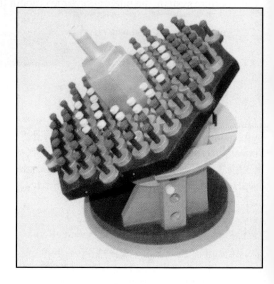

Figure 66 The Discus model.[37]

lifetime of 10 years. Over the full lifetime of the mission it can cover the entire sky.

Probably the most critical technology driver is the weight of the mirror. It is meant to be large, with a diameter of 6 m. NASA originally chose four pathways for an appropriate lightweight mirror: a lightweight egg-crate structure with a borosilicate glass faceplate, a similar structure with a Zerodur faceplate, a "hogged-out" beryllium mirror, and a carbon-reinforced silicon carbide lightweighted mirror. They settled on the use of 36 semirigid hexagonal segments, much like the Keck telescope. The optics will be deployed in space and will have an inflatable sun shield. The telescope will be sent to a point in space called the second Lagrange point where the gravitational attractions of the Earth and sun just cancel each other, and where a single shield can protect it from the heat of both the sun and the Earth, so it can be better maintained at a temperature of about 50 K.

---

36   Seery, B. and E. Smith, "NASA's Next Generation Space Telescope," *Optics and Photonics News*, 29, July 1998,

Spectrometers

Spectrometers are devices that measure the spectra of light that is either emitted or absorbed by various materials. They come in different forms and are very important optical instruments, as there are many applications for measuring spectra. We can categorize spectrometers as dispersive devices, transform devices, and laser spectrometers. A spectrum is a representation of the amount of light as a function of wavelength. It can be portrayed on film (with a spectrograph), as an electrical signal (a spectrometer), or directly to the eye (a spectroscope). I will call them all spectrometers. They are useful for identifying all sorts of materials, since each material has a specific spectrum, as unique as a fingerprint.

Dispersive Spectrometers

At the heart of these devices is either a prism or a grating to separate light into its constituent colors to obtain a spectrum. They can be emissive or absorptive. An emissive, dispersive spectrometer that uses a prism is shown in its basic form in Fig. 70. The light from a source to be analyzed is placed at the focus of a lens. The lens focuses the light onto the entrance slit. The collimating lens then collimates the beam to shine it onto the prism, which breaks it up into its colors. The camera (focusing) lens directs the light to the focal plane, where there is an exit slit. The exit slit allows only one color to pass through to the detector, where the amount of the light of that color is measured. In operation, the prism is rotated so that one color after another passes through the exit slit to the detector. A record is made of the amount of the light for each color. This is called the spectrum of the light, and it applies not only to visible colors but to light of all wavelengths. I have shown only two of the many colors from the prism. The part of the device between the slits is called the *monochromator* because it separates the light into its monochromatic components.

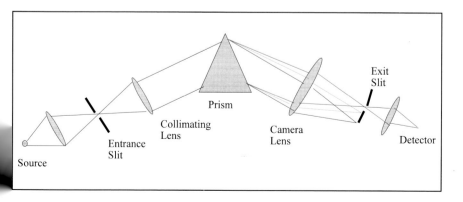

Figure 70 Basic emission spectrometer.

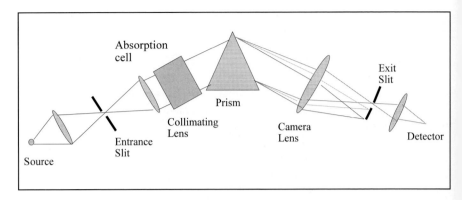

Figure 71 Absorption spectrometer.

A spectrograph has film at the position of the exit slit, and does not have an exit slit or detector. The entire spectrum is recorded on the film. A spectroscope also does not have an exit slit; the exit lens collimates the light to the eye. The entire spectrum is seen by the user.

An important variation on this design is to use a grating instead of a prism. This involves advantages and disadvantages too numerous to elaborate, but prism characteristics depend upon the materials, whereas gratings can be fabricated with various line densities. Thus, the dispersion can be adjusted with a grating, and gratings can be made larger than many prisms. Gratings can also be either transmissive or reflective, and some gratings are concave, thereby accomplishing both focusing and dispersing.

Many spectrometers are used in the absorptive mode; that is they measure the spectrum of light that is absorbed. The light from a known source that is part of the spectrometer is handled in just the same way as shown, but after the entrance slit and before the prism, there is an absorption cell that contains the material (usually a liquid or gas) to be analyzed. With this basic system, two runs must be made: The first to characterize the source, the second to measure the unknown. A ratio is then calculated to obtain the spectrum from the unknown. I did some of my graduate work in the Middle Ages with such a single-beam spectrometer. It was very tedious. Modern instruments use two beams and use computers to calculate the ratios.

Spectrometers come in many guises. One is a double-pass instrument. Figure 72 shows one example of how this can be arranged. By using a plane mirror with the prism, you can get the beam to pass through the prism twice to get twice the dispersion and therefore the spectral resolution, compared to a single-pass instrument. There is a price to pay, and that is space. Notice how far apart the components are. That is because the incident and reflected beams have to be separated.

Double-beam spectrometers are used to automatically obtain the spectrum of the unknown. The monochromator portion of the spectrometer is one of the versions described above or below. The key is obtaining both a sample beam and a ref

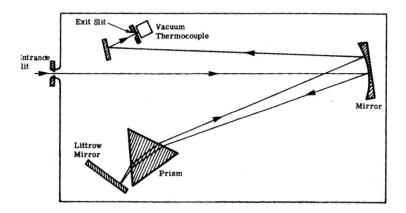

Figure 72 Double pass with a Littrow mount.

erence beam. There are several ways to do this. Figure 73 shows one example. The absorption cell shown in Fig. 71 is replaced by the configuration shown in Fig. 73. The light comes in from the upper left. It is generated by an appropriate source and is collimated by appropriate optics.

The optical chopper, a device much like a household fan, with blades and spaces, chops it (Fig. 73). When a blade is in the beam, the beam goes down and through the sample cell. When a space is there, the beam goes through the reference cell. The two beams are combined by the beamsplitter and sent to the detector. The detector measures the alternate pulses that are generated, and takes their ratio.

An alternative scheme replaces the chopper with a beamsplitter and uses a detector at the output of each of the cells. Although this produces a device that has no moving parts, we must make sure both detectors have the same response.

The schemes and layouts I have shown here are representative and basic. Just to show that these spectrometers can be much more complicated, I have included a diagram of a very popular design of some years ago in Fig. 74.

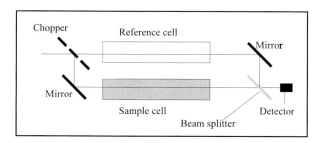

Figure 73 Example of a double beam.

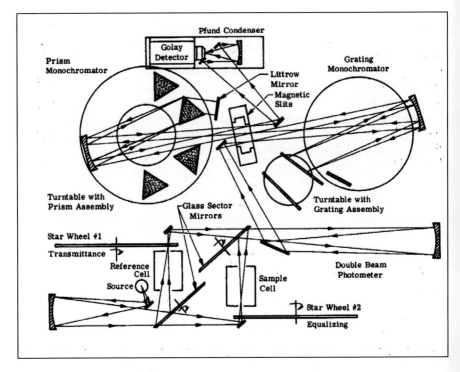

Figure 74 The Unicam spectrometer of Perkin Elmer.

Nondispersive Spectrometers

These devices do not use a grating or prism; the light is not dispersed. They are interferometers that first obtain an interferogram and then calculate the spectrum from that. They are described in the section on interferometers.

Laser Spectrometers

These devices use an array of lasers or a tunable laser so that light of different wavelengths is shone onto the sample. A detector measures the amount of reflected or transmitted light, with calibration, to determine the spectrum. They are accurate and have high resolution because the spectral width of the lasers is so small. No prism or grating is necessary. No dispersion is involved.

Microscopes and Magnifiers

Introduction

These devices make small objects appear larger. Magnifiers are often used for such things as reading maps and the fine print on contracts, or by age-advantaged people. Whereas magnifiers magnify by about 5 to 10 times, microscopes can attain much larger magnifications and are therefore used for such things as biological imaging, identifying germs, circuit-board inspection, and forensic work.

Simple Magnifier

This is just a lens, a so-called reading glass. The magnification is the ratio of the image distance to the object distance, and the ratio of image size to the object size is equal to this magnification. This simple geometric relation is shown in Fig. 75, including the rays from the object to the image for a given position. As shown, the magnification is about four to one. Note the ray construction is such that a ray from the object parallel to the axis passes through the rear focal point. A ray through the front focus emerges from the lens parallel to the axis. The image is located where the rays intersect. Greater magnification can be obtained by moving the object closer to the focus (but not inside the focal point). Some less-simple magnifiers are shown in Fig. 76. The biconvex version is the simplest, cheapest, and most common. The next-most-used is the separated doublet. The Coddington is a solid piece, but is also essentially a doublet. The Hastings triplet (not shown) is a contact triplet, and the achromat is triplet of lenses that are essentially the reverse of those of the Hastings—positive for negative and negative for positive lenses.

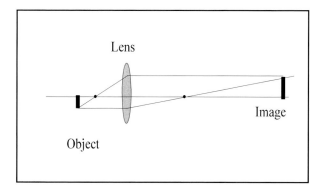

Figure 75 Simple magnifier.

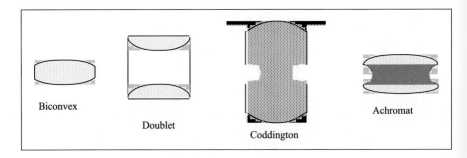

Biconvex

Doublet

Coddington

Achromat

Figure 76 Magnifiers.

Simple Microscope

The standard optical microscope was invented by Galileo in 1610. It consists of
two lenses (or lens combinations), the objective and the
eyepiece. The objective,
which has a short focal
length, is close to the object
and forms a magnified im-
age of it between the two
lenses. The eyepiece forms
an image that is greatly magnified. The eye sees this
magnified image of the original object. Most classical
microscopes of this type
have three different objectives that realize three dif-

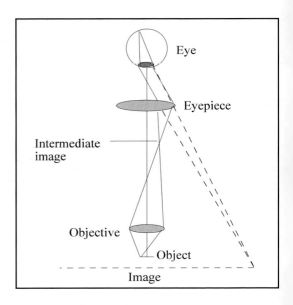

Figure 77 Simple microscope.

ferent overall magnifications. They are ordinarily arranged in turrets that can be rotated in front of the eyepiece.[41]

There are various designs for both the eyepiece and the objective. Most microscopes have a fixed objective, the design of which depends largely upon the cost.
They then usually have three different eyepieces that provide different magnifications by having different focal lengths.[42]

---

41   Jenkins, F., and H. White, *Fundamentals of Optics*, McGraw Hill, 1957. (Image
     courtesy of McGraw-Hill, copyright 1957.)
42   ibid.

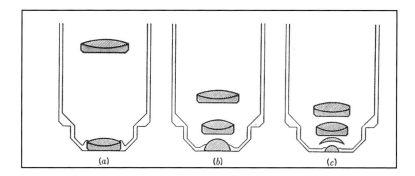

Figure 78 Microscope objectives.[41]

Microscope Objectives

Figure 78 shows three microscope objectives. They are low, medium, and high power objectives, and are usually mounted on the same stand so that they can be interchanged. The low-power objective (a) is just a pair of double lenses. The medium power objective (b) adds a third lens, a hemisphere, and adjusts the distances appropriately. The high-power version (c) has still another lens and uses oil immersion. The first two lenses do not come in contact with the object, but the highest power objective touches the object in an oil bath. They are all designed to correct for as many aberrations as possible. Of course, the more surfaces and spacings, the more correction is available. Modern microscopes have even more complicated (and expensive) objectives than these for greater aberration correction.

Eyepieces

These are also called oculars, and logically enough are right next to the eye. They correct the aberrations of the objectives (as much as possible) and send a collimated beam to the viewer's eye with enough eye relief (distance behind the lens, where the eye can be positioned) that using the microscope is not harder than it needs to be. Several eyepieces are shown in Fig. 79. They all collimate the light to the eye on the right just out of the figure.

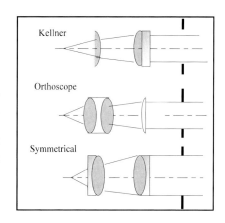

Figure 79 Eyepieces.

Phase-Contrast Microscopes

Transparent objects cannot be imaged by an ordinary microscope. To solve this problem, Frits Zernicke invented the phase-contrast microscope. Its basic function

is the interference of two beams. In
the diagram (Fig. 80), light comes
from the bottom, perhaps a mir-
ror-based illumination system. It is
collimated by the condenser and
passes through the specimen. Here,
no contrast is generated because it is
completely transparent, but it does
change the phase of the light across
the wavefront, except for the center.
A phase plate (a plate that shifts the
phase of the wave by a given amount)
is introduced so that the wave from
the rest of the region can interfere
with this reference wave. The interference then provides the contrast in
the image plane.

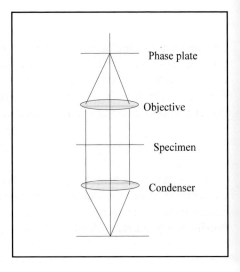

Figure 80 Phase-contrast principle.

Confocal Microscopes

In a confocal microscope, the source of light, a
pinhole, the object, and the detector are all images of one another; they are confocal. The arrangement is shown in Fig. 81. This means
that, unlike the normal microscope, only a
small spot on the object is seen, but it is seen
clearly with no background or other interference. This arrangement also allows the operator to focus a little below the surface to do a little subsurface inspection. Of course, to obtain
an areal image one must scan the spot over the
field.[43] This can be done either with a mirror in
the microscope or by moving the stage.

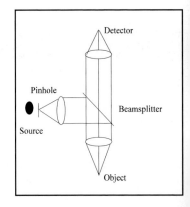

Figure 81 Confocal microscope.

Interference Microscope

This device—and there are many versions—is just a combination of a microscope
(or two) and an interferometer. One can imagine any of the interferometers discussed in that section with microscope optics in each of the arms. On the other
hand, one can imagine an interferometer that has microscope optics for its output.

---

43   Keller, H. E., *Handbook of Biological Confocal Microscopy*, 1995.

Two-Photon Microscopy

This technique is similar to confocal fluorescence microscopy, but is not quite the same. It uses a source laser that is twice the wavelength of absorption of the treatment dye. It then takes two photons arriving at the same time to excite fluorescence in the dye. The laser light is outside the measurement spectrum, and it therefore causes no background or other interference.[44]

Tomographic Microscope

A microscope using the principles of tomography and phase-shifting interferometry has been designed and built. A 633-nanometer (nm) laser illuminates the object successively from several different angles. During each illumination, a piezoelectrically driven mirror shifts the phase of the reference beam three times, each 120 deg., thereby generating three interference patterns that are sensed by a CCD. A computer program takes each interferogram from each angle and calculates a 3D model. Once the information is in the computer, all sorts of sections and views can be generated.[45]

Outputs

The eyepiece is normally the output of a microscope, but all sorts of options are available once the microscopic image has been generated. We can easily imagine replacing the eye with a camera, and a photographic microscope is the result. We can use a beamsplitter and have a microscope that provides an image to both the eye and a camera. Or we can affix two eyepieces to create a microscope. Then, to extend things even more, the output can be a spectrometer, a Raman spectrometer,[46] a fluorescence spectrometer, or other analysis device. Figure 82 shows a microscope fitted with a Raman spectrometer; it illustrates the use of several output ports and a special means of illumination.

Microspectroscopy

By using special optical techniques, researchers have been able to perform spectroscopy with a resolution spot of less than 100 nm. The process is to use a fiber optic probe that has been narrowed at its end to a diameter of 50 to 100 nm. This probe is brought to within about 5 nm of the sample. Light is shone from an appropriate

---

44 "Confocal or multiphoton: what's the difference?," *Biophotonics International*, September/October 1997.
45 Russell, N. D., "Tomographic microscope produces 3-D images of cells," *Biophotonics International*, December 2000.
46 Hollricher, O., "Combine and conquer," *OEmagazine*, November 2003.

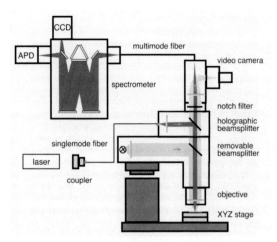

Figure 82 A confocal Raman microscope consists of a dual-output port spectrometer integrated with a confocal microscope. A single-mode optical fiber provides point-source illumination and the core diameter of a multimode fiber provides the confocal pinhole in the focal plane.

source, like a laser, down the fiber to the sample and is picked up by a high numerical aperture receiver. The light is then sent to a spectrometer of some sort—filter, wheel, prism, grating, array, or other. The sample is then moved in x and y directions to obtain an image by scanning the array of 100-nm pixels.[47] The technique is relatively inefficient of light, and the tips are hard to manufacture and maintain, but it does work.

Other Scopes

Endoscopes

These devices are used to explore the interior parts of our bodies. Typically, they are inserted into our mouths and threaded down our throats to get to the stomach and other interior parts. They are about 10–12 mm in diameter. The sigmoidoscope, commonly known as the *flexi sig,* is inserted in the other end, and explores the colon. These endoscopes, meaning scopes that go inside, come in essentially two forms. One is a collection of fiber optics that sends light down some of the fibers and relays an image of the object that is at the anterior end of the probe. This is the classical and older form of an endoscope. The more modern version has a light source, a very tiny camera at the anterior end. This digital camera takes a picture of

47   Robinson, M., *Photonics Spectra*, September 1997.

what is around it and relays it to the end of the endoscope by wires, and in some cases by transmitting in space. Further variations of these endoscopes consist of the other functions they may have at the anterior end. These may include appropriate cutters to remove polyps or other things, dyes that can be inserted to aid either fluorescence imaging, or x-ray imaging.[48]

One fascinating endoscope is a free-floating pill! The patient swallows a pill that is 11×27 mm. This travels down the gastrointestinal tract and on the way it takes pictures, transmits them to a receiver on the belt of the patient, and keeps track of where it is by calculation. The doctor then views the record that has been obtained some 24 hours later. A white-light LED illuminates the areas. The 256×256 CCD camera records the imagery. Although it takes some 5 hours to download all this information, the doctor can view what is effectively a movie of the gastrointestinal tract in a much shorter time. Initial tests have proven encouraging, but there are some drawbacks. The MD cannot direct the pill in any way–back it up, have it look to the side, etc. The pill is, however, fairly well oriented by its geometry: it is cylindrical in a tubular track.[49]

Another similar capsule is called "robotic." It is intended to be maneuverable from outside the body, although no details have been given about how this will work. We can speculate that magnets would be used. If it had feet or tracks, it could be instructed to back up, although this could be somewhat painful. Other functions could also be incorporated.[50]

A very unusual endoscope is applied to a woman's breast. It is only 0.9–1.2 mm in diameter and is inserted through the nipple, provides a 6000-pixel image, and is used to map the breast ducts for things like hyperplasia and carcinoma. In practice, after insertion a saline solution is injected to expand the ducts. The scope must be small, so the CCD is very small. In preliminary tests, the endoscope found 75% of the lesions that were confirmed with biopsies. It was also reported that the endoscope was used to help define the edges of a tumor in breast conservation surgery. Nothing was said about pain or discomfort.[51]

Stroboscopes

These devices are cameras with pulsed light sources. They have the ability to make it appear that moving things stand still. Imagine a butterfly flapping its wings 20 times a second. This means that every twentieth of a second the wings are in exactly the same position. If the light source is pulsed at 20 times a second and the camera is

---

48 Leggett, K., "Endoscopy: many pluses, still a few minuses," *Biophotonics International*, March/April 1999.
49 Rowell, N. D., "Endoscopes go wireless," *Photonics Spectra*, March 2001.
50 Ibid.
51 "Endoscope improves breast cancer detection and surgery," *Biophotonics International*, November 2000.

synchronized to the light source, the wings are pictured only when they are in that particular position. The stroboscope can be of the type just described, with its own source of light, or it can just be a camera with a fast, repetitive shutter. It depends upon how much light is available.

One interesting stroboscopic event appears on our television sets. TV pictures come to us at a frame rate of about 30 per second. So TVs are a form of stroboscope. In some ads, cars are shown rolling along on the road, but their wheels seem to be rotating backwards. This is a stroboscopic effect. The TV frames would make the tires look stationary if they rotated at 30 times per second, but they usually rotate a little slower, so the TV makes them look as if they rotate backwards because the TV rate is just a little faster than the tire rotation rate.

Periscopes

These are optical instruments in long tubes. We are probably all familiar with their use in submarines. They allow the captain to raise the periscope above the water surface and hunt for enemy ships. How do the optics work in such a long tube? The answer is by relays. A periscope consists of alternating relay lenses and field lenses, as shown in Fig. 83.[52] The objective forms an image of the object in the first field lens. The field lens controls the angular field of view, and prevents the image from extending beyond the sides of the periscope. The relay lenses reimage the field lenses. This is repeated as many times as necessary.

Kaleidoscopes

These toys use bits of glass held loosely in a tube with two or more mirrors, which reflect their images to the eye in changing patterns as the tube is rotated.

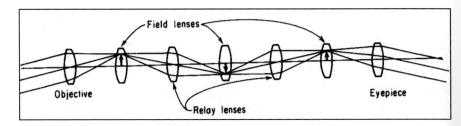

Figure 83 Periscope optics.[52]

---

52   Smith, W., Chapter 2, "Image formation," *The Handbook of Optics*, Driscoll W., and W. Vaughan, eds., McGraw-Hill, 1978. (Image courtesy of McGraw-Hill, copyright 1978.)

Borescopes

These devices image the inside surfaces of cylinders (and similar hollow structures). Typically, they contain a camera and a rotating mirror. They may also incorporate fiber optics. Figure 84 shows one such design. The fiber optics could, in some cases, be a relay telescope or a periscope.

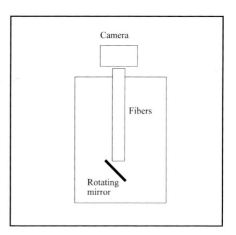

Figure 84 Borescope.

Colposcopes

These devices are used for inspecting the cervix. One is shown schematically in Fig. 85. A light is shone into the cervical cavity down the middle of the optical system. A lens is used to image the cervix onto both a camera and a binocular viewer. This allows the physician to both see what he wants and to record it. Some training devices have two binocular viewers. Some have interchangeable setups so that either a camera or a viewer can be used. The figure is obviously a schematic. There may be other optics for the light source and more complicated optics for the viewers. Most designs use a little folding mirror in the center of the optics to reflect the light toward the cervix. It obscures a small portion of the return beam.

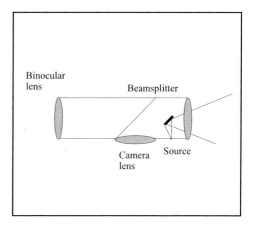

Figure 85 Colposcope.

Lasers

These absolutely wonderful sources of light produce coherent, bright, monochromatic beams that are useful because of these properties. Lasers come in a variety of sizes, shapes, and mechanisms, but every one of them relies upon an inversion of stable states. One way to view lasers is that they are super-luminescent sources. Electrons are raised to a higher state of energy, a metastable state. Then they fall to lower energy states and in the process emit photons. The difference between this and the generation of ordinary light is that this process occurs in a special cavity. The cavity is sometimes a cylinder with a mirror at one end and a partial mirror at the other. It is not hollow, but filled with the laser material. As described in the section on interferometers, the spacing determines that only waves of a certain frequency can exist in such a cavity. This makes the laser essentially monochromatic. Where the amplitude of the wave is at its maximum, it triggers other electrons to drop down from the metastable states in synchrony with the waves moving back and forth in the cavity. So the amplification is done in phase with synchrony. The waves are reflected from the back (completely reflective) mirror, while on each pass some of the light passes through the partially reflective mirror at the front end. Because the electrons are triggered at the maxima of the waves that move back and forth in the cavity, the light is enhanced at the peaks and is therefore coherent. Because the light moves back and forth many, many times in the cavity, the light is well collimated. (In one second, light in a one-foot long laser will go back and forth about 100 million times.)

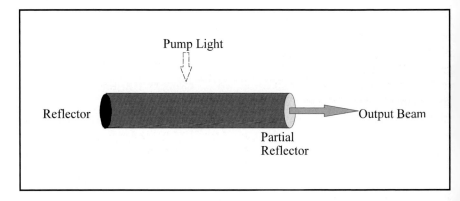

Figure 86 Laser schematic.

Solid Lasers

The first laser was a cylindrical ruby rod with flat ends that were reflective and partially reflective, as described. A flash lamp was the source of energy to raise the electrons to their metastable states. The beam was almost monochromatic, in phase and red. It was very bright.

Since then, many other solid rods have been used. A popular one is made of yttrium-aluminum-garnet doped with neodymium, abbreviated Nd:YAG and pronounced in the trade as "nid-yag." Many other dopants are used to obtain laser action at many different wavelengths, because the impurities used as dopants set up different energy levels in the material, analogous to impurities in semiconductors.

Gas Lasers

Gas can be used as the active material in a laser. Two of the most commonly used are carbon dioxide and a combination of helium and neon. The carbon-dioxide laser operates at about 10 μm and can be very powerful (in kilowatts). The helium-neon (nicknamed a heenie for the element symbols, He and Ne) laser operates in the red and is much less powerful (milliwatts). They have in common the cylinder with mirrors, and usually an electrical stimulation.

Diode Lasers

In a very real sense these are super LEDs. An LED (light-emitting diode) is formed between two parallel flat mirrors, one of which is partially transparent. The p and the n regions are above and below the active region. The mirrors are on the front and the back. The photons are generated by the current that flows between the p and n regions of this diode. The photons so generated traverse back and

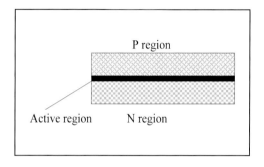

Figure 87 Diode laser.

forth between the mirrors, sometimes exiting the partially reflecting mirror. The same things that apply to gas lasers apply here: the light is essentially monochromatic, coherent, and well collimated. However, the light is collimated in only one direction since the diode is essentially a planar structure. Thus, the inherent beam of the laser diode is collimated in one direction, but spreads in the other direction. As shown in Fig. 87, the light is emitted out of the page toward the reader, and the beam would be narrow vertically, but spread horizontally. The origin of these lasers has been nicely described recently.[53] Most commercial semiconductor lasers have an anamorphic lens (collimates in one direction only) to shape the beam so that it is symmetric, if that is what they want.

Ultraviolet Lasers

The ultraviolet part of the spectrum provides advantages in some applications. The diffraction-limited spot is smaller and the more energetic photons are more useful in breaking some chemical bonds. One type of ultraviolet laser is the excimer laser; another is the frequency-tripled, lamp-pumped, solid-state laser. The most recent is

---

53   Dupuis, R., "The diode laser, the first 30 days, 40 years ago," *Optics and Photonics News*, April 2004.

the diode-pumped, tripled laser. The original light comes from a Nd:YAG at 1064 nm and triples it with nonlinear crystals to 355. (The frequency is tripled; the wavelength is thirded). Excimer lasers generally are multimode lasers with almost rectangular cross sections, low repetition rates, but high-pulse energy. They are EX-Cited monoMERs (single molecules) of gases like XeCl. The exact chemistry is not known, but the transitions are. The tripled lasers are circular in cross section, in a single mode, but they suffer from the inefficiency of the tripling process. This requires high power densities in the original beam and a consequent damaging of the tripling crystal. The first diode-pumped lasers attained an average power of 200 mW, pulse repetition rate of 30 kHz, resulting in a pulse energy of 10 μJ. Improvements have led to 1.5 W average power with a pulse rate of 15 kHz and variations around these numbers. Applications have included making small holes in plastics and circuit boards, like 20 μm holes in Kapton that was only 0.005-inch thick.[54]

Frequency Doublers

These devices are used with lasers. They double or even triple the frequency of the light that enters them. As mentioned in the previous section on lasers, this is one way to obtain ultraviolet laser light. Of course, when the frequency is doubled, the wavelength is halved, but they are always called doublers. Frequency doubling is a relatively inefficient process; typically the doubled light is about ten percent of the intensity of the input light. Of course, it depends upon the material and the design.

The simple explanation is that some electrons can take up the energy of two photons at the same time. These electrons jump to a higher energy level based on the sum of the two photon energies. Then they return to the ground state, emitting a photon of this doubled energy and doubled frequency. This requires many photons in a dense distribution, so that there can be two of them in almost the same place at the same time, much of the time. The input beam must be very intense. The output beam will be much less intense. The very first demonstration of frequency doubling was done by my friend Peter Franken, then at the University of Michigan. He later became director of the Optical Sciences Center at the University of Arizona.

Some years later, frequency tripling was accomplished. Based on the same logic of doubling—that is, the absorption of two photons at the same time—tripling occurs when three photons are absorbed at the same time. Clearly, it is an even weaker process, requiring an even higher intensity of input light.

---

54   Gitin, M., "UV lasers," *Photonics Spectra*, 136, September 1998.

Binoculars

Binoculars may be considered a connected pair of telescopes. The magnification process is the same, but they have been adapted to work in parallel and be handled conveniently by the user.

The first patent on binoculars was by Ernst Abbe in 1894. These used an objective lens and an eyepiece connected optically by a Porro prism. Later, people incorporated a pentaprism, one with five sides. Figure 88 shows a pair of binoculars, with the right hand side cut away. As shown,[55] the rays of light come in from the bottom. The image is inverted by normal lensing action. The first Porro prism reinverts the image, making it erect. The second prism inverts the image from left to right. Thus, after passing through the objective lens and two Porro prisms, the image is erect and correct from left to right. The eyepiece then relays that image to infinity, actually to the eye. The design must have enough eye relief so that you do not have to smush your eye against the lens. It was not until the mid to late 1950s that eye relief was sufficient so spectacle wearers could wear them and use binoculars at the same time. The binocular must also have enough of a field so that there is room to move the eye back and forth.

Figure 88 Binoculars with Porro prisms.[55]

The pentaprism system uses just one prism to perform the functions of the two Porros. Of course, it is a more complex element that has reflection from two different surfaces. In both forms, the prisms put the image in the right geometrical arrangement, and reduce the length of the telescopes, making them easier to handle.

Binoculars are described by their magnification and aperture size. For instance, a pair of 7×50 bin-

Figure 89 Binoculars with pentaprisms.[55]

55   Jenkins F., and H. White, *Fundamentals of Optics*, McGraw Hill, 1957. (Images courtesy of McGraw-Hill, copyright 1957.)

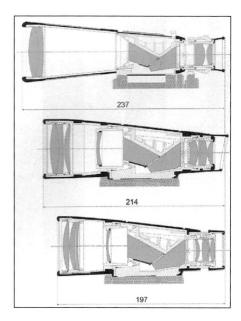

Figure 90 Modern designs.[56]

oculars means that the magnification is 7 times and the aperture diameter is 50 mm. Possibly the ultimate binocular is the 8×56 because it has greater magnification and a larger aperture. The next consideration is the field of view. The user wants a fairly large field of view, say 50 to 60 deg. In order to approach these values, a new prism system was introduced, the dialyte. As shown in Fig. 89, it has three reflections and does both the inversion and reversion. It is an in-line system that results in a longer but slimmer envelope.[56]

The most recent designs for the challenging 8×56 binocular result from optimization of the objective, use of the dialyte prism, and a fairly standard eyepiece. One nice design is shown (Fig. 90). It uses four lenses in the objective, low-dispersion glass for lightness, and the other elements are standard. The illustration shows the classic design on top plus two recent modifications that result in a shorter 8×56 binocular with a 60 deg field of view.

Interferometers

Interferometers come in many shapes and forms, and they are used for many different purposes.

The Michelson Interferometer[57]

Since it was used in the classic Michelson Morley experiment, I list it first (see p. 249). As shown, it consists of an extended source, S, a beamsplitter, BS, two plane mirrors, M1 and M2, and an image plane, where a sensor of some sort may be located. The interference is between the two beams that are generated by the

56   Besenmatter, W., "Recent progress in binocular design, the 8×56," *Optics and Photonics News*, November 2000. (Image courtesy OSA, copyright 2000.)
57   Wyatt J. C., and W. L. Wolfe, "Interferometers," *Optical Engineer's Desk Reference,* W. L. Wolfe, ed., OSA and SPIE Press, 2003.

beamsplitter and then are recombined by it. They will recombine in or out of phase, depending on the relative lengths of the two paths. An interference pattern will be generated at the image plane. Mirror M1 has an image at M1', shown with the dashed line. Then it is easy to see how these two beams are separated linearly, and can then interfere.

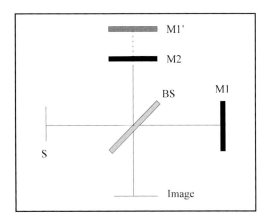

Figure 91 Michelson interferometer.

The Twyman-Green Interferometer[58]

This device is a Michelson interferometer with a small source and a collimating optic (and focusing lens). The elements are identified the same as in Fig. 91, but there are two lenses in addition; one to collimate, the second to focus. Thus, the beams that interfere are collimated. One of the flat mirrors can be replaced by an optical element to be tested. The interference pattern in the image plane will then be a map of the profile of the optical element. This is an important use of this interferometer.

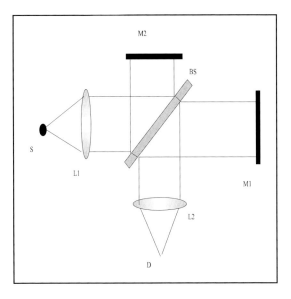

Figure 92 Twyman-Green interferometer.

The Interferometer Spectrometer

This is often called a Fourier transform infrared (FTIR) interferometer. It is a Twyman-Green, but is used dynamically. Imagine that a monochromatic beam is the source. The interferometer is arranged so that the two optical paths are exactly alike. There is then constructive interference and a high signal at the image plane. Now

---

58 Ibid.

imagine that one of the mirrors is moved a little. The two beams will then be a little out of phase and the signal will be lower, until the beams are 180 deg out of phase and there is a null. As the mirror moves further, the two beams will again move back into phase. Now imagine that there are two such sources, but of different frequencies. Then there will be two peaks and additional interference. Then—go for it—many, many such sources. Each of the many peaks is an indication of constructive interference of one of the frequencies, which is a map of the different colors in the source. It is called an interferogram; its Fourier transform is the spectrum of the light. Thus, it is called a Fourier transform interferometer, and because its main use is in the infrared part of the spectrum, it is called a Fourier transform infrared spectrometer. The Fourier transform is a mathematical process invented by Joseph Fourier to accomplish certain analyses.

The Sagnac Interferometer

In this device, a beam-splitter is used with three mirrors. The beams travel around the interferometer in clockwise and counter-clockwise directions and are recombined by the beamsplitter. They travel exactly the same path, but in opposite directions. Therefore, without anything additional, they will generate constructive interference. One of the important uses of this device is as a gyroscope. The interferometer is spun, and therefore the beams are Doppler shifted up and down and a measure of their shift is used to determine rotation angle. By the way, it is pronounced sahn-yak.

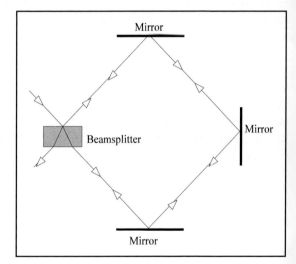

Figure 93 Sagnac interferometer.

The Rayleigh Interferometer

This instrument is used to measure the refractive index of gases. As shown, two beams are generated by a lens and apertures and directed down two separate paths (tubes). The beams are recombined with another pair of lenses and apertures and the interference is generated at a detector. One tube is usually evacuated and the other gradually filled with gas. The fringes thereby generated are counted, and the

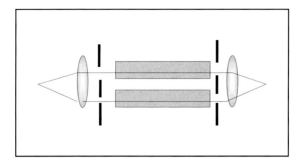

Figure 94 Rayleigh interferometer.

optical path difference inferred. Since the optical path is the refractive index times the distance, and the distances are identical, the difference is due only to the different refractive indexes—that of vacuum and that of the gas. Compare this arrangement to the double-beam spectrometer.

The Fabry-Perot Interferometer

This is a multiple-beam interferometer and therefore is more spectrally sensitive. As shown in Fig. 95, it consists of two parallel plates. Each is partially reflecting, partially transmitting. The light enters from the left (in the drawing) and reflects off the surface of the second plate back to the second surface of the first plate, and then repeats many times. This generates many beams; they are all combined by the lens to the focus, where a bulls-eye interference pattern can be viewed. As a result of this multiplication effect, the interference fringes are much sharper.

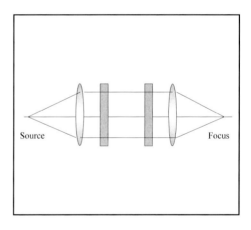

Figure 95 Fabry-Perot interferometer.

Phase-Shifting Interferometers

These interferometers are used to measure the profile of the height of a surface. An interferometer is set up as shown schematically in Fig. 96. Light from a source is collimated by a lens and sent to the test surface by reflection from the beamsplitter. The other beam goes to the mirror and is reflected back to the beamsplitter. From here it goes up with the beam from the test surface. The two beams interfere at the

detector. This produces an interferogram of the surface. Then, either
the source or the detector assembly
is moved a little and another interferogram is taken. The process is repeated twice more. The four interfe-
rograms are digitized and compared
to obtain the surface profile. Although this looks simple, there are
complications; errors can occur.[59]
These measurements can be made
with an uncertainty of about 0.1 nm
in the surface height. There are other
variations of this basic instrument.[60]

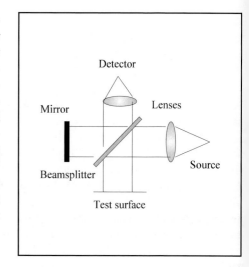

Radiometers

Figure 96 Phase-shifting interferometer.

Round and Round She Goes

How do those little radiometers they
sell at planetariums work? Which way
do they spin? What are they for? Are
they just decorative gadgets? Why
are they called radiometers? Enough
questions; how about answers? Oh,
that was another question!

The little devices are panels
painted black on one side and white
on the other, as shown in Fig. 97.
Usually, four such panels are arranged abound a hub placed on top of
a narrow spike, so that they can rotate
freely. The wheel of panels is placed

Figure 97 Radiometer.

inside a bulb, and the inside may or may not be evacuated, but it is isolated from the
atmosphere. They are called radiometers, actually Crooke radiometers, after the
man who invented them. They are called this because at one time they were used to

---

59   Koliopoulis, K., "Avoiding phase-measuring interferometry's pitfalls," *Photonics
     Spectra*, 169, October 1988.
60   Bristow, T., and K. Arackellian, "New device monitors optical surfaces," *Photonic
     Spectra*, 113, January 1987.

measure the amount of radiation that impinged upon them. The speed at which they spun was an indication of the amount of light radiation that was incident. Today, they are strictly interesting, decorative gadgets.

They can spin either way, depending upon whether they are in a good vacuum or not. If they are not in a vacuum, then the incident light is absorbed more by the black side than the white side. Accordingly, the black side heats up more and transfers that heat to the air around it. As the air warms up, the air molecules are more active and bang on the black side. Therefore the black side pushes the white side in front of it—the white sides go first. If the wheel is in a good vacuum, there is no air to heat. Then we can explain the action in terms of photons. The photon is absorbed by the black side, which then receives one photon momentum. The photon is reflected by the white or reflecting side. Since the photon then bounces back, it transfers two photon momenta to the white side (coming and going). The white side, therefore, pushes the black side—the black sides go first.

There is an interesting, personal side note to this. I taught radiometry at the University of Arizona. I tested one of my students by asking him how the radiometer would spin. As I put it on the windowsill I gave it an unintentional twist. So as he gave the second explanation, the vanes gradually came to a stop, and reversed their direction. He quickly said, "on the other hand…," and gave the first and correct explanation. Almost all the radiometers sold today have no vacuum; it would just be too expensive.

Lights

The sun, stars, and moon are natural lights. This section deals with artificial ones. As described in Chapter 1, almost all light arises from the acceleration of charges. The most familiar light, technically called a luminaire, is the incandescent bulb, invented by Edison. Others in frequent use are fluorescent lights, neon lights, so-called natural (or day) lights, and diodes.

Incandescent Light Bulbs

Thin wires are mounted inside an evacuated envelope. A current is passed through the wires, which once were carbon but now are mostly made of tungsten. The current, an alternating one, causes the electrons to vibrate frantically, thereby giving rise to heat and light. The typical spectrum of such a bulb is shown in Fig. 98 along

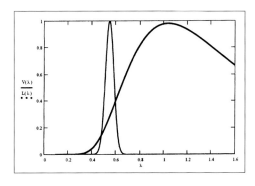

Figure 98 Tunsten bulb and eye response.

with the response of the photopic (daylight) eye. The bulb output is the broad curve to the right; the eye response is the narrow one on the left. The overlap region is the part of the light from the bulb that is useful to our eyes; it is called, by optical techies, the luminous efficacy. It is abundantly clear that a tungsten bulb radiates much more heat than light. Halogen gas has recently been introduced to the evacuated bulbs to extend their lifetime. Careful measurements show that the light actually fluctuates in intensity at a rate of 120 cycles per second, twice the frequency of house current. These bulbs can also be used in flashlights, where there is no fluctuation from the direct current source.

Fluorescent Bulbs

These bulbs, usually long tubes, have electrical actuators and use the fluorescence effect described in Chapter 1. The choice of the powder in the tube determines the spectral output, and they therefore can have a much better luminous efficacy than incandescent bulbs. Manufacturers have recently produced smaller versions that fit in to standard sockets. They have the additional advantage of long life.

Neon Lights

Walk down Broadway near Times Square in New York City and notice all the different-colored lights used to hawk just about everything. The lights are tubes filled with various gases. Each gas has its own color; and they are not all neon.

Arcs

This source of light is used mostly in searchlights to obtain very high brightness. An anode (the positive terminal) and a cathode (the negative one) are brought in fairly close proximity—about an inch apart—and a high voltage is generated between them. If the gap is set correctly for the voltage that is applied, a spark jumps across the gap. The spark is set at the focus of a large mirror to generate the searchlight beam.

This is not a stable light source. After the gap has been set just right, the electrodes gradually wear away. The gap tends to get larger and the arc goes away. Mechanisms have been developed to gradually feed the electrodes to get around this problem. Lightning is an arc, but on a grand scale—millions of volts and miles of arc!

Diodes and Laser Diodes

These modern light sources come in essentially monochromatic versions. They can be used nicely for taillights and stop lights, but for white light applications, three different colors need to be combined. They can be tuned to give high luminous efficacy, but in evaluating the overall efficiency of lighting systems one must calculate what I call the plug efficiency. How many watts are useful to the eye for the number of watts coming from the house (or other) current? A recent development in flashlights uses diodes as sources. They have very blue-white beams, essentially infinite life, and they use little power.

Other Instruments

Differential Absorption LIDAR

This system, the acronym for which is DIAL, shines two pulses of light at slightly different frequencies (wavelengths) into the atmosphere, a smoke trail, or other place to be investigated. The wavelengths are chosen such that light of one wavelength is and the other is not absorbed by the gas to be detected. The detector then makes the measurement, and this modest, active two-wavelength spectrometer does its job. The DIAL can have separately spaced emitters and absorbers or use a cube corner to return the beam to colocated emitters and receivers. For the detection of various gases, various pairs of wavelengths are used. (A similar instrument, the LIDAR is a light detector and ranger, a sort of optical radar that sends out a laser pulse and measures its return for distance, velocity, or, in this case, difference in absorption.)

Laser Tweezers

Laser light can be used to grab, hold, and manipulate very small objects like cells, vesicles, and organelles. The process is somewhat similar to the way balloons can be held in space by a column of air. The air pushes the balloon up, and the momentum of the air molecules keeps the balloon from moving out of the side of the beam. (Bernoulli's law states that faster-moving air in the presence of slower-moving air has a lower pressure). Similarly, the momentum of the photons in the laser beam can trap these very small particles with forces on the order of a pico pound of force—a millionth millionth of a pound. Laser scissors can be used in conjunction with the tweezers. It is an ultraviolet laser beam that disrupts the cells that have been trapped.[61] I have yet to read about laser emery boards!

Fiber Optic Strain Gauges

Two ultraviolet lasers are used to illuminate the same area of a fiber, about 1-cm long. The resulting interference pattern generates a regular pattern of refractive index variation, called a Bragg diffraction grating. The light that shines on this grat-

---

61 Robinson, K., "Laser tweezers grab a share of the spotlight," *Photonics Spectra,* January 1999.

ing will be reflected when its wavelength matches that of the wavelength of the diffraction grating. This wavelength or period is determined by the distance between the peaks of the interference pattern and the refractive index. The light will vary with expansion and contraction of the fiber and with a change in refractive index. Strain in turn changes both of these properties. Thus, we can shine broadband light onto the grating and sense the wavelength of maximum reflection, typically with the use of a linear CCD. Most installations have more than one grating, several to measure at different wavelengths and several in regions where there is no strain to measure any changes caused by temperature changes.[62]

Retroreflectors

There are two main retroreflectors in use today: a cube corner and a convex-plano lens. The cube corner can be either refractive, or hollow and reflective. In the refractive version, the cube is made of an appropriate transparent material. It is the corner of a cube with right angles in both directions. A ray that enters at any reasonable angle reflects off one surface, then a second surface, and exits the cube in exactly the opposite direction from which it came.

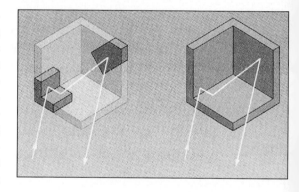

Figure 99 Cube corners.

The hollow version contains three mirrors arranged in the same way. Since the principle is the same, reflection off two orthogonal surfaces, the same thing happens. One application is for boresighting and alignment. The military has used beryllium mirrors since they are very light for a given strength. One version with an inset can displace the ray a chosen amount.[63]

The lens version uses a lens that focuses the light to a mirror surface. The mirror then sends the light right back out.

---

62   Friebele, E., "Fiber bragg grating strain sensors," *Optics and Photonics News*, August 1998.

63   Lipkins, J., and Z. Bleier, "Beryllium retroreflectors expand boresight uses," *Laser Focus World*, November 1996. (Image courtesy of Pennwell Publishers.)

The Convex-Plano Lens

The front surface of the lens is spherical and of the correct curvature for the refractive index of the material so that the collimated light incident upon it is focused onto the back surface. The light then is reflected by the back surface and is collimated by the lens. These are not retroreflectors for as wide a range of incident angles as the cube corners, but they are very cheap to make and are used in many roadside signs.

Polarimeter

This is an instrument designed to determine the state of polarization of a beam of light. Light can be linearly polarized in any direction, circularly polarized either clockwise or counterclockwise, or unpolarized. Several measurements are needed to make this determination. Four filters are used that transmit unpolarized light equally. The first has no polarization; the second is polarized linearly in the horizontal direction; the third is polarized linearly in the +45 deg direction; the last has right circular polarization. These are used one after another, independently in no particular order. The first gives information about the first Stokes vector or the degree of unpolarized light. The difference between the first and second filters gives the second Stokes vector, or the degree of linear polarization. The difference between the first and third gives information about the angle of linear polarization. The fourth and first measurements give information about the degree of circular polarization. There are different manifestations of this scheme, with automatic insertion of the four filters, automatic recording, and automatic calculation. Other schemes have been promoted, but this gives you the basics.[64]

Acousto-Optic Modulators and Filters

These devices combine optical and acoustical processes in order to modulate light. They can also be operated as a type of spectrometer. There are two types, collinear and noncollinear; that is, one transmits the beam of light with no deviation, while the other deviates the beam a certain amount.

The collinear one is pictured in Fig. 100.[65] The acousto-optical tunable filter (AOTF) is usually a rectangular cylinder of the proper material. Light enters through a polarizer from the left, as shown. It passes through a polarizer and enters the material. A piezoelectric transducer is placed on the side of the material, and it is driven by a tunable electric oscillator. As the oscillator changes electric frequency, the piezoelectric transducer vibrates mechanically. Thus, electrical oscilla-

---

64 Wolfe, W., Chapter 4, "Polarization," *The Optical Engineer's Desk Reference*, W. L. Wolfe, ed., Optical Society of America, 2003.

65 Wolfe, W., *Introduction to Imaging Spectrometers*, SPIE Press, 1997.

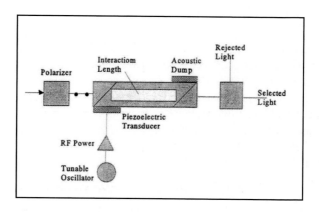

Figure 100 Collinear AOTF.[63]

tions are converted to mechanical oscillations. They propagate down the interaction zone where the waves combine. The output wave has a frequency that is the sum of the input optical frequency and the acoustic frequency, somewhat like the Doppler effect.

The other type is a form of diffraction grating. As shown in Fig. 101, the acoustic waves now propagate across the active region. The piezoelectric transducers are spaced along the sides and generate changes in refractive index where the transducers occur and when they are activated. The incident light will be diffracted just as with a diffraction grating. Some of it can be blocked, as shown, to make this a filter. The tunability comes from the strength of the acoustic waves, which determines the refractive index variations.

A modulator can be fashioned from the first type by filtering the output and varying the coupling so the filter becomes an on-off filter. The same technique can be used for a monochromatic input in the second type.

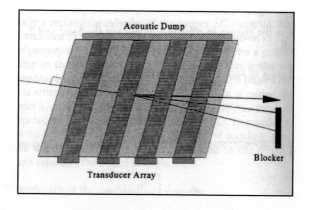

Figure 101 Noncollinear AOTF.[63]

Photo Tubes

These are electronic photon detectors. They have largely been replaced by photodiodes. As shown in Fig. 102, they consist of an ordinary electronic diode with a cathode and an anode, separated by an evacuated space. There is an electric voltage between the two. One electrode contains a photosensitive surface, so that when a photon is absorbed, an electron is emitted. Thus, an electronic current is generated by a photonic current.

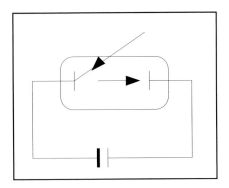

Figure 102 Phototube.

Photomultiplier Tubes

These are phototubes with multiplication. A phototube like that just described is equipped with a number of additional electrodes along its length, called *dynodes*. Each of these is at a certain voltage that causes the electrons to be accelerated along the length of the tube. These are called voltage taps in the figure. As each electrode smashes into each dynode, three to five electrons are emitted. This is the multiplication. This increases the sensitivity of the tube. It also increases the noise.

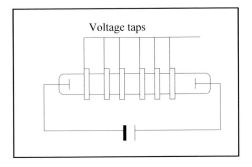

Figure 103 Photomultiplier tube.

Kerr Cell

This is a device that can be used to modulate the intensity of light. A Kerr cell consists of a polarizer in front of and behind two electric plates, as shown in Fig. 104. The electric plates are of opposite polarity so that there is a strong electric field in the material between them. The electric field causes the material to be optically active; that is, it rotates the plane of polarization. The polarizers are crossed, that is, for instance, one is horizontal and the other is vertical. Thus, light coming in is polarized in a particular direction, say horizontal. It passes through the electric cell. If there is no applied voltage, it reaches the second polarizer and does not pass through it, since they are of opposite polarities. When a voltage is applied, the plane of polarization of the light in the electric cell is rotated and therefore is transmitted by the second polarizer. Thus, in its simplest form, it is a light switch. Since the

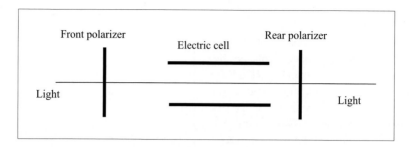

Figure 104 The Kerr cell.

electrical voltage can be of any form, and any time varying form, it is also a light modulator, a light shutter.

Pockels Cell

If the electric field is parallel to the direction of the light beam, the same results may be obtained. This, then, is a Pockels cell.

Faraday Cell

The Faraday cell is the magnetic analog of the Kerr cell. It is identical, except that a magnetic field is used rather than an electric field. The relative performance of the two depends on the sensitivity of the materials used to either a magnetic field or an electric one. In this effect, the magnetic field is parallel to the direction of the light beam. If it is perpendicular, similar results may be obtained, but they are far less efficient.

The Human Eye

The human eye is the most remarkable optical instrument. It can change sensitivity; it has stereoscopic viewing; it can sense color; it can change lens power; it can detect as little as one photon; it has varying resolution over its field of view; it covers a field of view of about 180 deg; it has central resolution of about one minute of arc; and it does all this in a volume of about one cubic inch. The designer of this optical instrument was certainly omniscient.

Figure 105 shows a cross-sectional view of a representative human eye.[66] The cornea is the front and gives the eye its color. Behind this is a material that is essentially a saltwater (saline) solution called the aqueous humor. (There is nothing

---

66   Allergan, wall chart. (Image courtesy of Allergan, Inc.)

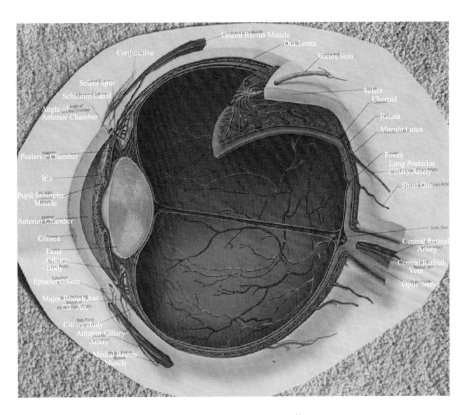

Figure 105 Eye structure.[66]

funny about this; "humor" means "bodily fluid" in Latin). In translation then, this is liquid bodily material. Then comes the iris, right behind the anterior chamber, which is the stop of the optical system. It blocks the light and can cause the opening to vary from about 2 mm to almost 10 mm. Behind the iris is the lens, a rather complicated singlet that is aspheric and has a radial variation in refractive index. The lens focuses the light onto the retinal surface, almost 20 mm away. The retina consists of rods and cones that detect the light, turning the pattern of incident photons into nerve signals that are sent by the optic nerve to the brain. The material between the lens and the retina is called the vitreous humor, the glasslike fluid (because it is more viscous than the aqueous humor).

The figure came from a poster in my optometrist's office. They are more interested in the many things shown here than optical people are. I have overlaid my titles, mostly the same as theirs, in white.

Spectral Response

The spectral response of the eye is controlled by the spectral transmission of the cornea, lens, aqueous and vitreous humors, and the responses of the rods and cones. The main effect is the spectral response of the rods and cones.

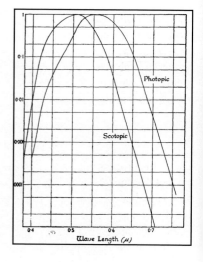

Figure 106 Spectral response of the human eye.[67]

Figure 106 shows the overall photopic response, that is, the response of the eye when there is plenty of light. Of course, this is a representative curve. Originally it was obtained by averaging the response of many volunteers. It also shows the scotopic response, when there is little light, say as on a moonlit night. Note the photopic response has more response in the red, at longer wave lengths. These curves are both normalized to one. The absolute scotopic response is higher than the photopic response. These curves come from a classic book on photometry;[67] both are shown on a logarithmic basis.

Spatial Response

The spatial response of the eye is determined by the quality of the lens and the density of the rods and cones on the retina. The rods and cones perform different functions. Rods serve to detect images under low levels of illumination, while the cones are used when the light is bright. The cones peak in the foveal region, which is on the optical axis, where our vision is most acute. Over a field of view of about 1 degree, the cones have a density of more than 200 per degree and there are no rods. The cones drop to about 20 per degree outside this region, one-tenth the number.

Eye Movements

The eye is in constant motion; it never stops. It exhibits small swift motions and larger ones, too. Even when we attempt to stare at a fixed point, like we are asked to do in the optometrist's office (a process called fixation), the eye makes small, swift motions. These are called tremor, drift, and microsaccades. Tremors happen from 10 to 200 times per second and with an amplitude of about 24 arcseconds. Drift occurs at the slower rate of about 4 arcminutes per second (240 arcseconds per sec-

---

67   Walsh, J. W. T., *Photometry*, Dover, 1958.

ond), with amplitudes of about 2 to 5 minutes of arc. The microsaccades are much more variable, perhaps because they are controllable. They occur at rates of 0.2 to 3 per second with amplitudes of 1 to 23 arcminutes. Experiments have been performed to stabilize the image on the retina in spite of these motions. When this is done, the image breaks up and even disappears. So these relatively small motions are essential to the visual process.

Stereopsis

This is the process of seeing depth, or stereoscopic vision. The basis of stereopsis is the fact that the two eyes view objects from slightly different angles. It is somewhat surprising that our binocular stereo viewing is useful at best to about one kilometer. We determine distance and positions at ranges longer than that by a variety of different cues and clues—size, perspective, obscuration, etc.

One interesting application of stereoscopic vision is the use of three-dimensional type fonts. By printing letters twice with an appropriate spacing between them (they can overlap), they appear to have depth. This has been developed by Professor Martin Sussman of Tufts University.[68]

Eye Integration

Nothing in this world responds instantaneously. I don't; ask my wife. Even the human eye has a response time, and it is approximately one-tenth of a second. This information is useful in calculating such things as the distance one should stay behind a car. The response of the eye is one part of the entire time that it takes to respond to some action on the part of the car in front. Notice that at 60 mph (88 feet per second), your car will travel 8.8 feet in just the time it takes for the eye to respond. It will take at least another second for your mind to respond and another for your foot to hit the brake.

It is shown in the section on television that the normal TV set flashes 30 frames per second at you. Therefore, your eye integrates three frames, thereby creating what appears to be a better image. When a freeze frame is viewed, it looks less good, noisier, because the integration is no longer operable.

Optical Defects

The normal eye is considered to be emmetropic (*emmetros*, in measure); the abnormal eye is said to have one or more forms of ametropia (*ametros*, irregular and *opia*, eye state). The simplest of these are myopia (*myops*, short-sighted) and hypermetropia (*hypermetros*, beyond measure)—near- and far-sightedness. The myopic eye has a lens that forms an image of a distant point source in front of the retina.

---

68 *The Arizona Daily Star*, "Startech," 2, September 22, 1997.

Therefore, distant objects are out of focus and only close objects are well defined to the near-sighted.

The opposite is true for the far-sighted person. The distant object is focused behind the retina, and only distant objects can be seen with clarity. These can both be corrected with simple spectacle lenses.

Presbyopia (old-age eye), describes the problem in which our arms get too short! We can no longer make our eyes focus at a normal close distance of about 25 cm. When I was 35-years old at The University of Michigan, I was part of a large study and underwent an incredibly thorough physical exam. I was told that my eyes were great, but that when I got to be 45, I would begin to experience presbyopia. Sure enough, when I got to be 45, I went to buy my first magnifiers at the drugstore. The cause is a combination of increased viscosity of the humors and a weakening of the muscles that expand and contract the lens. It is considered to be a lack of accommodation—squeezing or pulling on the lens to change its focus. At the other end of the age spectrum, some children are afflcited with amblyopia, often called lazy eye. The two eyes do not track together.

The lenses used for these corrections are often specified in diopters, but sometimes in magnification. A diopter is the reciprocal of the focal length of the lens in meters. It is easier to pick out the spectacles from the rack by checking the magnification.

Astigmatism is caused by an eye lens that is not circularly symmetric. Two mutually perpendicular line images are formed from a single point object. Usually the maximum and minimum powers of the lens are perpendicular and almost as often are vertical and horizontal. This condition is corrected with the use of a properly shaped cylindrical lens.

Your friendly optometrist has an instrument to measure the approximate shape of your lens. His next process—constantly asking which is better—is a trial-and-error process with lenses of various power and cylindrical shapes. He also checks the appearance of your retina and puffs on your eye to test for undue internal pressure, a symptom of glaucoma.

Interference Films and Filters

These devices consist of one or more layers of materials of different refractive index. The waves of different frequencies interfere in transmission and reflection as they pass through these layers. Probably the best known of these is the antireflection coating, often used on eyeglasses. This is a single-layer coating of the proper refractive index and thickness that is applied to a material-like glass to reduce the reflection to almost zero over a range of wavelengths. Figure 107 shows how this works. A beam designated by A is incident upon the thin film on top of a substrate such as glass. It generates two reflected rays: B from the top of the film, and C from the first surface of the substrate. If the beams are out of phase by a half cycle (the maximum of one is on the minimum of the other), then the waves interfere destructively, and there is no reflection. This is accomplished at a single wavelength by adjusting the film thickness and refractive index just right. (The optical thickness, that is, the refractive index times the physical thickness, must be a quarter wavelength of the light.) This adjustment can only be exactly right for a single wavelength, but it is pretty good over a range of wavelengths and angles.

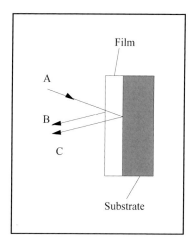

Figure 107 Antireflection coating.

More complicated filters and antireflection coatings can be generated with additional layers. A filter is generated by putting several coatings on a chosen substrate. Filters such as these used for photography can be made to reduce reflection or to transmit light of only a certain wavelength or range of wavelengths. It is not too hard to imagine a two-layer filter. The first layer is designed to reduce the reflection, or enhance the transmission at one wavelength, and the second layer is adjusted to do the same for a second wavelength. Then three layers; and some filters have 90 layers. The design of these filters has been described in a number of texts[69,70] and in a course that is taught at my school.

69 Madsen, C., *Optical Filter Design and Analysis: A Signal-Processing Approach*, Wiley, 1999.

70 Baumeister, P., *Optical Coating Technology*, SPIE Press, 2004.

Chapter 3

Natural Optical Phenomena

As we look around us, we see light in nature everywhere we turn. Many of these natural light phenomena are not appreciated, and others are not well understood by many. Some, like rainbows, are beautiful, and some, like lightning, are frightening—and dangerous. Hummingbirds show us beautiful iridescent colors; the sky is blue; sunsets are red; oil slicks are multicolored; and halos glow around the sun and in clouds. Wow!

Environment

The Sun

It is not our undoing, as one play says it is. It is our source of life, of energy, and of light. The sun has an output spectrum that is shown in Fig. 1. The overall curve,

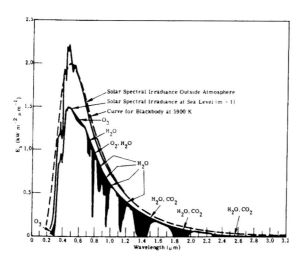

Figure 1 Solar spectrum.[1]

1   Wolfe W., and G. Zissis, *The Infrared Handbook*, Environmental Research Institute of Michigan, 1978.

sunlight outside of the atmosphere, is smooth, but there are regions in which the atmosphere absorbs part of the sunlight. These are shown in black. These are not in the visible, but rather in the ultraviolet and infrared.

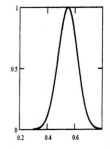

The eye is well matched to the sun; that is, the sun is a very efficient illuminator for the human eye. I have plotted the eye response on the same scale as the solar spectrum to show that in Fig. 2. It was too complicated to overlap them.

Figure 2 Eye response.

Seasons

We orbit around the sun in an elliptical orbit and we are tilted toward it. It is a little surprising that summer occurs when we are farthest from the sun, and winter when we make our closest approach. The relative difference in distance is small, about 5.5%. The effect that causes summer and winter is the tilt of the Earth from about 18 to 28 deg. We are more straight-on to the solar rays in summer and more oblique to them in the winter. It is, if you will, the glancing blow that causes winter. If you doubt this, consider that the southern hemisphere has winter when the northern hemisphere has summer, and vice versa. If it were a distance effect, this would not be so.

Solar Variability

The output of the sun is not constant. It has a regular, cyclic variation of about 0.5% over a 13-year period. It has smaller, random variations thanks to sun spots and spatial variations in the thermonuclear reactions that create all that energy.

The Moon

Our only natural satellite, the moon is not made of green cheese, but consists of rocks and dirt, of hills and dales. The moon is essentially a flat (nonspectrally selective) reflector of the sun's radiation, adding no color to it. The overall reflectivity is diffuse and about 10%. The man in the moon is a visual image caused by the variations in the reflectivity over the surface. The phases of the moon are caused by the angles of the sun and Earth to the moon. A simple experiment with a ball and a flashlight will demonstrate this.

The Stars

The stars twinkle in the sky and all look about the same color. They are, in fact, many different colors in the sense that they have many different temperatures. Whereas our sun is about 6000 K, and therefore has peak radiation at about 500 nm, many stars are much hotter and therefore peak more in the blue or even ultraviolet parts of the spectrum. They radiate just as steadily as our Sol; the fluctuations and turbulence of the atmosphere make them look like they twinkle.

The Planets

The planets themselves do not radiate, but reflect the sun's light. Although it is hard to tell with the naked eye, the planets subtend a larger angle than the stars. A good telescope will let you see the rings of Saturn and the canals on Mars, but gives no structural information about stars. The fact that planets do subtend larger angles means that they are less affected by the atmospheric turbulence. In a sense, they average it out. Thus, you can usually tell a star from a planet by its degree of twinkle, and, of course, some of the planets appear very bright.

The Sky, Sunrise, Sunset

Here in Arizona we have beautiful, deep blue skies almost every day of the year. Why are they so blue? The simple answer is scattering. Light is scattered by the molecules and small particulates in the atmosphere. These particles are less than a micrometer in size, are more or less spherical, and float in the air. They scatter different colors of light differently. The shorter wavelengths, the blues, are scattered more than the longer ones, the reds. This is because the particle, relative to the wavelength of the light, is larger for a shorter wavelength. Thus, the sunlight that is essentially white light is scattered to us more in the blue than in the red, and we see a blue sky away from the sun.

As I wrote this on September 7, 2003, I paused to listen to National Public Radio (NPR) explain the blue sky. They said it is because blue light is more energetic than the other colors and therefore bounces more. They added that this was the explanation of Rayleigh. Well, it is true that blue photons are more energetic than the longer-wavelength photons, and the argument is not wrong, but I think it is not quite right, either, and I am sure that was not Rayleigh's explanation! He was the master of waves, and photons were not discovered until 1905.

The history of the explanation of the blue sky goes back to an Arab, Aby Yusuf Yaquib ibn Ishaq al-Sabbah Al-Kindi, who lived about 800 AD. He thought that the blue sky was a mixture of the darkness of the night plus the sunlit particles of haze. Leonardo da Vinci attributed the blue color to scattering of sunlight by minute water particles. Other famous physicists, such as Isaac Newton, Pierre Bouguer, Dominique Arago, and John Tyndall, continued to believe that the blue color came from scattering from minute water droplets. Then, in 1871, John William Strutt, the third Baron Rayleigh, showed that it was scattering from molecules, and that the scattering from particles smaller than the wavelength of light is inversely proportional to the fourth power of the wavelength. Blue light of about 400 nm scatters about sixteen times as much as red light at 800 nm.[2]

As you can see in Fig. 3, the sky is especially blue, in this case, away from the sun. The scene is a part of my favorite fishing spot—Lee's Ferry on the Colorado River.

---

2   Lilienfeld, P., "A blue-sky history," *Optics and Photonics News*, June 2004.

Figure 3 An Arizona blue sky.

Figure 4 An Arizona sunset.

As the sun sets, and as it rises, too, it sends its light to us along a path that is close to the horizon. The reds are scattered less, so they get through this long atmospheric path better than the blues. So we get red sunsets (and sunrises), and they are redder if there are more particles in the path, as with some clouds. The sunsets are usually more spectacular because there is more "stuff" in the air there.

Clouds

These are white, black, and shades of gray. The particles in clouds, nascent water droplets, are bigger than the particles in the clear sky. They scatter all wavelengths equally. If there is not too much water, the droplets scatter all colors of light in all directions and the clouds look white. If they are bigger, and therefore have more water in them, the water absorbs some of the light and the clouds look gray or even black.

Mirages

Those wet-looking dry spots on the desert road ahead are a mirage caused by a form of total internal reflection. It happens more in the desert because the mirage is a function of heat near the surface of a road, usually. The heat coming off the road increases the temperature of the air. This causes a gradient of refractive index of the air in which the lower index is closer to the road. The rays from the background horizon are bent in the way shown in Fig. 5, so that the area of the horizon is seen by the viewer. This appears as a reflection and the mind says there must be water there to make this reflection. It was really a refraction. We do not see things that are not there; we see things that are in a different place as if reflected by water—in the road or even an oasis that is not there!

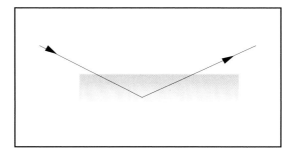

Figure 5 Mirage.

Rainbows

There is no pot of gold at the end of a rainbow, but there are some lovely optics in its generation. Arizona is a wonderful place to see rainbows. We have seen complete arcs, from horizon to horizon. We have seen double rainbows. Next time you get the chance, observe that the second rainbow is higher in the sky and upside down compared to the primary arc. It is also somewhat fainter. (It is barely visible in Fig. 6.) The triple is still lower and in the same orientation as the primary bow. The angles are all critical. Rainbows usually occur in the morning or evening, but only when it rains! The light from the sun comes over your shoulder and is refracted by the droplets in the rain. It is enough to understand how the spectrum is generated in a single droplet.

The light ray refracts into the droplet, as shown in Fig. 7, and breaks up into colors as in a prism. The colored rays are reflected from the back of the droplet and refracted back out the front

Figure 6 Rainbow.

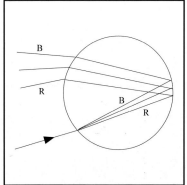

Figure 7 Primary rainbow.

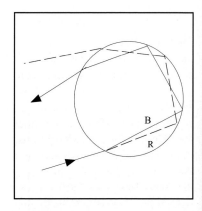

Figure 8 Secondary rainbow.

to your eye. The ray from the sun, indicated by the arrow, is refracted at the surface of the droplet into a rainbow of colored rays (R and B for red and blue are shown, but all the rest are in between) that go in slightly different directions because the refractive index is slightly different for the different colors. They all reach the back surface and are reflected back to the front surface by the law of reflection. They are then refracted one more time back to the eye of the beholder. The reflection off the back surface is not a total internal reflection. Some rays also pass through the droplet. Thus, the reflectivity is about 4%. The rainbow is not nearly as bright as the sun.

The secondary rainbow, barely visible in the photograph, starts the same way, but there are two reflections in the droplet. The second reflection reverses the colors because there are two reflections, and the rainbow is therefore dimmer. The tertiary rainbow is formed in an analogous way. The colors are in the same order as the primary; it is lowest, and dimmest.

Other Bows

The processes that form bows in rain, i.e., rainbows, also form bows in fogs and on dewy lawns, sometimes called Ulloa's mystery. These are fog bows and bows without names. It is also possible that the moon can form bows. These have somewhat different characteristics since the geometries and the drops are different.[3]

---

3   Wilk, S., "Antonio de Ulloa's mystery," *Optics and Photonics News*, April 2004.

Glories

These can be seen in clouds, looking down from airplanes, and they
can be seen from the ground to the
sides of the sun in the sky. They
are caused by collections of ice
crystals that diffract and refract
the light as if they are little prisms.
They are little prisms, although
they are not triangular in shape,
but more irregular. They operate
as both prisms and gratings to give
nice colored figures. The one
shown here is faint; it looks like a
rainbow, but comes from the crystals in the sky. The sun is off to the
right.

Figure 9 Glory.

Lightning

This mighty electrical phenomenon is both beautiful and deadly. Ninety-five percent
of lightning bolts have more than 10 million watt of light; 50% exceed a billion watt;
and 5% exceed 10 billion watt. This makes golf one of the deadliest sports in the
United States. Lightning can go inside a cloud, between clouds, or from clouds to the
ground. During electrical storms, thunderstorms, a tremendous voltage is generated
between the earth and clouds. At likely spots, high spots, a corona builds up and an
electrical leader of low voltage starts from the earth skyward for about a meter. This
establishes a path for the subsequent lightning flash. Each flash consists of one to 25
strokes (typically 5) about 30 ms apart.

One technique for ameliorating or at least diverting lightning strikes uses a device to sense the corona and then focuses powerful laser beams near the object to be
protected but far enough away to make the strike benign. The focused laser beams
form a plasma that (we hope) guides the bolt.[4]

Japanese investigators have reported attracting lightning with the use of a directed carbon-dioxide laser. They created a plasma channel from the top of a metal
lightning tower. A monitoring system told the researchers when the cloud was
charged enough to bolt. Two 1-kJ, 50-ns pulses were sent. The publication[5] did not
say whether the report from the investigators was posthumous.

---

4   Carts-Powell, Y., "Laser-triggered lightning discharges harmlessly," *OE Reports*, July 1999.
5   "Laser triggers lightning," *Photonics Spectra*, August 1997.

My group at the University of Arizona had the opportunity to design a global lightning detector. In the process, we learned that a phenomenal number of flashes occur per day over the globe. The problem was not detection; we could do that with a telescope and CCD focal plane that took up no more room than the proverbial breadbox. The problem was processing the enormous amount of data. There are many more cloud-to-cloud lightning flashes, which are all visible from a geosynchronous satellite, than cloud-to-ground flashes. It is the latter, clearly, that cause damage on Earth. They all had to be processed. The project ended, and as far as I know, NASA never did go any further with it. We did find a way to detect lightning. It was then a question of whether it was worth doing so.

Weather

It is always with us, and we always want to know about it. We now see wonderful depictions of clouds and storms, taken by the weather satellite called GOES, the Geosynchronous Orbiting Earth Surveyor, on our TV sets each night. The satellite is at an altitude of 24,000 miles over the equator. There, it orbits at the same rate that Earth rotates, so that it is stationary with respect to points on Earth. Sometimes this is called a geostationary orbit. GOES has in it an infrared imaging device that scans, line by line, the entire projection of the Earth below it.

For complete global coverage, more than one satellite is used. The infrared system consists of a single solid-state semiconductor detector (with a backup for redundancy), a flat mirror to do the scanning, a telescope to obtain the instantaneous image, and a passive cooler to keep the detector at operating temperature, about 200 K.

Since weather phenomena do not move all that fast, the time for a full scan can be on the order of 30 minutes. The infrared system measures differences in thermal radiation and infers temperature differences. The tops of clouds are much cooler than the surface of the Earth, so that GOES really measures the location of clouds. It can also measure their paths, since new scans are taken every few minutes. That is how hurricanes and fronts are portrayed on TV. The colors are added by the computer guys. In an early, undoctored version, I saw portrayed the temperature difference between the top of Mount Whitney in California and the neighboring Mojave Valley. These are extreme; the system can sense differences of about one deg. NASA is funding studies that will improve the GOES by allowing it to point at various places and zoom in on them.

The Greenhouse Effect

We read rather alarming tales about global warming due to the greenhouse effect. This connection is still an unproven theory, but the effect is very real. The sun shines down its radiation, most of which is in the visible. It warms the Earth, which in turn radiates back to out space. The Earth's radiation is mostly in the infrared where the atmosphere is not completely transparent. In fact, absorption bands result from water, carbon dioxide, and other less important gases. Therefore, not all of the heat absorbed from the sun can radiate away. We warm up, and it is a good thing.

But if the gases that do the absorption increase unduly, then we will warm up too much. That is the concern. Figure 10 shows the overall transmission of the atmosphere at the bottom. Each of the curves above it shows the absorption of one of the constituent gases. It is clear that water and carbon dioxide are the primary absorbers. The outputs from the sun and from the Earth are shown in Fig. 11. It is aligned with the transmission figure so that the two curves may be readily compared. The output from the sun is at the left and is completely transmitted by the atmosphere (not shown in the transmission curve, which starts at 1 μm). The radiation from the Earth is contained mostly in the region from 6 to 14 μm as shown.

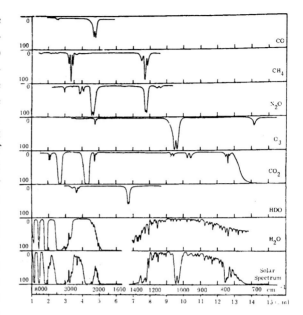

Figure 10 Atmospheric transmission.

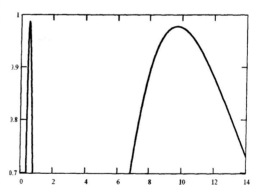

Figure 11 Solar and Earth emission spectra.

Other factors, such as the variability of the solar output, can also cause global warming—and cooling. We surely have had both with the Ice Age and age of the dinosaurs.

Consider solar variability. The sun provides almost 1500 watts per square meter on the surface of the Earth that it illuminates. That amounts to 300 billion watts on the hemisphere it illuminates (if there are no clouds). If the sun varies by as little as 0.5%, as it does over its solar cycle, that is a variation of 1.5 billion W. That kind of variation is surely enough to cause variations in the average temperature of the Earth. I think we should be aware of the possible problem of man-made greenhouse gases causing global warming, but we must also not panic nor ignore other, natural effects.

The Green Flash

As the sun sets, we can sometimes view a transient green flash right at the horizon. The phenomenon can be very complex, but in its simplest form it is light from the edge of the setting (or rising) sun that is dispersed and partly absorbed by the atmosphere. It has been stated elsewhere in this book that the atmosphere is transparent in the visible. There is a little absorption, and in this long atmospheric path it manifests itself a little.

There are those who have proposed that this is a physiological phenomenon, that it is an afterimage. You can investigate afterimages if you have not already observed them. Stare at a red square for some time. Then look away at a piece of white paper. You will see a green square. Similarly for other color opposites. The rods of the

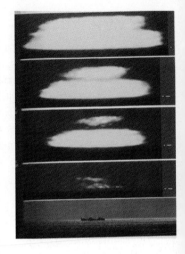

Figure 12 Green flash.[6]

retina are bleached by the long staring at a single color. Then, when something white is observed, the bleached rods do not respond, and a false complementary color is sensed.

This afterimage theory is proven wrong by the image shown here (Fig. 12). It is a beautiful photograph taken by the Vatican Observatory.[6] If it is taken by a camera, it is not a physiological effect. Note that this is a sequence of five pictures taken seconds apart at the setting of the sun, in sequence from top to bottom. First, a big yellow sun is seen with a few green edges. Then the sun separates. This is a mirage effect. Then more separation and more green. Then the sun disappears and the green flash is left. That is what we really see, because in the earlier situations there is too much direct sunlight for the little flash to be visible. Finally, there is the red sunset with a ship on the sea. It is all over.

Life

Chameleons

These lizards and some frogs and other amphibians change their skin color according to their background as a means of protection. They have color-sensitive photoreceptors. As they receive the chromatic light from the background, they process it and release pigments called melanopsin.

---

6   O'Connell, D., *The Green Flash*, North Holland, 1958.

Hummingbirds

Hummingbirds and other creatures create delightful optical effects. They are said to be irridescent, a term often associated with metallic reflection. However, their beautiful colors result from interference effects in their feathers. Males have lovely reds and blues and greens on their throats and heads, called gorgets. The females usually have only iridescent back feathers. The gorgets only show their brilliance at certain angles, whereas the back colors can be seen from many directions. This is because the head and neck feathers are flat, whereas the back feathers are convex. These effects may also be found on pigeons, peacocks, and ducks, but surely not as brilliantly.[7]

Butterflies and Moths

The iridescent colors of some butterflies and moths result from the arrangement of their scales, which are essentially flattened sacs that may be hollow or filled with stacks of thin films. This gives rise to interference effects, and in some cases even diffraction, from the structures.

Flutter by Butterfly

It was reported in the *Los Angeles Times*[8] that butterflies navigate by using the polarized ultraviolet light in the sky. The researchers further indicated that "to butterflies it appears as a grid in the sky that emanates from the sun." I believe they are on the right track. It has long been known that some birds navigate by the polarization of the light of the sky. As described earlier, the degree of polarization changes with angle from the sun. I believe that the birds and the butterflies navigate by monitoring the degree of polarization, but in an analog way. I find the concept of a grid in the sky difficult to accept. An internal clock keeps track of the position of the sun in the sky.

Insects

The iridescence in beetles comes from interference effects as well. There are two types of structure: One has microfibrils arranged in parallel to each other in distinct layers, with the successive layers oriented in the same direction. Others have the layers angled slightly to each other. Some also have half-wave separations to effect the polarization. Both left-handed and right-handed polarization have been observed—but not at the same time or in the same bug.[9]

---

7   Turner-Valle, J., "Optical interference coatings in nature," *Optics and Photonics News*, August 1998.
8   Kaplan, K., *Los Angeles Times*, May 7, 2005.
9   Ghiradella, H., "Shining armor: structural colors in insects," *Optics and Photonics News*, March 1999.

Marine Mammal Eyes

When you stop and think about it, the eyes of marine creatures are remarkable. When we go swimming underwater without a snorkel or mask, we find it very hard to see. Everything is a blur. The lens of our eye consists mostly of aqueous humor, which is essentially water. It has virtually the same refractive index as water, and therefore becomes ineffective.

But the seals and whales in Sea World come charging from the depths and snare little fish out of the air with unerring accuracy. They can see underwater (without a mask) and they can see in the air (also without a mask). Their eyes must have some very rapid adaptation mechanism.

The three parts of the eye that seem available for this function are the cornea, the pupil and the lens. The cornea rather than the lens may change its shape and actually adapt the focus. The pupils of these aquatic animals have a greater range than those of humans. A closing of the pupil reduces aberrations and increases the depth of focus. Finally, the shape of the lens can be altered by contraction and expansion of the ciliary muscles. These muscles in well-developed species can also move the lens axially somewhat, but maybe enough. The bottom line is that we do not know how they do it, but they do it.[10]

Pit Vipers

These snakes, including most rattlesnakes, have vision both from their eyes and infrared or heat sensing from the pits near their eyes. Their infrared vision seems to be as good as their visible vision. Very small temperature differences are detectable, so that they can actually follow the heat trail that kangaroo rats leave in the desert at night. And surely there is no trouble detecting the rat or other prey.[11]

Note that I disagree with the title of the cited article, but the vipers' systems are sensitive, about 0.01 K.

Figure 13 illustrates an experiment to prove the use of the infrared imagery. The snake is blindfolded. The light bulb on the left is on; the other is off. The snakes goes for the hot bulb. Other investigations have added to this and determined the number of little thermal sensors and the quality of the imagery.

Figure 13 Rattlesnake.

10   Zorn, H. M., "Eye optics of marine mammals," *Optics and Photonics News*, March 1999
11   Robinson, K., "Snake IR vision beats top imaging technology," *Biophotonic. International*, May 2002.

Mosquitos

These nasty little critters—and some are dangerous—bite, draw blood, and leave a little deposit. They
find us by homing in on warm carbon dioxide vapor.
So one piece of advice to avoid mosquitos is never to
exhale. There is now a device on the market that at-
tracts them and kills them by the use of warm carbon
dioxide. I cannot help but note that only the female
mosquitos bite.

Figure 14 Mosquito.

Moths

These sexy little critters have a phenomenal way of attracting those of the other sex.
Experiments have been performed to show that they use infrared to sense each
other at distances of miles. No full explanation has been given for the source of this
sensitivity, but it is a fact.

Squids

In an experiment at Woods Hole Oceanographic Institute, it was found that squids
much prefer polarizing beads to little beads that do not polarize light. This probably
means that one of the mechanisms they use to find prey is polarized light. I do not
know why they liked these beads at all. Perhaps they were impregnated with food. I
don't think the squids were doing macrame, but imagine how fast they could be
with all those arms!

Bumblebees

Bumblebees should not be able to fly. They do not have the right aerodynamics. A
professor at the University of Tokyo wanted to understand the ways bees and other
such insects fly. "...if we could understand this mechanism well...that would help
us understand excellent artificial wings."

The experiment consisted of a stainless steel rod 30-cm long and 2×2 mm in
cross section. One end was attached to a rigid wall, while the other held the bee. A
laser was aimed through an acousto-optic deflector that sent the beam at different
angles according to the voltage applied to the deflector. The process of using two
beams in sequence to measure the two different sides of the block is known as time
sharing or time sequencing. It had to be fast with respect to the rate of wing beating.
The force could be calculated based on the bending of the cantilever beam and its
stiffness. The bee wing beats at about 130 Hz. The scanning frequency was about 2
kHz and as a result they sampled about 30 points in each direction per wing beat.
They found that the instantaneous vertical force was almost five time the bee's

weight and the horizontal force almost eight times. To paraphrase Simon Scarle's comments in *New Scientist*, if a bumblebee is in the air and apparently flying, it probably is flying.[12]

Fits and Starts

Plants are very sensitive (so talk to them nicely). They stress when they are touched or even when the air around them is disturbed. So researchers in Canada developed a "black box" to observe plants growing in an undisturbed state. It was a wooden box with a black cloth covering. The inside of the box was uniformly illuminated by light conducted from an incandescent bulb via fiber optics. Thus there was no heat, no touching, and no air motion. A mirror was placed inside so that an image of the corn seedlings inside could be relayed to a CCD camera outside. In this way plant growth could be monitored. The researchers found that plants do not grow uniformly, but in spurts (like children).[13] What is significant, however, is that this is a technique to monitor all the different things that can be done to alter plant growth for the better.

Am I Blue?

Researchers at UCLA have determined that flowers have both red and blue photoreceptors. The reds work to inhibit blooming and the blues promote blooms. This experiment was done on *Arabidopsis thaliana*, whatever that is.[14] Yes, there is more blue light in spring than in winter. The sun is higher in the sky and the days are longer.

I Hear They are Growing

A very unusual application of lasers is listening to plants! The Germans wondered why so many of their geranium seedlings died during their transit from the Mediterranean countries, where they were grown from seeds, to Germany. The unusual solution was to use a very sensitive hearing aid and a laser to sense the ethylene gases that are emitted from the plants. This gas is emitted when the plants are exposed to drought, cold, or other stresses. The more ethylene "exhaled" by the plants, the louder the "noise" from the hearing aid. The laser is used to make the gas molecules vibrate, and this occurs when the laser optical frequency matches the natural vibra-

---

12   Whipple, C. T., "Bumblebees can't fly, can they?," *Biophotonics International*, July/August 1998.
13   Leggett, K., "Imaging reveals fitful plant growth," *Biophotonics International*, January/ February 1998.
14   "Photoreceptors herald spring," *Biophotonics International*, May/June 1998.

tion frequency of these molecules.[15] This sensing technique permitted them to monitor and maintain the proper moisture and temperature during transit.

Grow Lights

Many gardeners buy these lights specially to enhance the growth of their indoor plants. What is wrong with just a tungsten light? The plants are genetically attuned to the spectral distribution of sunlight. That is shown in Fig. 15, along with the spectral distribution of the light from a regular household tungsten lightbulb. I have normalized both curves to the same value; the relative values are not important. The sunlight curve is the solid line on the left. The spectrum from a normal tungsten bulb is the dotted line on the right. There is far less blue light (shorter wavelengths) in the tungsten bulb than in the sunlight. Does

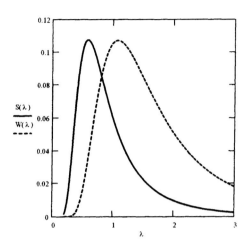

Figure 15 Solar and incandescent light spectra.

this also apply to fluorescent lights? Not as much. A fluorescent light is a much whiter light, matching the solar spectrum better in some ways. The grow light maximizes this to get as good a match to sunlight as possible.

Insect Extinction

Ultraviolet and blue lights are used in connection with electrical circuits to attract and kill a variety of insects. The ultraviolet radiation is a powerful attractant for moths and many other insects. However, Douglas Tallamy and his students have counted these insects in a number of cases. In at least one count, 13,789 insects were found dead in the bottom of one of these devices. Of these, only 18 were found to be female mosquitoes and 13 other biting insects were found. Only 0.022% of the insects killed were biters. One way to improve this is to redesign the insect attractors using a heated canister of carbon dioxide or a properly filtered thermal source.[16]

---

15 *Scientific American*, 22, June 1997.
16 *Scientific American*, 30, June 1997.

Chlorophyll Detection

Researchers at NASA's Stennis Lab have developed a chlorophyll detector. It uses ambient light and three CCD cameras that use the same telescope. One has a filter centered at 700 nm, one at 840 nm, and one is unfiltered. Chlorophyll absorbs at 700 nm and has no influence at 840 nm, so the former is the chlorophyll detector and the latter a reference.[17] The amount of chlorophyll is an important diagnostic for plant health. The unfiltered CCD gives an image.

Photosynthesis Measurement

Photosynthesis, the generation of complex organic materials in leaves from water, carbon dioxide, and sunlight, is an essential part of the human life cycle. It does not happen in humans, but it is basic to the food chain, shade, and aesthetics. A technique has been developed to measure just where and under what conditions this happens on various leaves.

An array of light-emitting diodes (LEDs) is used to illuminate the leaf with light at 470 nm. The resultant fluorescence from the leaf is imaged by a camera with a filtered CCD array. The test instrument used a 659×494 array and an RG 495 infrared filter. This common technique of fluorescence measurement is used to block any blue light coming from the illuminator. The investigators used a pulse technique to further reduce any background interference. They checked against the standard gas-exchange methods the quantity of ethylene emitted by the plants. They found, for instance, in wild parsnip leaves, that photosynthesis was reduced over an area six times as large as that eaten by a caterpillar. Speculation was that the leaf was expending more energy in defense than in photosynthesis.

---

17   Robinson, K., "NASA builds chlorophyll measurement system," *Photonics Spectra*, August 1998.

Chapter 4

Applications

This chapter is a collection of optical applications I have gathered for more than ten years. They range from some very simple detectors for security to complex devices to control manufacturing processes, aircraft, and rockets. I have divided them into various categories to provide some organization, but they could just as well have been presented in a different order. There are surely more optics applications in our lives, but these are all I have found or remembered.

Aerospace

This section groups applications that are nonmilitary in nature but are part of our aeronautics and space applications and ventures. Many of the applications and instruments have been developed by the National Aeronautics and Space Agency (NASA).

The Laser Gyroscope

As many readers already know, the gyroscope has long been a part of the navigational equipment of aircraft. Familiar mechanical versions consist of two or more spinning members that react to external forces. These reactions are monitored and used to show when the aircraft begins to veer off course. When the vehicle, usually a plane, turns from the direct-line path it was sent on, the gyros sense the acceleration in the different direction, and make a correction to the course. Lasers have been used to replace these "iron" gyros, and they have been far more accurate, more compact, and even less expensive.

A laser, with its very narrow spectral band of light, is directed into a Sagnac interferometer. Recall that this interferometer has a beam that is split and then has two beams that rotate clockwise and counterclockwise, respectively. They then combine and interfere. If there is no rotation of the interferometer, there is constructive interference, but if there is rotation, there is a frequency shift in opposite directions because of the Doppler effect. Thus, any tendency to go off course is sensed by the rotation of the laser gyroscope. This is a very sensitive measurement, and these laser gyros have better performance than the old spinning gyroscopes.

The Fiber Optic Gyroscope[1]

The fiber optic gyro is similar to the laser gyro, but is even more compact and less expensive. These instruments have appeared on Boeing 777s, Dormier commuter aircraft, remotely piloted helicopters, lawn mowers, and shopping-mall floor scrubbers. An accuracy of 0.00038 deg per hour has been demonstrated. This means that on a cross-country airline flight taking five hours, the direction will be off by 0.0019 deg or 33.16 microradians, and therefore 0.099 miles or 525 feet. The flight from New York to Los Angeles should not miss the airport!

One example is a high-sensitivity I-FOG, or interferometric fiber optic gyroscope, that can obtain an accuracy of 0.15 deg per hour with a coiled loop that is 10 cm in diameter, 1-km long, and uses light of 1550 nm. The coil consists of approximately 30 loops.

Almost monochromatic light from the source is passed through a beamsplitter and polarizer to a spatial filter, consisting of two lenses and a pinhole. Then it enters the coil via a beamsplitter, which causes the two different beams to propagate in different directions. They pass through the entire coil and emerge, where they are recombined by the beamsplitter, spatially filtered again, and go to the detector, which senses the degree to which they are out of phase. Other schemes have been devised that make use of a variety of different solid-state beamsplitters and combiners. The devices can operate with sensitivities ranging from 0.001 deg per hour to 100 deg per hour.[2]

Check-In Safety System[3]

Several airlines have implemented a face-recognition system to ensure that passengers and their luggage agree. A lipstick-size camera takes a digital photograph of the person who checks a bag. The image is embedded on a smart-card that is used both as a boarding pass and a baggage check. During the boarding process, every passenger is checked. The recognition system must find the facial image anywhere in the field of view in a variety of orientations. It also ignores hair length and facial hair and concentrates on several unique features. It operates in the ambient light of an airport. This ensures that every person who checked a bag is on the plane.

Hot Air Gas Detection

At the Stennis Center of NASA, where there are many rocket pads, one concern is small hydrogen flames that can cause much larger flames and even explosions. A

1   Tebo, A., *OE Reports*, 158, February 1997.
2   Burns, W., "Fiber optic gyroscopes–light is better," *Optics and Photonic News*, May 1998.
3   Mendonsa, R., "Face-recognition technology makes air travel safer," *Photonics Spectra*, 20, September 1997.

hydrogen flame is essentially invisible to the human eye and to visible cameras and TVs. So a system has been developed to detect these small flames in the infrared. The system uses a zoom lens in the front, followed by a beamsplitter that directs the visible light to a standard three-color CCD. The other beam is then split into two infrared wavelengths, one at 2.7 μm to detect the emission from heated water molecules in the flame, the other at nearby but different wavelengths to get the background. The background image is subtracted from the flame image and the result is processed. The flame can then be displayed as red (or some other color) superimposed on the standard color image.[4]

In related research, I investigated a way to detect the flames but prevent similar, much larger, hydrogen flames from rockets taking off or being tested, from creating false detections. This enabled the detection of small hydrogen flames that should not be there on gantries that are nearby, while preventing false alarms from real flames from distant gantries. The basic technique is to pick wavelengths in which the flame radiation is highly attenuated by the atmosphere. This required carefully adjusting the spectral band on the edge of the line emission of the water molecules. It worked on paper, and it has never been published, but it was reported to Stennis.

The Red Planet

At the dawn of 2004, we landed a rover on Mars to explore its composition, history, and the possibility (probability) that life was ever there. It is loaded with optical instruments. It has a microscopic imager on an arm out front. It has navigational cameras on a four-foot pedestal. It is powered by solar arrays. It has high-resolution panoramic cameras and two different kinds of spectrometers.

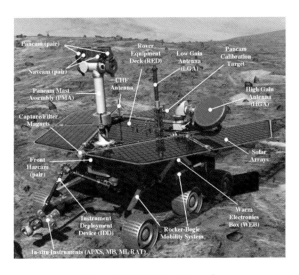

Figure 1 The Mars Rover.[5]

The orbiting mother ship kept track of the lander with an arrangement of laser diodes and a CCD camera. It sent the laser beams to an array of retroreflectors on

4 "Camera images hydrogen fires in three wavelength bands," Stennis Space Center, *Photonic Tech Briefs*, July 1999.
5 Image courtesy of NASA/JPL-Caltech.

the lander and used the geometry to determine its aspect; the range may be monitored. The lasers emit 2 W at 800 and 850 nm.[6]

A Small-Time Rover

The Mars Rover is discussed elsewhere. This one is a tunnel rover. Two students at the University of Arizona put together a small 18-inch platform that can probe the nooks and crannies of mines.[7] It has two 12-volt halogen lamps and a pan-and-tilt video camera—180 deg horizontally, 90 deg vertically. It has a 900 MHz telemetry unit with a range of 1500 feet, and is powered by three lithium batteries. The entire assemblage weighs 3.4 pounds and can move at 1.6 miles per hour. Although this is a limited unit, others can be envisaged: a greater telemetry range, pickup arms, shovels, a winch, and more. Size and cost will, as always, be critical. It could eventually be used as a remote digger in mines, or as a remote tram. And it has potential for other applications, such as cleanups in dangerous areas, and even search-and-rescue missions.

Figure 2 The small-time Mars Rover.[7]

The Venus Probe

In the late 1970s, NASA sent a probe to the planet Venus to learn more about that mysterious planet. My group had a role in that mission; we designed and built a probe that would drop through the atmosphere and take measurements on the way down. The aim was to measure the deposition of sunlight in the atmosphere as a function of altitude to determine the degree of the greenhouse effect on that planet. The instrument would fall and spin, its rate of descent reduced by the use of a parachute.

---

6   Howard, R., Bryan, T., Brook, M., and Rogers, L., "Photonics makes connections in space," *Photonics Spectra*, pp May 1999.
7   Fischer, A. L., "Students build a rover for remote mine detection," *Photonics Spectra*, January 2005. (Image courtesy of Jessica Brock and Keith Brock.)

There were a few problems. The atmosphere is not hospitable! The surface temperature is about 700 K; the gases are mostly carbon dioxide, but with clouds of sulfuric and nitric acids.

The device we designed, mostly by my then-student, Jim Palmer, is shown in Fig. 3. We included five channels, determined by the light pipes and detectors (Fig. 4). The windows and light pipes were made of sapphire. The detectors were cadmium sulfide and we had a temperature-controlling mechanism that kept the unit cool enough for long enough to make the measurements. It was a solid material that would liquify at these temperatures, but the time it took to melt the material kept the temperature low enough for the device to be effective.

Figure 3 Outside view of the Venus probe instrument.

Figure 4 Inside of Venus device, showing light pipes.

Lightcraft Propulsion

Why not use the power in a laser beam to propel an aerospace vehicle? Why not, indeed? It has been done. So far, small vehicles have been propelled about 30 m by the use of a carbon-dioxide laser beam. It is estimated that a million watts are necessary for each kilogram of payload that gets into orbit. That could be accomplished with multiple beams, and, although it sounds exorbitant, such light-propelling systems stay on the ground and can be used over and over again. Other applications include levitation of various objects and local propulsion.[8]

Go with the Flow

In some applications, including synthetic aperture radar and satellite-based cell phones, it has been proposed to use hundreds to thousands of miniature satellites. Researchers need to know how to optimize the miniature thrusters for these minia-

8   "Lightcraft propulsion," *Optics and Photonics News*, January 1999.

ture satellites. One technique has been coating tiny latex particles with fluorescent dye and injecting them into the microthrusters. A doubled Nd:YAG laser operating at 532 nm is used to illuminate the particles in the plume. The resultant images are used to evaluate the flow of the thrusters.[9]

Gas Gauge

NASA has been investigating an optical device for measuring the amount of fuel in a gas tank. This is for aircraft, but it applies to other tanks that hold liquids. A rod made of a material that has a refractive index close to that of the fuel is inserted into the liquid. It is actually mounted in the tank, and the liquid is poured in. There are several fiducial marks scratched in the side of the rod indicating the levels. Light is shone into the rod. The marks will appear dark in the liquid, but bright in the air above. A camera is used to view the rod.[10]

Harder Fan Blades

Jet engine fan blades, in turbo fan jets, lead a tough life. During takeoff and landing, they are battered and bruised by sticks and stones, ice, and even geese. The smaller objects dent and damage them, thereby shortening their lives.

However, laser peening can restore their strength to a considerable degree. The process uses a neodymium-phosphate glass laser and an absorbant coating, which together generate a shock wave that produces stress in the blades.[11]

Agricultural Exploits

Optical applications in agriculture range from checking out the products—beef, poultry, grain—to improving their production by keeping hogs happy, cotton watered just right, and others. Here are a few.

Happy as a Hog in...

Hongwei Xin at Iowa State University has employed optics to observe pigs.[12] It seems that the perfect pork chop requires perfect conditions for growing piglets.

9   Werely, S., "Mini-Nd:YAG laser illuminates microfluids," *Photonics Spectra*, May 1999.
10   "Optoelectronic liquid-level gauges for aircraft fuel tanks," *NASA Tech Briefs*, February 1999.
11   Mendonsa, R., "Laser increases lifetime of jet engine fan blades," *Photonics Spectra*, 26, August 1998.
12   Anonymous, "Porcine comfort tops priority list," *Photonics Spectra*, September 1997.

The proper temperature is vital. Xin found that the perfect temperature can be determined by how close the pigs snuggle up to or avoid each other. If they are barely touching, it seems, they are blissful. So a video camera coupled to a central computer monitors their proximity and adjusts the temperature accordingly. The pigs actually seem to like different temperatures at different times, so an areal thermometer will not do the job.

Breeding Better Beef

Cattle and swine have been monitored by infrared cameras to find lesions and inflammation, or sickness. It has since been learned, not surprisingly, that different cattle have different metabolic rates. Now they can be separated into groups and fed according to their different metabolisms. Researches have also found that sick animals release less energy, and this can be used as a diagnostic tool.[13]

Infrared cameras are also used to carry out temperature assessments to see if cattle are stressed out. Too much stress causes less flavorful meat. The correlation between stress and temperature is not certain, but higher stress probably means higher temperature.

How's the Beef?

The problems of *E. coli* have been chronicled in the popular press, usually in terms of cooking hamburger meat to well done. But inspection for it goes on in the meat-packing plant. The problem is inspecting a 9-foot by 3-foot slab of white beef that has flecks of blood and oil on it. For this, a photonic system based upon fluorescence is used. The output of a mercury-vapor lamp, filtered to a 40 nm band centered at 400 nm, is used to illuminate a small area on the carcass. The fecal matter provides a detectable fluorescence in the red at 670 nm. Detection statistics were not available.[14]

A related application is a hand scanner that uses the same technology to determine whether a worker's hands really are clean—or at least free of fecal matter.[15] My experience with fluorescence detection tells me that the instrument could be broadened to detect other contaminants.

The Danish Meat Research Institute in Roskilde has developed a way to inspect beef carcasses. Several light sources produce stripes across the meat at an angle in order to calculate the thickness. The conveyor belt stops at regular intervals and the carcass is imaged both under and without illumination to eliminate ambient light

13 "Infrared imaging keeps feed animals fit," *Photonics Spectra*, March 2001.
14 "Fluorescence finds contamination," *Biophotonics International*, July/August 1999.
15 Bridis, T., "From slaughterhouse to hospitals, scanners to expose fecal germs," *Arizona Daily Star* via AP, April 4, 2004.

effects. Neural networks, also a form of computer learning, are used to classify the meat by color and other clues.

Thermal imagers are now used to determine the size and quality of cattle to see if they qualify as choice meat[16] (and get the highest prices). Visible imagers were found to have difficulties with the dust in the area and the variability of the colors of the cattle. In this application, handlers send the animals down a chute and take thermal images of them from above. They can then determine size, frame size, and muscle thickness. If inadequate, their lives are saved for a while—till they grow up to be choice!

Finer Fillets

VE Tech in St. Johns, Newfoundland, has developed a technique for grading fish fillets. The details of how they discriminate between blemishes and natural differences have not been revealed, but I surmise that they go through a fairly long learning procedure and are still not 100%. Although the challenges are great, progress is being made on the inspection of fish fillets by machine vision. The problems are defining exactly what is a defect and what is merely a variation in flesh.[17]

Poultry Inspection

Poultry is inspected by the USDA, using a multispectral sensor and analyzing the spectra of the carcasses.[16]

Go with the Grain

The University of Saskatchewan is developing a color CCD that will identify grain discoloration, hull peeling, and broken kernels for use in barley inspection. Other applications include using a laser for three-dimensional inspection of lentils.[18] A similar system with similar problems is used for beef carcasses and barley.[19]

---

16   Kummer, S., "Thermal imaging takes the guesswork out of feeder cattle sizing," *Photonics Spectra*, January 2005.
17   Ibid.
18   Grant, B., *Photonics Spectra*, October 1998.
19   Grant, B., "Photonic eyes separate the wheat from the chaff," *Photonics Spectra*, October 1998.

Cut It Out

A line-scan camera makes single-line scans of beef as it goes by on a belt at 500 feet per second. The generated imagery allows them to trim the fat with water jets. They can also use the deflections of a strip of light to get a vertical profile.[20]

Cotton-Pickin's Better Cotton Picking

A system for checking the maturity of cotton consists of a near-infrared spectrometer. The spectrum is indicative of the state of maturity, and a simple, diode-array spectrometer is used to make this assessment of the fibers in about two seconds with an uncertainty of about two percent. When the boll opens, the tubular fibers lose moisture, and the degree of this moisture is the key.

Viniculture

The growth of really good grapes for wine has long been an art—some things are understood, but many are not.[21] White wines taste fruitier if aged in stainless steel tanks, and Zinfandels are more flavorful if they are stressed a little, causing more complex sugars. Vintners do know that microclimate is important. Different part of their vineyards, not very far apart, produce different results.

This is where remote sensing can help. One of the most influential factors in growing grapes is the soil water content, and therefore the density of grape leaves. By mapping the vineyards in different colors, the grapes may be harvested at their absolute peak, and the best grapes can be segregated from the mediocre ones. One system that flies in a plane at about 14,000 ft altitude uses four CCD cameras, each with a different color filter—red, green, blue, and infrared. Color-ratioing algorithms are used and a geometrical grid is overlaid on the processed imagery. As satellite imagery gets better resolution, there may be more coverage with that modality. Some 50,100 California vintners are now using this technology, but it is unlikely to be used in France. They have tradition and Appelation Controlee!

Weevils and Borers, the Kernel of the Problem

These nasty devils do their dirty work inside the kernels of grain, so they cannot be inspected visually. The kernels are relatively transparent to near-infrared radiation in the range of 1.00 to 1.35 μm and 1.65 to 1.80 μm, so modern spectroscopy can be used. The test system, which operates from 0.4 μm to 1.7 μm, can only examine two

20   McCarthy, D., "Flexible-frame-rate camera guides cutting robot," *Photonics Spectra*, March 1999.

21   Drollette, D., "Photonics meets the French resistance," *Photonics Spectra*, August 2000.

grains per second since, it is reported, the spectrometer that is used can only take 30 spectra per second. It would seem that they could do 30 grains per second on that basis, but it would still have to be faster.

Every engineer tries to improve on a system that is inadequate, and I am no exception. First, cut the spectral scan so that it runs from 1.0 to 1.7 μm. If the spectrometer has uniform wavelength resolution, this will cut the scan time in about half, up to 60 grains per second.

The report did say that grain-handling equipment works at about 1000 grains per second. So an entirely different approach is needed. I say investigate the spectra; see where the differences are and use just a few bands. When detected, the grains might be separated and then treated with a laser to kill the weevils.[22] But do you want dead weevils in your Wheaties?

Orange Juicing

A very interesting application of the use of remote sensing is that of Florida's Department of Citrus.[23] They are using the Quickbird satellite with a ground resolution of 0.6 m that takes 57 images per orbit to monitor Brazil's orange groves. They claim that Brazil both underrates and overrates their orange product as they choose, thereby adversely affecting the prices of Florida's orange juice!

Another application is the early detection of citrus canker in the trees. The trees emit a special chemical to fight cancer, and this creates a reflection spectrum different from that of the healthy leaves. This technique has been used with spectral imaging from the air.[24] The spectrometer has a resolution of 3 nm and fits into a single-engine airplane.

One Fish, Two Fish

About half of the salmon that swim downstream and into the Pacific are raised in hatcheries. Since 1971, Northwest Marine Technology has tagged the small hatchery fish with 1.1×0.25-mm stainless steel tags to monitor their migration habits. The former spark-erosion etching method of writing the information has recently been replaced with a Nd:YAG laser system that can etch alpha-numeric characters rather than just binary codes.[25]

22   Robinson, K., "Spectroscopy takes on agricultural pests," *Biophotonics International* November, December, 1998.
23   "Did you know?" *Optics and Photonics News*, September 2003.
24   Drollette, D., "Hyperspectral aerial imaging may conquer canker," *Photonics Spectra*, August 1999.
25   McCarthy, D. C., "Nd:YAG improves the fine print in fish tags," *Photonics Spectra*, August 1999.

Clean Beans

A small portion of every soybean crop gets infested with mold—green, white, or brown. It is important, of course, to search and eliminate these from the good ones. Researchers at Osaka University have invented a technique that analyzes multicolor reflection ratios. They were able to determine the density of green mold distribution without destroying the beans. The other colors are yet to be addressed.[26]

Spreading the Manure

Most applications of fertilizers to crops are uniform; every plant gets the same amount. But some do not need as much as others for one reason or another. A system called the N-Sensor is used in Europe to fertilize crops where the crops need fertilized. Two spectrometers monitor the spectrum in the chlorophyll region. One looks up to obtain a reference, while the other makes the measurement.

Figure 5 Spectrometer spreader.[27]

(I would use a flip mirror and a single instrument.) The measurement of the chlorophyll is sent to the spreader and more or less fertilizer is delivered, based on the need. The device is shown in the illustration (Fig. 5).[27] The spectrometer is indicated by the white arrow.

Out, Out Damned Spot

A similar but simpler system has been used to detect *karnal bunt*, or fungal spores. A simple black-and-white 480×640 CCD camera was mounted on a reaper. Special pattern-recognition software was used to identify the spores. This has allowed farmers to increase their productivity by ten times and ensure that their crops are good.[28]

---

26 *Photonics Spectra*, August 1999.
27 McCarthy, D., "Sensor cultivates agricultural market," *Photonics Spectra*, August 1999. (Image courtesy of Yara International.)
28 Wheeler, M., "Machine vision spots spoiled wheat," *Photonics Spectra*, June 1998.

Wearin' of the Green

One test for chlorophyll is to measure the relative absorption by chlorophyll at 700 nm. This can be done by measuring the relative reflectance at 700 nm and 840 nm, the second being used as a reference. One system does this by imaging with two filters and adding a standard color video image for reference.[29]

Seeds can also be tested for chlorophyll, but in this case the less chlorophyll, the riper it is, and the better it will germinate. The process is to illuminate the seeds with red laser light and monitor the amount of light that fluoresces at the chlorophyll wavelength of about 700 nm.[30]

How Dry Am I

Multispectral imagery can be used by farmers to determine when their crops exhibit water stress and need to be watered. Several bands can be used. One set is 653.668 nm, 830.870 nm and 8.12 μm. These systems range from very simple three-camera systems with filters to satellite-borne devices with diffraction gratings and the other components of a spectrometer. They can be in satellites, in crop dusters or aerial mapping planes, and even in towers or tractors. When used correctly, they can optimize the watering for good, healthy crops, and not overwater.[31]

From Pillar to Post

Actually, from farm to store. Ultraviolet light is now used in some places to prevent fruit rot from occurring during the time from picking at the farm to delivery at the supermarket. Although the germicidal properties of ultraviolet light have long been known, and discussed elsewhere in this book, the new methods use pulsed, high-peak power to kill microbes. This technique is better than the use of ionizing radiation or fumigation techniques. It causes no internal changes and does not leave any residue. It has generated a shelf life of 30 to 40 days for grapes and "a long time at room temperature" for tomatoes.[32]

Perfect Bubbly

As champagne bottles move along the production line, they are inspected by a machine-vision system to see that they have exactly the right amount of bubbly in

29 Robinson, K., "NASA builds chlorophyll measurement system," *Photonics Spectra*, August 1998.

30 "Testing for chlorophyll content," *Optics and Photonics News*, August 1998.

31 Hogan, H., "Photonics spots thirsty plants," *Biophotonics International*, March/April 1999.

32 Pini, R., "UV light stops the rot," *Biophotonics International*, May/June 1999.

them and that their corks are on straight. This is accomplished with a calibrated CCD camera.

Better Fleecing

In Australia, where sheep breeding is very important, a new strain called Primerino has been introduced. It is a breed whose fleece is finer than even Merinos—about 12-μm thick as opposed to cashmere at 15 μm and human hairs at 20 μm. The device that tests this is a CCD camera that has means for correcting for object distance variations. It can test some 1200 skins per day, giving information on diameter, length, thick and thin regions, and curvature (a measure of curliness). It can even do random sampling for lanolin, creating a grease-correction factor.[33]

Remote-Sensing Satellite Instruments

Several mappers have been designed and built to assess crop damage and other phenomena on the Earth. The Environmental Protection Agency (EPA) has used one of these remote sensors to assess the situation in Leadville, CO, where there are almost 1200 abandoned mines. The EPA was able to assess rapidly the potential impact and danger of these mines and openings. According to Sam Vance of the EPA, they were able to save some $2.5 million and two years as compared to conventional methods (airplane photography).

Art

Optics have been used in art in at least two ways. As described briefly in the section on the camera obscura, it is believed that some artists during the Renaissance used the camera to trace certain figures before they sketched and painted, possibly over the tracings. Optics have also been used to hunt for forgeries and for underpaintings. It was not uncommon for the old masters to decide a painting was a loser (surely not their phrase), and simply start a new painting over the top of it. I discovered in my art class long ago that oil is a wonderful medium. When (not if) I made a mistake, I could paint right over it after it dried. Such is surely not the case with watercolors. So infrared cameras have been used to hunt for what is below the surface. Other applications involve the restoration of buildings and statues.

---

33 "Shear profits," *Photonics Spectra*, June 2004.

The Real Renoir

Infrared cameras in the spectral region from 0.9 to 1.7 μm have been used to examine paintings for forgeries. In this part of the spectrum, the paints are translucent, and underpaintings can be examined. In a Renoir, "The Luncheon of the Boat Party," components of a bridge were found underneath the lovely picture by the curator of the Phillips Collection in Washington, D. C. The camera contained an array of 128×128 elements of InGaAs detectors with pixels that are 60 μm on a side with a well capacity of 10^7 electrons. Other museums have also used this camera, which records the images digitally and stores them in a computer memory.[34]

Not So Obscure

The highly controvesial case for the use of the camera obscura by the masters has been made by David Hockney and Charles Falco.[35] Their main arguments are that shortly after the invention of the camera obscura, paintings took on a new and better reality and definition. Many people in these paintings are left handed. This would be a natural result if a camera was used, in that the image of a camera obscura is both inverted and reverted. That is, it is upside down and reversed left to right. Another clue is that objects that are somewhat in the background are portrayed as a little fuzzy. If they are a little out of focus in the camera image, they will be a little fuzzy. If they are viewed directly, the eye refocuses. Another phenomenon is that some of the photographs have more than one vanishing point. This is the point we learned about when we did perspectives. We drew lines in the figure that converged to a point in the distance. If a camera of some sort was used and refocused to get sharper imagery of a different part of the picture, there would be more than one vanishing point.

Laser Carving

One other advent of optics in art is laser carving. It is very simple in concept. A nice piece of wood is fixed to a table. A fairly high-power laser, probably a carbon dioxide laser, is shone on the piece. Then either the wood or the laser is moved in a programmed way by numerical control. It can be done by hand, but today's commercial ones are surely controlled by computer.

Laser Etching

During our visit to the Boulder County Fair, we saw some very nice etchings in glass. They were inside the glass. The trick was to program two lasers, each with

---

34 "Penetrating art with a near IR camera," *Optics and Photonics News*, November, 1997.
35 Hockney, D., and C. Falco, "Optical insights into renaissance art," *Optics and Photonics News*, July, 2000.

about half the power necessary to etch the glass. Where they intersected, however, there was enough power to do the job. Thus, one could get an etching inside a block or globe of glass. Of course this was also done by a computer.

Remember the Alamo

That famous shrine to Texas statehood is slowly deteriorating. The limestone and mortar walls, 4-foot thick, are being attacked by water. It wicks up from the ground and causes the limestone to deteriorate. Now, accurate, fast measurements can be made with an infrared camera. The walls absorb heat in the warm Texas weather, and the walls cool in the evening. The moisture retains the heat, partly because of the high heat capacity of water, so that the warm spots show clearly the accumulations of moisture, with a sensitivity of about $0.02°C$.[36]

Get the Soot Out

Historic statues are now being cleaned by laser techniques. As we all know, many ancient Greek and Roman statues have darkened with age. They are no longer pristine and white. Cleaning with a Nd:YAG laser is a natural. The black dirt nicely absorbs the laser beam, but the white marble reflects almost all of it. So shining the laser on the dirty statue heats the dirt, which expands and pops off the statue. If the laser is not too powerful, it will not be absorbed by the marble. Workers have chosen different powers; some prefer to leave a little dirt on to indicate age, while others clean "to the bone."[37] As indicated below, the technique has also been applied to buildings.

Everything Old is New Again

The French have developed a laser system that removes paint and other deposits from some of their architectural treasures. A Nd:YAG laser supplies a mean output power of 20 W in 10-ns pulses to a 36-foot fiber optic cord in a protective casing. At the end of the cord is a three-pound gun that delivers the energy to the building. Thresholds are set so that the power is great enough to ablate the stains but not great enough to destroy the substrate. The dark stains absorb the laser light and vaporize.

36   Mendonsa, R., "IR imager helps preserve the Alamo," *Photonics Spectra*, July 1998.

37   Drollette, D., "Photonics advances the science of art," *Photonics Spectra*, March 2001.

Forgery Detection

Real old masters are worth millions; fakes are virtually worthless. Verification is now done with the help of optics. A typical investigation begins with a detailed "eyeballing" of the picture for any tell-tale signs of forgery. Then the work is illuminated with ultraviolet light. General fluorescence is an indication of validity, since varnishes, binders, coatings, and other materials have aged enough to form unsaturated double bonds that fluoresce. Areas that do not do so may have been touched up at a later date, and are not worthy of further investigation. The next step is removal of minuscule amounts of material for spectroscopic analysis. In one example, "La Dolorosa," some of the paints were found to consist of materials available only centuries after the painting was said to have been created, and the wood base was primed with a coat of white paint with polyvinyl acetate.[38]

Automotive

Automobiles use all kinds of optics, from the headlights to the interior and exterior mirrors, the colors, the windshields, moon roofs, and all the way to the taillights. There are automatic driving systems, display systems, control systems, and even a variety of driver's aids. This section describes some of them.

It's All How You Look at It

A car paint has been developed recently, although it was described years ago by A. Francis Turner, that changes color with aspect angle. It is called ChromaFlair; it consists of an ultrathin, multilayer, interference filter that is formed into flakes that are opaque, flat, and highly specular. The films are colorless; the paint color is generated by the interference and the color determined by the thickness of the layers.

There are several advantageous features of this new paint. It enhances the look of a car, even making it look like it's moving when it isn't as a result of the angular color change. It is easier to apply than metallic paint and it has no organics that can be altered and degraded by the sun.

But it is very expensive, some 100 times as expensive as metallic paints.[39] As Turner put it, "There goes the red, no green, no blue [getaway] car," in the event of a robbery. If the police are up to date, that will actually limit it to the relatively few cars that have this rainbow paint.

---

38   Drollette, D., ibid.
39   Reiss, S., "Coatings for cars and communications," *Optics and Photonics News* October 1997.

Paint

It is good to have an even coat of paint on a car. Too much tends to delaminate; too little, to wear thin. A sophisticated method to ensure optimal thickness has been developed by Perceptron. A Nd:YAG laser sends a short pulse that creates an ultrasonic vibration in the paint. A stable, almost monochromatic continuous laser shines on the sample, and a detector senses the Doppler shift caused by the ultrasonic wave. In practice, the laser must be scanned over the entire surface to be measured.[40]

In Germany they use a similar system called PaintCheck. A short laser pulse is sent to the paint, and an infrared sensor measures the resultant heat, which is reradiated. The speed of the heating is an indicator of the thickness of the paint. A very sensitive detector is used so that the laser can be of low power and not affect the paint.[41]

Headlights

These have had only minor changes in many years. A tungsten bulb is placed near the focus of a concave mirror, ideally parabolic, but usually spherical for economy. The beam is then projected out front for nighttime driving. Engineers work out how much power is needed to get the correct illumination at a specified distance. High beams result from a different bulb at a different place. Actually, it's placed a little lower than the optical axis in order for the beam to go a little higher. Some may also be a little more powerful. Recently, bluish, high-power beams have been introduced on some cars.

Many years ago, Edwin Land of Polaroid introduced the concept of polarized headlights. This would greatly reduce the glare from oncoming headlights. Imagine that your lights and your windshield both are polarized at 45 degrees from lower left to upper right. You can see perfectly well the reflections from objects illuminated by the polarized light from your headlights, which have the same polarization orientation (and get depolarized to some extent on reflection). Now imagine an identically equipped car coming the other way. Since he is facing the opposite way, his headlights are polarized from lower right to upper left from your point of view. This means that there will be considerable extinction of his headlight illumination.

Although this sounds like a wonderful idea, there are some drawbacks. The first is that the efficiency at best is 25% for the illumination that gets from your headlights back through your windshield—50% for the headlights and 50% for the windshield. In addition, some of the light that is reflected from the road and other objects ahead will be depolarized, causing further loss in efficiency. The additional

---

40 "Paint measuring laser gives good vibrations," *Photonics Spectra*, September 2000.

41 McCarthy, D., "Compact cooler chills compact detector," *Photonics Spectra*, May 1999.

cost of providing all windshields and all headlights with polarizers was not lost on the auto industry–nor on Land!

Audi has introduced white light-emitting diodes (LEDs) into some of their models to be used as daytime running lights. The LEDs are so efficient that they have no influence on gas mileage.[42]

Windshields and Windows

All windshields today are made of safety glass. Safety glass has a laminate of plastic along with its glass composition. In case of an accident and glass breakage, the glass mostly stays together and prevents shards and flying pieces. Windshields are also tinted, but that is a straightforward dyeing process in the glass manufacture.

Side windows are now made of tempered glass. This is safety glass of a different type. When it breaks, it breaks into many small pieces of about an inch or so. These, too, are not dangerous shards. Tempered glass is made by applying heat to the surface of the glass after most of the manufacture has been done. This introduces strain throughout the material. When the glass is broken, or even if the surface is badly scratched, the strain is relaxed and the pane shatters into all those small pieces. If you want to check on whether your car windows are tempered, look at them through polarizing sunglasses. You will observe various colored contours all over the glass, a result of stress birefringence, which is described elsewhere.

I recall a demonstration at Barr and Stroud in Scotland, which makes such glass. They supported one of their panes at two ends and invited us to stand on it. I did, and it held. Another companion did. Same result. But our largest companion caused the pane to sag enough to just touch the concrete floor. This was enough to scratch the surface and cause the pane to shatter in a million pieces. There was a little embarrassment, but the pane really did do what it was supposed to: It showed considerable strength and it shattered in a safe way.

Sew What

Each car that comes off the assembly line has many stitches in it, the seats, the rugs, around visors, and elsewhere. Studies have been made on the temperature of the needles used in automated stitching of these fabrics. The needles can go at least 2000 strokes per second; the friction between the needle and the fabric can increase the temperature of the needle to the point where it bends or even breaks as the melting point is approached.

General Motors and the University of Windsor used computer analysis to calculate the temperatures, and infrared imaging devices to measure them. The results are used to optimize the needle speeds for different types of fabrics.[43]

---

42   "White LEDs to appear in Audi headlights," *Photonics Spectra*, February 2004.
43   Kaplan, H., "Study assesses needle heat," *Photonics Spectra*, June 1999.

Manufacturing

It is truly amazing the degree to which optics has entered the automobile manufacturing plant—and the impact it has had. In many plants, the production line workers are now dressed in white smocks, and the floors are immaculately clean. This is because robots do much of the work, and optics lets the robots measure and position. One example is the attachment of the windshield to the front of the car. As the car approaches the windshield installation site, robot arms reach forth to measure with CCD cameras the exact dimensions of the windshield frame and of the windshield. Comparisons are made to see if it is a perfect fit. If so, the robot, which holds the glass with a large suction cup, extends the windshield to the frame, releases it and moves on. Then a through-beam sensor measures the color and attenuation of the windshield and compares it to the specification for this car. As the car goes by, another sensor counts the wires on the rear window to see that it has the right number of heating coils (for defrosting).

At the engine plant or station, sensors count and inspect pistons as they roll down the line. Others check that the O-rings have been installed correctly and for any breakage in valve assemblies. Even the amount of coating on gaskets can be checked, and the positions of radiator fins. A major difference in modern automobile production is the constant measurement and inspection all along the line so that everything fits exactly in its place. This can be done because of the measuring capabilities of machine-vision systems that measure lateral displacement with CCD cameras and longitudinal ones with lasers.[44]

An infrared camera has been incorporated with welding by both carbon dioxide and Nd:YAG lasers to monitor the quality of the weld. These welds—in air-bag canisters, transmissions, and other parts—must be of high quality. The previous technique used ultrasonic testing in a water tank following the weld. The optical system checks the weld as it is made and is far simpler. So both time and money are saved, and the yield is higher.[45]

To a Tee

The automobile industry has for many years been using robots guided by photonics. Some examples include the insertion of a windshield on a Lincoln in one of Ford's plants. The robot places the windshield within ±25 mm to a specified place (and can probably do it better today). Another application is door attachment. The door and the frame are measured by a three-dimensional sensing system, and gradually the door is moved into the right spot as the continuous measurements guide the robot. The process is that a laser shines a line of light on the part, thereby outlin-

---

44 Whipple, C., "In search of the perfect car, *Photonics Spectra*, June 1999.
45 Wheeler, M., "IR monitor tracks weld defects in auto plant," *Photonics Spectra*, September 1999.

ing the contour. Two or more cameras then triangulate on some 500 points on the line. Other variations include flooding the entire area of the part with light and triangulating on many points over the surface.[46]

A Better Plug

One spark plug company tests its plugs for 100% performance, with no out-of-spec plugs. This means that the points had to be correctly seated and straight, the gap be the right size, and the model and type numbers be legible and complete. This latter was the most difficult since they wrap around the cylindrical base of the plug. This was accomplished with a line scanner and rotation of the plug in front of the imager. This is a process they called "peeling the plug."[47]

The Die Is Cast

Infrared imaging rather than a few thermocouples is now being used to map the thermal patterns of die-cast parts such as transmission cover dies, engine blocks, catalytic converters, and the like.[48]

This Is Not Boring

Mercedes uses a borescope (an optical device that drops into a cylinder and images the inside surface) to investigate fuel injection, valve movements, and other engine functions in its Indy car engines, while they race at 14,000 rpm (in place). The chamber is illuminated with a stroboscopic light source timed to match the firing of the fuel injectors. The image is taken by a wide-angle analog camera and frame grabber. It is important that the scope can be inserted in a hole only 8 mm in diameter; this minimizes alterations in the operation of the engine.[49]

All Fired Up

The study of combustion and combustion products is very important to understanding better the optimum way to inject and ignite in many different kinds of engines. One way to do this is with laser-induced fluorescence. Cylindrical (anamorphic) optics transform the circular beam that exits a tunable laser into a planar beam that

46 Kaplan, H., "Laser alignment helps appearance, safety, efficiency," *Photonics Spectra*, July 1998.
47 "Line-scan camera 'peels' spark plugs," *Photonics Spectra*, June 1998.
48 Phillips, L., "Infrared thermography streamlines automotive R&D," *Photonics Spectra*, February 2004.
49 McCarthy, D., "Borescope evaluates Mercedes engine performance," *Photonics Spectra*, October 1998.

is perpendicular to the flame flow field. A filtered CCD camera images the induced fluorescence.

The type of combustion products—carbon monoxide, carbon dioxide, various organics—is determined by the fluorescence spectrum from the flame; the temperature can also be found from taking ratios of different excitation levels.

Mitsubishi did this with a full-size turbine engine. Their planar sheet was 50-mm wide and 1-mm thick. They probed in successive 50-mm segments covering a total area of about 300 mm square. They used an excitation line of 284.458 nm for OH and 225.786 for NO. The broadband fluorescence was from 306 to 340 nm and 240 to 300 nm for these two gases, respectively. It was this broadband fluorescence that was imaged by the camera. Detection in parts per million of the combustion products is possible.[50]

Slick as a ...

Japanese researchers have developed a film that repels both water and some oils. A thin polycrystalline film of TiO_2 obtained from anastase gel is annealed at 773 K and then irradiated with ultraviolet light. The mirrors and windows thus coated repel for as long as the ultraviolet light is maintained. Daylight is good enough. The film can be reactivated after being in the dark for a while, and it forms activated oxygen that is strong enough to decompose organic materials and bacteria. This could be a water and oil repellant that also sterilizes, deodorizes, and defouls.[51]

Score One

Glass for automobiles and other applications can be cut to the exact size by photonic scoring. A nick is put in the glass mechanically. Then a carbon dioxide laser draws a line across the glass from the nick. The glass is heated just above the annealing point and then chilled with water. This quenching step induces tension in the glass and the crack follows the zone drawn by the laser, the tensile zone. The result is two pieces of glass with no chips or microcracks at the edge as with mechanical scoring.[52]

Another Score

A laser can be used to create pits and surrounding hills in the walls of automobile cylinders. Then the cylinder can be partially reground to remove the high spots. In

50 Margalith, E., Y. Deguchi, H. Nishida and R. Hanson, "Laser-induced fluorescence fires up engine research," *Photonics Spectra*, March 1997.
51 Whipple, C., "Coated mirrors and glass repel fog, dirt," *Photonics Spectra*, October 1997.
52 Sheppard, L., "Laser scoring improves glass," *Photonics Spectra*, June 1999.

this way a cylinder wall with pits is generated, and this extra surface and topography leads to less cylinder wear and better lubrication.[53]

Cleanliness is Next to...

In some facilities, a laser is now used to clean the molds used to make tires. The molds define the tread and the rest of the tire. After many tires have been formed, the molds get clogged with leftover rubber and related materials. Mechanical means for removing these also remove a little of the mold each time, until the molds have to be replaced. The laser, partly because the rubber is black and absorbs the radiation while the mold itself does not, does not eat away at the mold. So the process is both more efficient and preserves the molds.[54]

Night Vision

About 15 years ago, General Motors started the development of a night driving system. It was based on the infrared sensors that had been used on military vehicles for some years. The first design incorporated mercury-cadmium-telluride detectors cooled with a Peltier cooler (solid state) to about 200 K. Soon, however, the advent of uncooled detector arrays led to a different design. Many decisions had to be made before a final design was accepted. One approach was the use of reflective optics formed by injection molding. It was replaced by refractive optics of a special glass.[55] Another was the use of ferroelectric versus bolometric detectors. There was even an intensive study on the location of the sensor—in the grill versus high on the windshield, versus on the back of the side-view mirrors. Another trade-off was the display. Early designs included a cathode-ray tube (CRT) in the dash. The final choice was a head-up display on the windshield. Although this has the advantage of not requiring the driver to look away from the road, it obviates the use of the imager in daylight.[56] In some fogs and mists, the infrared system performs better than the human eye, with or without headlights.

The Optical Patternator

So help me, that is the developers' name for it, a device that can characterize sprays. A diode laser is equipped with a lens that ensures it sends out a planar beam. A camera captures both scattered and fluorescent light from each slice through the spray. The laser moves and illuminates successive slices of the spray. Applications in-

53   "Laser texturing slashes cylinder wear," *Photonics Spectra*, June 1998.
54   "Photonic cleaning process moves to heavy industry," *Photonics Spectra,* March 1997.
55   "New process dramatically reduces time, cost of precision IR lens production," *OE Reports*, March 1999.
56   Kaplan, H., "Users grapple with display brightness issues," *Photonics Spectra*, January 1999.

clude analysis of automobile fuel injectors, which need to be optimized for best fuel economy and lowest pollution.[57]

Time Is of the Essence

High-speed cameras, whether they use film or are digital, are crucial in many applications. One is crash testing. A car, with dummies inside, traveling at 30 mph finishes its crash in 100 to 200 ms (0.1 to 0.2 s). At standard TV rates, this would be less than one frame (0.33 s). A standard camera has about the same time of exposure, 1/30 s. The situation for air bags is even more critical. They explode and take about 5 to 10 ms to be completely expanded. Engineers want to see the procedure, the steps along the way. Thus, frames must be less than 1 ms. This takes special cameras and lighting. Exposure is the key. In film, the trade-off is between time of exposure and amount of light in order to get a picture with sufficient dynamic range and resolution. The same is true for digital cameras, only more so. So in these scenarios, the cars are illuminated very brightly to provide more photons to the camera.[58]

Wake UP!

Sleepy drivers cause accidents, whether they drive trucks, highway semis, sedans, or sports cars. A new system uses an array of 15 LEDs that shines 6-mm diameter spots on the driver's eye. He wears a special hat with a visor in front. The visor is mostly transparent in the visible, and can even incorporate polarization to improve driving, but it reflects the invisible infrared spots to the eye. The eye itself has a relatively low reflectivity to this radiation compared to the eyelid. Thus, a sensor that receives the light reflected from the eye or lid via the visor can monitor the change in return light. If the return is too high for too long, say 2 seconds, a warning to wake up is given.[59]

Engine Deposits

Workers in England have used Fourier transform spectroscopy to analyze deposits on pistons. They scraped them off the pistons, used an array of different chemicals to separate them, and then did the spectroscopy. Deposits closer to the top of the piston showed a higher level of lubrication than those lower down.[60]

---

57 Sankar, S., "Planar fluorescence imager characterizes sprays," *Laser Focus World*, March 1997.
58 Weiss, S., "High-speed cameras improve vehicle performance and safety," *Photonics Spectra*, July 1998.
59 Robinson, K., "Infrared sensor works better than coffee," *Photonics Spectra*, Marc 1998.
60 "FTIR examines engine deposits," *Photonics Spectra*, October 1997.

Communication

The field of optical communication is a broad one. It includes televison, computers, fiber optic cables, displays, camcorders, cameras of all kinds, and more. In order to understand some of the concepts involving optical communication, we need to understand bandwidth, information rate, and modulation. This section deals only with transmission; displays, cameras, and other applications are treated separately.

Information Rate

In a broad sense, this is how fast information is transmitted from one person or place to another. In a technical sense, the information may not be useful, as with many television programs, but it is information. Some people talk faster than others; they speak more words per second than others (New Yorkers vs Southerners). However, words are of varying lengths and this measure is definitely ambiguous. In this day of computers, a "bit" is the fundamental unit of information. It is either a one or a zero in text, a black or a white line in bar-code patterns, and a voltage above a threshold or below in most electronics systems. A "byte" is a row of eight bits. (A "nibble" is half a byte, four bits). Bytes and bits circulate through computers and over transmission lines, but we do not notice them because they are converted into higher-order computer languages. A baud is a bit per second. Bits and bytes are units of information, but a baud is a unit of information rate. The history of information rates is summarized in Table 1.[61]

Table 1. History of information rate transmission.

Mode	Date	Rate (baud)
Smoke Signals	?	1
Telegraph	1844	5
Telephone	1876	2000
Transcontinental calls	1915	30,000
Coaxial cable	1940	7,680,000
Transatlantic cable	1956	1,152,000
Telstar (the first communication satellife)	1962	768,000
Fiber	1983	45,000,000
Faster fiber	1996	40,000,000,000
Today	1997	100,000,000,000

---

61   Banks, H., "The law of the photon," *Forbes*, 66, Oct. 6, 1997.

Older Optical Methods

Table 1 reminds us that long ago we had optical means of communication besides signing and nodding and wagging. We had semaphore, which I once learned. The flags wig-wagged in various positions, probably at a rate of 1 baud, assuming a byte per letter. Smoke signals were older. Although I never learned them, one has to assume that the codes were something like Morse code. Morse code, of course, was not meant to be optical, but meant as a way of communicating with dots and dashes, representing shorter and longer sounds, over the wires, although the Navy used it with searchlights at night.

Modulation

Information, like the TV news broadcast or even music, is sent on a modulated wave. A sine wave is modulated, that is, mixed with a higher frequency carrier. Figure 6 shows a modulated wave. It consists of the high-frequency carrier and the low-frequency one, the envelope, that contains the information. The carrier wave must be of a sufficiently high frequency that it represents all of the peaks and valleys of the information wave—a rule of thumb is ten times. The inverse statement is that the information bandwidth (rate) can only be as high as one-tenth the frequency of the carrier.

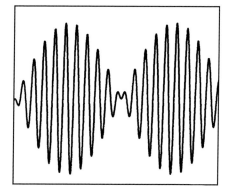

Figure 6 Modulated wave.

The standard AM broadcast bands run from about 500 to about 1600 kHz. This means that sound broadcast over these waves can only be as high as about 160 kHz. That is all right because we can only hear sounds up to about 20 kHz. If each AM band is 20 kHz wide, then the AM band can handle about 60 individual stations. Most channels are not this wide, and that is why radio has fidelity limitations. Televison requires about 6 MHz and therefore uses carrier frequencies of about 60 MHz. Cable can transmit about 30 Mb per second. When light is used as the carrier, however, the carrier frequency is about 3×10^{14}, thereby permitting information rates of about 3×10^8 Mb per second or, stated another way, 300 terabits per second. This is about ten million times the capacity of cable. It is this tremendous increase in available bandwidth that makes light the transmission medium of the future.

Light transmission can be of the free-space or cable variety.

Fiber Optic Cables

These cables are rapidly replacing copper cables throughout the nation and across the Atlantic Ocean. They are reliable, cheap, and can carry much more information than the old copper cables or even the more-expensive coaxial cables. The reason for this was just described. Standard television carriers have frequencies of tens of MHz, while light has frequencies of about 600 million MHz! Fiber optic cables are based on the principle of total internal reflection. In most of these high-tech cables, there are many different electromagnetic modes that I just cannot show. This means that a single cable can carry many different channels. The cables are actually designed so that even though they may be bent to some extent, the light is still internally reflected, the modes are not distorted.

Free-Space Light Communication

Since light is drastically attenuated by clouds, fog, and rain, free-space communication is limited in its areas of applicability. Satellite communication in space is surely one of these applications. Indoors is another area of use, and some outdoors, short-range applications exist. There exist some building-to-building systems that operate on a line-of-sight basis. These are, of course, subject to weather interference, but they are smaller and have higher data rates than radio-frequency systems and are less costly to install than fiber optic lines.[62]

NASA sponsored a program in the late 1960s to develop a laser communication system between two (Advanced Technology) satellites. It would have been a CO_2 laser modulated at high rates. The issues at that time involved not only the lasers and modulation schemes but also the pointing systems that would keep the lasers aimed at the receivers. Unfortunately, that project fell to the greed of the contractor who received the bid. The contractor, who of course shall not be named, underbid by a lot to get the job and then filed for new money soon after he got it. NASA had the wisdom to just say no.

We do have such technology in place now.

Dentistry

Optics have entered the field of dentistry in several ways: in diagnostics, drilling assessing bonds, and making prosthetics.

---

62 "Fiber-free laser communication finds niche in commercial market," *Optics and Photonics News*, July 1997.

Defining Decay

Raman spectra and infrared luminescent spectra are being investigated as means for detecting incipient dental caries (decay). The results so far have been mixed, but are promising.[63]

Other researchers have used a 1-mW red-diode laser at 655 nm as an illuminator through a quartz fiber. The return is collected by the fibers, filtered, and fed to a detector that measures the degree of fluorescence at its wavelength. Apparently the fluorescence is from porphyrins that leach into the partially decayed subsurface region of the tooth, according to Daniel Fried at San Francisco University. Although the fluorescence probe has proven to be more reliable than a steel probe, the teeth have to be clean and virtually free of plaque and calculus. The instrument presently costs about $2600, a little more than the mechanical probe! Other approaches use simpler equipment, but will still be more expensive.

Still other techniques shine light from an arc lamp on one side of the tooth and image from the other side. Dark areas indicate decay.[64]

Locating Cracks

A new and relatively untested technique for finding caries and cracks is the combination of luminscence and thermal imaging. A short-wavelength laser of 488 nm is modulated at frequencies of 10 to 10 kHz by the use of an acousto-optical modulator for more precise control of the heat application. The laser raises the temperature about a degree and the resultant thermal return can be analyzed in intensity and phase to determine whether a given anomaly is a crack or a fissure. The luminescence from healthy teeth is higher than that from the caries material of decaying teeth.[65]

Drilling

Lasers offer the possibility of fast, painless, but expensive drilling procedures. The FDA has approved an erbium YAG laser for the treatment of tooth decay in adults. The light is delivered by way of a fiber optic cable and provides painless removal of decay by ablation.[66] (The article cited points out that the many exacting drilling applications in manufacturing can be applied to dentistry, but I hope in a kinder, gentler way). Other studies on pulled teeth showed that a CO_2 laser can also perform

63 "Raman imaging adds perspective to dental bond studies," *Biophotonics International*, March/April 1998.
64 *Biophotonics International*, September/October 2001.
65 Robinson, K., "Luminescence, IR imaging find cracks in teeth," *Biophotonics International*, November 2000.
66 Morley, J. L., "Dentistry: manufacturing technology works on teeth," *Photonics Spectra*, August 1997.

the drilling operation. The laser was pulsed with groups of 10 pulses each from 100 to 700 μs long and 200 to 1000 μs apart some 7 mm from the tooth. A water spray is necessary to prevent charring and cracking, and some kind of manual smoothing is necessary to finish it off. Drilling the hole took from 2 to 100 seconds. The trade-off is that a small laser spot is necessary for good application, but this can generate irregular surfaces.[67] I anticipate that future instruments will have a means for adjusting the beam size; there are many ways.

There are two primary applications of lasers in dental drilling. One is penetrating the hard enamel dentin to remove caries; the other is working on soft tissue, to treat, for example, gingivitis. For the former, the erbium YAG laser mentioned above has been approved and is used. The major drawbacks have been cost and some awkward delivery systems, such as fibers. For softer applications, several different lasers with less power have been approved. These include YAGs with other dopants and carbon dioxide. Most patients have been very happy with the laser techniques.[68]

Root Canals

The very thought makes some people ache, but a new tool has the potential to ease the pain of root canals or at least shorten it. It is a 0.7-mm diameter fiber optic endoscope. It relays an image to a video imager and tape recorder with 500 lines of resolution. In the conventional procedure, the dentist must rely on relating the x-ray image to what he feels with his probe. With this, he can see both the drill and the inside of the tooth. It greatly reduces chair time and should not cost more than the conventional technique. Results should be better and patient anxiety lessened.[69]

Prosthetics

These include single caps and replacement teeth as well as bridges and dentures. The piece is formed from plaster in the usual manner. Then it is put on a table where it is measured by a laser probe in five axes, up, down, left and right, back and forth, as well as two angles. This gives enough data to define the shape completely. This information is then fed to computer-aided drafting (CAD) software that can show the tooth in three dimensions. The technician can then adapt the image, adjusting margin line where the crown meets a root, to give more or less space. The corrected information is then sent to a computer-aided manufacturing (CAM) machine where

---

67   Rowell, N. D., "CO$_2$ laser could prevent dentist's drill," *Biophotonics International* November 2000.

68   Wheeler, M., "Dental lasers: better for the patient, but are they too expensive," *Biophotonics International*, January/February 1999.

69   Calabrese, D. M., "Microfiber optics ease root canal procedures," *Biophotonics International*, September/October 2000.

the prosthesis is formed. The combined measurement and manufacturing processes take about 40 minutes.[70]

A Little Bonding

Investigations are ongoing on the use of a krypton laser at 647 nm to assess dental bonds. The laser is shone on the bond via a microscope, and the reflected light is examined with Raman spectroscopy. The sample is scanned in x and y directions by the microscope stage. Data are taken about every 1 μm. The Raman spectra could be interpreted in terms of whether the area was dentin, interface, or adhesive. A mathematical model was used to determine the degree to which the adhesive had diffused into the dentin. They found some adhesives better than others and some acid-etch preparations more effective than others. No surprise, but they identified the better ones. They also found that Raman spectroscopy was better than infrared spectroscopy, which was plagued by background signals from water. The krypton laser had less fluorescent background than the argon laser.[71]

Displays

We see displays all around us, and they come in many different forms. In this section I deal with artificial displays. Among others, these include the ubiquitous televison screen, its probable successor, the flat-panel display, computer monitors and laptop screens, high-definition screens, and more. I have also included some special things for those with impaired vision and movie screens. Displays are accomplished with cathode-ray tubes, light-emitting diodes, dithering mirrors, special paper, and more.

The Nipkow Projector

This is an early precursor of the television tube in the era of black-and-white TV. As shown in Fig. 7, an image is formed on a disk that contains a spiral of holes. As the disc spins, the holes let light from different parts of the total field through to the projection lens. As each hole crosses the image, the light from that part goes to a detector, where it is sensed. The holes have to be spaced so that only one is in the im-

70   Whipple, C., "Putting your technology where your mouth is," *Biophotonic International,* July/August 1999; Grant, B., "3-D imager brings dentistry into the digital era," *Biophotonics International,* May/June 1999.

71   "Raman imaging adds perspective to dental bond studies," *Biophotonics International,* March/April 1998.

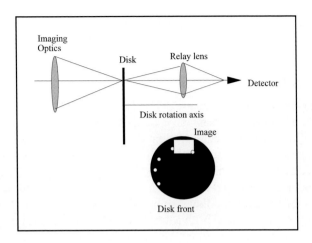

Figure 7 Nipkow disk.

age at a time, and they are a spiral that passes contiguous lines across the image. Therefore, a raster pattern is generated to the viewer.

Cathode-Ray Tubes

A cathode-ray tube (CRT) is shown schematically in Fig. 8. The cathode is shown on the left-hand side. It is heated and generates electrons. The emitted electrons are attracted to the anode, which is the phosphor screen, and they are guided by the electric fields at the sides, top and bottom of the tube. They impinge upon the phosphor screen at a point that is dictated by the voltages on the sides, the x direction, the top and bottom, and the y di-

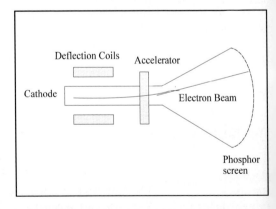

Figure 8 Cathode-ray tube for television.

rection. The voltages on the x and y fields are time-varying in such a way that a raster is scanned. The intensity of the beam is dictated by the time-varying voltage difference between the cathode and anode. This is dictated in turn by the signal. The phosphor then glows at the place and with the intensity dictated by these three voltages.

Color TV tubes have a complex phosphor screen. At each x,y position there are three phosphors in close proximity. The electron beam impinges on each of these.

one that glows red, another green, and the third blue, the RGB colors of the color TV tube.

Television Rasters

A typical television set displays its image with about 500 lines. The raster-generated information is sent from the transmitter essentially as a pair of triangular electrical signals. The horizontal line is the fast one and is repeated 500 times a second—250 a second to generate first one set of 250 lines, and then a second set of 250 lines that fit in between—an interlace. Figure 9 shows some of the lines. The solid black ones are those of the first field, the tilted dashed lines show a retrace to get back to the left to trace the next line. The retraces go much faster than the forward lines. The red set is similar, but generates the interlaced second field. The other voltage is a triangle that is 1/60 second long and drives the lines down for the first field. Then it repeats and drives it down a second time for the second field. The two make up a frame that repeats 30 times a second. These voltages direct an electron beam to the positions that are required. The electron beam, in turn, excites the three different-colored phosphors at each point on the screen.

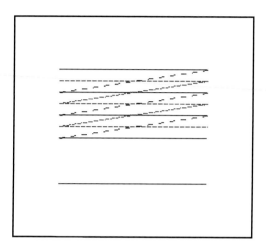

Figure 9 TV raster.

High-definition television works on exactly the same principle, but has more lines.

Laser Displays

A new laser-driven display is under development at the University of Central Florida. An inexpensive plastic screen is embedded with crystals that emit red, green, and blue light when illuminated with a near-infrared diode laser. The crystals are ytterbium doped with other rare-earth elements to get the desired colors. The display is in early development, but should be much more compact than a CRT, and probably less expensive and less consumptive of power.[72] The scanning of the

---

72 Smith, J. P., "Laser display challenges cathode-ray tubes," *Photonics Spectra*, August 2000.

laser beam has to be done with some sort of mirror system, which isn't as easy to steer as an electron beam.

Mirror, Mirror on the Chip

One of the modern developments for large-screen displays that are also very bright is the use of large arrays of hundreds of thousands of very small mirrors, typically about 14 μm on a side, all on a chip about 0.7 inch on a side. Lights of three different colors are shone on the mirrors. The mirrors flip back and forth about ±12 deg; in one position, the light is reflected to an absorber; in the other direction it goes to the viewer. The three colors are combined in the usual way to get a multitude of colors. The mirrors flip back and forth very quickly, in about a microsecond, and the average length of time determines the intensity of the light that is reflected to the viewer.[73] They can be brighter and have larger formats than other displays.

These arrays can display up to 15,000 frames per second with 768 rows of 1024 mirrors (as of this writing). They are thus capable of high-brightness displays as well as applications in lithography and photofinishing.[74]

Computers

Desktop computers have long had cathode-ray tube monitors that are very similar to television screens. The differences lie in the rates at which the rasters are scanned. Whereas television displays need to have fast rise and decay times to portray action, computers can have slower ones, although for video streaming and some games they must also be fast. Also, computers are driven by their internal clocks and do not have to march to the drummer of standard TV broadcast regulations.

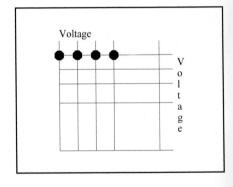

Figure 10 Voltages applied to an LED array.

The flat-panel displays consist of arrays of light-emitting diodes in three colors (Fig. 10). They come in a variety of styles depending upon how they are driven electrically. The drive voltages are applied by an array of interconnects. One method is to have two "wires" attached to each LED, so that it fires when the two are coincident. The voltages ramp across the lines and down the columns. The "wires" are interconnects in integrated circuit chips.

---

73   Hardin, R., "Digital micromirrors take tinsel town by storm," *OE Reports*, March 1999.
74   Dudley, D., "Micromirror technology enables more than projectors," *Photonics Spectra*, May 2004.

Large Displays

In the National Western Event Center in Denver, there is a 9 foot by 12 foot display screen that consists of 440,000 optical fibers, each representing one pixel of the screen. A projector focuses onto the input end of the fiber array and is magnified 36 times to get the display. Any image source can be used to project onto the input end. The screen provides a very wide viewing field, up to about 170 deg.

Direct Retinal Display[75]

Most displays are on screens. These include the standard television set, the computer screen, and the laptop computer screen. This device is a personal display that presents the image directly to the retina. A beam of light is incident onto an achromatic lens and then onto two scanning mirrors, one for horizontal scanning and one for vertical scanning. The beam then goes to an eyepiece that forms the image right onto the retina. The system provides a field of view that is 40 deg horizontally and 30 deg vertically. It can be a monochrome version or one with color (by using three lasers for the sources). The mirrors scan a 480×640 pixel field of view 60 times per second.

Retinal Scanning

Forget the screen; put the image directly on the retina. This development uses three LEDs and an array of micromirrors to display an image directly from the front of the eye to the retina. Such a display could be used for camera viewfinders, wearable screens for games, and other portable viewers. The image appears as if it were at normal viewing distance.[76]

Digital Pen and Paper

A form of display, perhaps. A pen that has a very small camera, image processor, and transmitter in it is used to write on special paper. The paper contains a pattern of small carbon dots that are imperceptible and do not show any visible writing. However, they help to absorb the light from the LED in the pen. The small IR camera then takes pictures every 10 ms so that the pattern of the pen on the paper is recorded. Some image processing to smooth and interpret is then done and the infor-

75 Reiss, R., "Retinal display projects imagery directly into human eye," *OE Reports*, 10, September 1997.
76 "LEDs shrink displays," *Photonics Spectra*, August 2000; "Retinal scanning unit tested in live operation," *Optics and Photonics News*, July 2000.

mation is transmitted to a selected receiver, such as a computer or a mobile phone. This could be the forerunner of digital forms that can be filled in by hand.[77]

A Very Unusual Display

Imagine a display that has no screen, no LEDs, no substantial mass, and that can operate in touch-screen mode. This was reported in the *New York Times* recently without very much technical detail. The Heliodisplay shoots a screen of particles into the air in an approximately vertical plane. The projector, a standard one, shines the image onto the plane of particles. The touch-screen function is accomplished by a laser and sensor monitoring where the finger is on the particle plane.[78]

A Very Bright Idea

The Boston Museum of Science has incorporated a laser-driven display for its daily announcements on a large, 7.5-foot by 10-foot screen. The screen is backlit with 5-W red, green, and blue solid state lasers that scan behind the screen to map out the information. The display is sufficiently bright that the ample ambient light from the windows has little or no effect on display performance.[79]

Another way to create a bright display is with laser pixels. A display made with a large array of LEDs is described elsewhere in this book. The close relationship between LEDs and laser diodes is described in Chapter 1. One attempt has been made to generate an array of laser diodes instead of LEDs.[80]

Electronic Ink

This is a display mechanism that may one day compete with CRTs, LCDs, and LEDs. It consists of capsules in a sheet of plastic. Each capsule is about 40 μm in diameter and has 1-μm particles inside it. The smaller particles are white and can be moved from side to side by the application of electric fields. When the voltage is applied, the white particles move to, for example, the right, turning the capsule off. When the voltage is canceled, they move the other way, turning it on. It can be printed on cheap materials, but it is, as of this writing, still experimental.[81]

77   Haras, A. J., "New technology: pen on paper," *Photonics Spectra*, August 2000.
78   Bernstein, D., "Making something out of nothing," *New York Times*, Dec. 18, 2003.
79   McCarthy, D., "Laser display's colors don't fade," *Photonics Spectra*, May 1999.
80   Lewotsky, K., "Lasing pixels produce projection display," *Laser Focus World*, March 1997.
81   Rice, J., "Electronic ink: the future of displays?," *Optics and Photonics News*, 8, September 1998.

Entertainment

Oldies but Goodies

The player pianos that were so popular in the early part of the last century are making a comeback, this time with a high-tech twist. Although computerized player pianos that store live performances and play them back have been around for several years, a new piano from Yamaha Corporation of America goes one step further by integrating stringless optical sensor technology.

The idea for the GranTouch was developed at the company's Japanese headquarters with the hope of revitalizing the piano market, which has been in a slump for two decades. At only 273 lbs, the GranTouch is less than half the weight of a traditional grand piano; its stringless structure makes it more compact as well. The company expects that these features will attract a segment of buyers who previously shied away from owning a piano because of space limitations.

The GranTouch features a traditional keyboard but is equipped with optical sensors instead of strings and an iron plate. When the user plays the instrument, a sensor on the bottom of each key breaks a beam of light, indicating which key is being played. Another optical sensor on the hammer tells the system the velocity at which the key is struck, converts the information into digital data, and selects the appropriate sound level. In addition to sensor technology, the piano has a floppy disk drive that allows users to listen to recordings from its 400-disk music library, make their own multitrack recordings, or receive digital signals from across the country. Concert pianists may find the GranTouch lacking some of the subtle nuances that characterize traditional instruments, but at a cost of less than $16,000, the photonic piano may prove to be an affordable alternative.

Play it Again, Sam

Remember 78 rpm record disks? They were about a foot across with a spiral groove that was impressed on resin or wax, and later vinyl. A metal stylus, a needle, followed the groove and changed the varying depth of the groove into varying musical sounds. This transformation was made by a piezoelectric or magnetic sensor. The abrasion of the needle and other mishandling of the disks eventually degraded the performance of these disks almost unbearably. Swiss scientists at the Lausanne have developed a fiber optic sensor that travels on the surface of the disk light as a feather, 1000 times lighter than the needle. A laser beam from a diode laser is shone down the fiber. It reflects off the groove and is thereby directed toward a position sensor. This information is then used to make the tunes. Not only does this preserve new 78 rpm disks, but it can reflect off of unmarred portions of the grooves of old ones.[82]

---

82   Morley, J., "Optical fibers restore old records," *Photonic Spectra*, November 1997.

ELP of Saitama, Japan, has a four-beam photonic system that reads these records. One pair of beams tracks the two sides of the lip, while the other two "peer" below the lip but above the damage and read the grooves. Photodiodes detect the reflected light. It was reported[83] that this system costs only about $12,000, so a whole new set of compact disks is probably the way to go. There are surely some old classics, performed by deceased artists, that will be played this way.

The Forests and the Trees[84]

A LIDAR satellite is being used to map our forests. It will provide direct measurements of canopy height, vertical and spatial structure, and subcanopy topography. These are vital for land-surface and climate modeling. The instrument will shine five 15-millijoule (mJ) Nd:YAG lasers with a 10-ns pulse that provide 25-m diameter spots around an 8-km circle. As the satellite moves, the lasers map out five lines of 25-m spots 30 m apart. Five silicon avalanche diodes detect the reflected pulses. The vertical resolution is less than a meter. This, way about 2–3% of the Earth's surface will be covered, but about 99% of the forests. This is a boon to preserving our camping, hunting, and fishing interests.

Upstaging the Stage

Tucson, my hometown, is the stage where the performance stage is getting smart.[85] Robb Lovell and John Mitchell are developing a stage that automatically controls the lighting, the audio, spotlights, video, and I guess everything but the actors. The system uses three video cameras with frame grabbers that measure the presence or absence of movement as well as the presence of figures. Then, such things as strong spots, diffuse lighting, increased audio volume, or sensitizing different mikes can all be controlled by a central computer. There is plenty of room for improvement, using some of the techniques discussed elsewhere in this publication such as triangulation, ranging, digitizing, and coloration.

They Shoot Horses, Don't They?

Infrared cameras can determine very small differences in temperature in the legs of racehorses, as well as people. This can be an important diagnostic sign for incipient or early injuries. The technique has been used to detect an inflamed flexor tendon before there was any observed lameness. By careful, early treatment, these horses can be saved, not shot.[86]

---

83   "A little light music," *Photonics Spectra*, October 1997.
84   Smith, J., "LIDAR satellite will analyze forests," *Photonics Spectra*, December 1999.
85   Hardin, R., "Machine vision steals the show," *Photonics Spectra*, 31, August 1997.
86   "IR camera sees early injuries in racehorses," *Biophotonics Spectra*, November/ December 1997.

Athletics

Optics are surely a part of the modern sports scene. Citing TV is enough to substantiate this, but there are other less obvious examples.[87] The photofinish of horse racing has been improved with an overhead HDTV video system. The system uses two such video cameras that take between 2000 and 4000 images per second. One is close to the finish line; the other some distance from it. Each makes a slit image of the line.

Shot-put distances and other field events are sometimes measured with an infrared triangulation system similar to surveying devices. The uncertainty in distance is about 2 mm.

Anyone for Tennis?

A test has been devised to determine how long a ball stays on the strings of a tennis racket. A shorter time correlates with a higher-velocity return; a longer time with more control. The racket is arranged to be fixed and horizontal. A laser beam is placed one ball diameter above the strings. Then you can drop tennis balls from a height of about 3.7 m (other distances are just as good). As the ball drops, it breaks the laser beam and generates a start signal in the detector electronics. When the ball leaves the racket and is one ball length away, the beam again shines on the detector. That is a measure of the time it is on the strings, plus the time for the ball to travel one ball diameter. The measurements discerned differences of as little as 0.1 ms[88] between different racquets strung differently.

Many of us avid tennis watchers have observed the MacCam and its derivatives in action. Named after the fine tennis pro John McEnroe, notorious for arguing umpires' calls, the camera is a high-speed video camera. Taking many more frames per second than the standard camera, it "sees" exactly where the ball hits, and the camera can be played back and forth to show this information. Hewlett Packard now has an HP camera that does much the same thing, and gives a cartoonlike representation of the ball's impression on the court.[89]

Racing, Baseball, Track

Other applications include[90] sensing the ignition wave pattern in the combustion in racing-car engines, using an infrared camera to monitor the heat that causes tread wear on these cars, using an infrared laser and camera to help train biathletes, laser

87 Rodriguez, M., *Optics and Photonics News*, November 1997.
88 Rodriquez, M., "On your mark, get set, go! Take a look at some novel uses of electro-optic devices," *Optics and Photonics News*, November 1997.
89 The 2004 Wimbledon broadcasts.
90 Robinson, K. and M. Wheeler, "Photonics goes for the gold," *Photonics Spectra*, December 1977.

scanning systems for better kayak designs, laser rangefinders for yacht racing, diode lasers and photodetectors to determine baseball bat speed, high-speed cameras to "watch" the curves in a curve-ball pitch, spectrometers that monitor the fuel mixture in race cars, high-speed cameras to monitor athletes' performances (including golf swings), and near-infrared blood-oxygen sensors to optimize athletic performance. Clearly, videotaping a gymnast on the uneven parallel bars is a useful training technique.

Other applications of optics in athletics include measuring the distance of javelin and discus throws as well as long and triple jumps. A pole with a reflector on top is jabbed into the spot where the javelin, hammer, discus, or foot landed. Care must be taken to put the pole at the near point and keep it erect. Then triangulation is carried out and the result calculated in the computer and displayed to the audience in 10 to 15 seconds.

Compact Disks (CDs)

This type of digital storage medium was first introduced by Sony and Philips in 1982. The disks are made by depositing a photoresist material on a high-quality substrate. The material resists optical exposure (hence the name photoresist). Then a laser is used to illuminate, spot by spot, the photoresist material. After it is developed in a chemical, which takes away the material where it has not been exposed by the laser, protrusions remain where it was exposed. This master is used as one face of a mold that is injected with molten plastic. The plastic solidifies, and the master's protrusions become pits in the copy. The pits are about 0.5 μm wide and from 0.833-μm to 3.054-μm long. The spiral has a pitch of 1.6 μm. The entire disk is covered with a reflective coating of aluminum alloy and overlaid with a protective acrylate coating.[91]

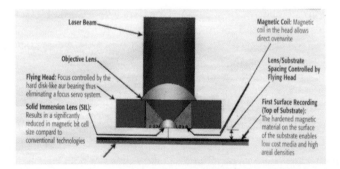

Figure 11 Writing a CD. TeraStor's flying magneto-optic head extended memory system (tera5) floats the write/read head approximately 6 microinches from the top of the recording material, reducing the bit size and eliminating the need for servo-controlled focusing.[91]

---

91   Stinson, D., "Compact disks," *Optics and Photonics News*, November 1997. (Image courtesy of OSA, copyright 1997.)

The CD player has a laser spot about 1 µm in diameter, larger than the width of the pit but smaller than the length. Both the pits and the surrounding area, the land, have the same reflectivity. The detection of a pit is therefore not done by reflection. However, the pit is about one-quarter wave deep. Thus the reflected light is one-half wave out of phase with the reflection from the land. These interfere, making the pit look dark. The information is actually contained in the pit edges. When there is a transition at the edge within a sampling window of the electronics, it is considered a "1"; otherwise it is a "0." The sequence of bits forms a special code that can correct for single-byte errors, scratches that can be as long as 2.5 mm. The 120-mm diameter disk holds 650 Mb of data or 74 minutes of sound. Note that this is about 65,000 bytes per square millimeter.

The single CD recordable (CD-R) disk is similar to the mass-produced one. The spiral exists in the unrecorded disk, and an organic dye is the recording medium. When exposed by a laser, the dye heats and either bleaches or makes a vesicle, depending upon the dye. This can then be read in the same way.

The rewritable CD, CD-RW, has an inorganic material instead of a dye. It switches between a crystalline and amorphous state. The crystalline material is more reflective than the amorphous material, and this provides the basis for data storage and retrieval.

The DVD, or digital versatile disks, were meant to be truly advanced. They were supposed to have these characteristics: 135 minutes of a movie on one side, with video quality better than a laser disk; five channels; three to five language sound tracks; copy protection; and parental control. So far, this has not been accomplished in one disk. There are, in fact, three DVDs: a video version, a ROM version, and a RAM version. They accomplish all this with spots, depressions, that are half the size, and light that is of a shorter wavelength. Thus, they get about four times as much data in the same area.

Holographic Data Storage[92]

This technique shows promise for even greater storage density than DVDs. The basic process is to encode a series of bits on an object beam by passing it through a spatial light modulator. The object beam is focused into an optically sensitive medium and superimposed with a reference beam. In this way a pattern of spatially varying refractive index is generated. When the reference beam is the only beam on this hologram, a faithful rendition of the pattern that was on the spatial light modulator is reproduced. This is the hologram playback.

It can be turned into electrical signals with arrays of detectors. In this way, a two-dimensional record or page is generated, and it can be read out as well. A set of such pages can be laid (figuratively) one on top of the other and read out by varying

---

92   Psaltis, D., and F. Mok, "Holographic memories," *Scientific American* 23(5), 70–76, 1995. (Image courtesy of D. Psaltis.)

the angles of incidence. So a 1-cm cube of material can record 10^{10} bits that can be read out with large-format CCDs at one gigabit per second. That is enormous! But the technology is not ready for commercial application yet.[93] And that is still true as of this writing.

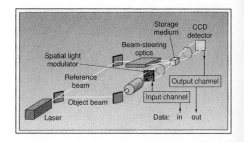

Pin It Down

A simple viewer with a rangefinder allows a golfer to determine exactly how far it is to the pin. This may or may not help him pick the right club or hit the right shot. The device is used to look at the pin with a field of view of about 450 feet at 1000 yards (or 45 feet at 100 yards). A button is pushed and the rangefinder is activated. The round-trip pulse is timed and range is found.[94]

Figure 12 Holographic storage. In a holographic digital storage system, the laser beam is split into object and reference beams. The object beam is expanded and passed through a spatial light modulator to impose a data-page pattern. It is focused into the storage medium, where it is superimposed with the reference beam whose angle is controlled with beam steering optics. During readout the data page is imaged on a CCD detector array. Data to be stored enter and exit through input-channel and output-channel electronics, which perform encoding and signal processing functions.[92]

Night-Vision Goggles

For the hunter, bird watcher, and others who enjoy the outdoors, these are versions of the World War II metascopes, which are the receiver parts of sniperscopes. As described in the military section, an invisible infrared light beam is projected to the target. The reflected light is sensed by a phosphor that converts it to visible and shows a green image in the scope.

Gemstones

Gemnological Research Centers in Switzerland, Thailand, and Italy are using Raman spectrometers to identify gemstones. A diamond is not a diamond is not a diamond—and neither is any other gemstone. They are minerals that consist of, for instance, carbon or sapphire and other trace minerals. Good ones have few impurities, but they all have some. The researchers are building a database so that eventually they will be able to trace gems almost as well as we trace fingerprints.[95]

93   "IBM holographic optical storage team," *Laser Focus World*, November 1996.
94   *SkyMall*, American Airlines, 2003.
95   Mendonsa, R., "Raman spectrometers 'fingerprint' gemstones," *Photonics Spectra*, March 1997.

Batter Up—and Down and Over

Laser measurements have come to the diamond—the baseball diamond. A system under development uses seven lasers mounted above a home plate containing embedded photodetectors. These monitor the speed, angle, and position of the bat relative to the plate.

A Touch of Gold

A high-speed photographic motion-picture camera was used to photograph one of Kerri Strug's gymnastics practice sessions. It ran faster than 259 frames per second. The results were shown to her coach, Bela Karolyi. He pointed out several areas for improvement, and she won the Olympic gold.

Tell-ing Imagery

The same high-speed camera that was used to photograph Strug was used to help Olympic archers. The area from their grip on the bow to their ear was imaged so that they could see exactly, in split-second timing, what they were doing. Was the release smooth? Did their arm and wrist remain locked? Were they steady?

The Big One Got Away

The State of Minnesota is in the process of making it illegal to use underwater photography for fishing. For my purposes, it points out that such cameras have been used along with sonar-type fish finders.[96] In a related report, there is now a compact, underwater infrared camera for locating fish.[97] The fish are still safe; water is opaque in the infrared!

Three Dimensions with Glasses

We probably all have seen three-dimensional presentations in the theatre. From a flat screen we actually sense three-dimensional presentations. How is this illusion created? Recall that we see in three dimensions because our eyes see objects from slightly different angles. One eye sees the front and part of one side; the other eye sees the front and a little of the other side. This effect is accomplished on the screen with two images. One image is taken of the object slightly from one side and is polarized vertically (for instance). The other image is taken from the other side and is polarized oppositely. Viewers put on special glasses. One side is polarized vertically; the other is polarized horizontally. Thus one eye sees the front and a little of one side. The other sees the front and a little of the other side, just the way it needs to be for 3D.

---

96 "Minnesota moves to limit underwater cameras," *Photonics Spectra*, April 1998.
97 "Meanwhile back at the lake," *Photonics Spectra*, March 1998.

Forensics

Optics now assist the police in many ways: apprehension by the use of night-vision cameras, prevention by recognition systems, analysis with various spectrometer systems, and more. There is even a stunning use—involving a tetanizer.

Finding the Bad Guys

Infrared cameras are in use by several communities. In particular, the US Department of Transportation and the Texas Transportation Institute have employed Raytheon imagers to detect criminals in the dark.[98]

The cameras are mounted on helicopters, cars, and are also held in the hand. The pursuit of criminals in cars is aided, as is the pursuit of any who leave the cars. A car that is in a chase and stops is easily detected by its heat pattern from among others that have been parked, and fugitives show up like glowing bulbs behind and amid foliage, as shown in Figure 13.[99] Note that the man's body parts are quite bright. The headlights, which are off, still glow because the filaments are still warm. The engine heat is reflected from the pavement up to the sensor.

A similar application involves small, unpiloted planes. Some were used in the fight against terrorism to locate and attack Al Qaeda members in Yemen. Other, smaller ones are used to hunt for felons. One very good application is the search for illegal aliens near our southern borders. The planes for these civilian applications so far have been about the size of radio-controlled model airplanes, with a

Figure 13 Caught infrared-handed.[99]

---

98   "IR Cameras Keep Texas Police ALERT," *Photonics Spectra*, October 1997.
99   Tatterson, K. G., "IR cameras keep Texas police ALERT," *Photonics Spectra*, October, 1997. (Images courtesy of Raytheon.)

wingspan of about six feet. They can carry either a visible camera or an infrared imager for about an hour with a range of about five miles.[100]

The Dallas-area police use the Raytheon night-vision device (which Cadillac also uses) to search for criminals.[101] ALERT is an acronym for their project. Even criminals who hide in the woods can be found with these infrared devices, as the picture in Fig. 14 shows. The top view is a picture taken in visible light of a man hidden in the trees. The bottom is the same scene taken with an infrared thermal camera. I think he is invisible on the top, but quite visible in the infrared. By the way, this is an old pair of images; today's infrared cameras are much better.

Figure 14 Visible and infrared images. See the man?[101]

Smile, You're on Digital Camera

This system may not work in all situations, but it worked this time.[102] A thief used keys from an earlier job to enter the victim's apartment. He took most of the computer equipment, but he left the disk drive that had copies of his image on it. The criminal had taken his own picture with a digital camera!

Recognition Systems[103]

Various systems exist for identifying people who wish to enter a secure area, extract money from an automatic teller, or perform similar tasks. These systems are the modern, optical versions of fingerprints. Some identify a person's face, others the veins in the hands or the pattern of blood-vessel distribution in the retina. They are all based on the use of a good, electronic camera and a set of pattern-matching

100 "Compact infrared camera takes wing," *Photonics Spectra*, July 2000.
101 Tatterson, K. G., "IR cameras keep Texas police ALERT," *Photonics Spectra*, October 1997.
102 "Smile and remain silent," *Photonics Spectra*, October 1997.
103 Hardin, R., "Biometric recognition," *Photonics Spectra*, November 1997.

algorithms. Some National Security Agency pioneers have suggested that you need a color camera with 24-bit true color, and a frame that is 480×640 pixels operated at 30 frames per second or better for the task. One application is in airports (see the section on Aerospace). A different version, intended for use in low- or varying illumination conditions, uses a light-emitting diode in the near-infrared to illuminate the face and a monochrome camera with filters to reduce the effect of ambient illumination. Another uses two monochrome cameras so that a stereoscopic image is obtained in order to distinguish between a real face and a photograph of one.

The iris identifier at an ATM illuminates the eye with a near-infrared beam and then makes 192 radial measurements on one frame, thereby creating a 256-byte template.[104] Before you get your money the template is compared to those on file. Each iris is unique in its pattern of rifts, crips, pits, and striations, just as each fingerprint is unique. A similar technique is used with the retina. Both of these require a close-up view of the user, and therefore his or her cooperation. I would put my eye up close to get my money!

Fingerprints have not been forgotten. MasterCard is still experimenting with them as the identifier. As with your iris and retina, you never leave home without them. Fingerprints are the most accepted method, but they also take up the most memory, a full two kilobytes.

It was estimated that in 1996 some 10,000 biometric recognition systems were in existence, representing about $17 million.

Drug Runners

An application about which I am not so proud is the use of an infrared beacon by drug runners. The beacon is about 3-feet high with a diameter of about one foot, and is dropped into the ocean so that they can locate floating cocaine shipments.[105] However, I am proud of the fact that similar systems are used in rescue operations.

A Telling Blush

At one time in my life, in order to get security clearance, I had to undergo the standard lie-detector or polygraph test. Examiners hooked me up with a whole bunch of wires and asked me embarrassing questions.

There is an alternative in the wings. Honeywell and the Mayo Clinic have collaborated to show that we can take an infrared image to detect very small changes in blood flow in the human face. Such changes are usually associated with telling a lie. An uncooled infrared imager, with the capability to sense about 0.1 deg. temperature difference, was used on some 20 test subjects. Some committed a fake crime

---

104 Reiss, R., "Iris recognition technology makes reliable identifier," *OE Reports*, November 1997.
105 *Arizona Daily Star*, July 1987.

and were then asked about it. The infrared device detected 75% of the guilty and 90% of the innocent. A typical polygraph, with all of its wires and electrodes, detected 75% of the guilty and 66% of the innocent. Although there are still embarrassing questions, there are no wires and the test is noncontact. Such a system could be used for real-time screening.

Fingering the Night Stalker

Lasers, with their inherent brightness, are a great aid in "lifting" fingerprints at the scene of a crime. The Night Stalker, Richard Ramirez, was nabbed by this technique. He had left a dim fingerprint in a Datsun station wagon. The print was found and illuminated by a laser and photographed for laboratory analysis. The laser of choice for most of these applications is an argon-ion laser operating at 514 nm, but for some applications a source that can emit at several wavelengths is preferred.[106]

It's a Crime

Optics play a big part in crime prevention, detection, and identification. Maybe the simplest optical device is the magnifier that Sherlock Holmes always carried. Modern devices also include a hand-held microscope with its own illuminator. Fluorescent powders are used that attach to oily fingerprints. A substance called Luminol can be sprayed around; it is phosphorescent in the presence of blood and therefore can show such things as blood spray patterns even though they are invisible to the eye.

An electrostatic imaging device allows the reading of indentations in paper—even five pages down from the original document. Certainly the microscope in all of its different forms—phase contrast, comparison, polarized, interferometric, spectroscopic—are essential in the crime lab.[107]

Double Overdose

Fourier transform infrared spectroscopy is a leading tool in many forensic labs. Functionally, it is simply a means of analyzing the spectra of relatively minute (or larger) quantities of material. One example was related to the death of two men who had pipes on their chests and a bottle labeled "meth" next to them. First blush says it is a double overdose, but these are rare. Analysis showed the "meth" was methadone (a heroin treatment) and not methamphetamine (a bad narcotic). Spectral analysis is a powerful tool for substance identification.

---

106 Wheeler, M. D., "Seeing the unseen, photonics assists investigators in gathering evidence," *Photonics Spectra*, November 1998.
107 Stoney, D., "Optical methods in forensic science," *Optics and Photonics News*, April 1998.

Can You Bear It?

One incredible example of the use of both FTIR and chromatography is the identification of bear bile. Why? Because in Chinese medicine, it is used to reduce fever and inflammation and to detoxify the body.

I do not see how the introduction of bear bile detoxifies, but that is what is said.

The first step is to separate bear bile from that of goats, pigs, or buffaloes. This can be done by FTIR, which can tell whether it is bear or goat bile, but not the others, because bear and goat bile both contain taurochoate.

The next step is chromatography, which measures the relative amounts of this acid. Then, similar to the old wine-joke punch line, "But what bear?"

Well, Asian bears have lower levels and therefore can be distinguished, but whether it was a wild bear or one that was "milked" on a farm is still anyone's guess.

Checkpoint Charlie

In Eastern Europe, a police officer entered a bus, strolled up and down the aisle, and left. He had just taken pictures of everyone on the bus with the digital camera in his spectacles. The pictures were relayed to a command center and scanned for any "wanteds."[108]

Escaped with His Pants Down

A man was accused of shoplifting underpants. An opened package lay where he had been shopping. Forensics used a green laser to cause fluorescence that was consistent with old urine and semen. He had old, worn underpants on. Microscopic examination of cotton fibers clinched his innocence.[109]

TNT

The detection of TNT, trinitroglycerine, can be made spectroscopically. The organic compound has a very distinct spectrum with two peaks above and below 1500 wave numbers. These can be detected whether using a spectrometer, which is needed, or a ratioing technique. The prototype instrument is a laser absorption spectrometer in order to get sufficient sensitivity for the minute amounts of gases that need to be detected.[110]

---

108 *Optics and Photonics News*, July 2000.

109 "Laser vindicates accused underwear thief," *Biophotonics International*, March/April 1998.

110 Effenerger, F., "Explosive vapor detection prevents bombs on board," *OE Reports*, April 1998.

Well-Equipped Guard Dogs

The (in)famous Sheriff Joe Arpaio (a very tough dude) in the wild west of Arizona has now added to the unusual ways he handles prisoners. Outside the tent city in which they reside, prisoners are now circled by German Shepherd guard dogs with miniature, wide-angle cameras and microphones—and antennas between their ears.[111]

Desktop Security

A very small imager in either the top of your computer keyboard or mouse will enable you to keep your computer secure from unauthorized users. In business and industry, this may be any co-worker who should not have access to data in your computer. At home, it may be a child who needs to be protected from the bad things on the Net.[112]

Laser Tetanizer

These devices now exist in one form called tasers. They shoot an electrical shock into a potential fugitive to disable him without killing him. First, two darts are shot at the target; they guide small wires. Then an electrical shock through the wires stuns the target.

In the Tetanizer, two ultraviolet laser beams are directed through the air to create ionized pathways. Then modulated, high-frequency charge pulses are con-

Figure 15 Well, with a little improvement.

---

111 "Alien dogs lay siege," *Photonics Spectra*, September 1997.
112 Mendonsa, R., *Photonics Spectra*, September 1998.

ducted to the target. The pulses are close approximations of the electrical impulses that control skeletal muscles. This means that persons who have been hit undergo sustained muscular contractions, stopping them in their tracks. The pulses do not affect muscles like the heart and diaphragm.[113] (A tetanizer is something that induces tetany. Tetanus is a disease that causes muscle spasms as described above). As of this writing, the tetanizer is still too large and bulky for practical use.

A Grave Investigation

In Morristown, NJ, the police have used infrared imaging to find both new and old graves (in order to have a corpse in murder investigations). The technique proved more convenient and cheaper than other techniques like radar and magnetometers.[114]

Eating (Less) Smoke

Infrared cameras are used by firefighters. They enable firefighters to see through smoke better, to evaluate the temperature of a wall to determine how dangerous the fire might be on the other side, to find people, and to find the source of the fire. The uncooled detector technology has made it possible for these devices to be small (they are head mounted) and inexpensive, while still quite capable.[115]

Some of these devices have color monitors so they can portray the seat of the fire as well as hot walls and so on. With all the smoke around, it is sometimes difficult to know exactly where the seat of the fire really is. The temperature displays use blue for the coolest to red for the hottest, and red is the seat. I had the pleasure of participating in litigation involving this kind of technique. The use of these colors has long been used to represent the hottest parts of the scene.[116]

Home Sweet Home

Optics works in the home, almost as much as the housewife. We have lights and flashlights and some more unusual devices at our disposal. Here they are, at least some of them.

---

113 "Exploring applications for a laser tetanizer," *Optics and Photonics News*, January 1999; "UV lasers stop people in their tracks," *Photonics Spectra*, January 1999.
114 "Infrared thermography unearths hidden graves," *Photonics Spectra*, June 1998.
115 "Photonics at work," *Photonics Spectra*, July 1998.
116 Proceedings of the IRE, September 1957.

Bright Bricks

One of the pleasant ways to landscape an entryway to your home is with bricks that light up. These are hollow, plastic bricks that interlock in a way that allows you to line the sides of a walkway. Some have lights inside them, and the low-voltage lighting system wires can be strung through the hollow, plastic brick.[117]

Solar Lights

I recently bought a set of solar lights to replace my set of Malibus. They are very interesting optical gadgets. On the top is a small solar panel. Inside is a rechargeable battery. The lights are LEDs. So the sun shines on them all day, every day (in Arizona). During this time, the solar cells recharge the batteries. A photoelectric sensor determines when the sunlight is gone, and it activates the LEDs. They stay on until about three in the morning in the summer. I bought a set of 15 for about $100. They are pretty cheap.

Quiet Time

In efforts to create quieter homes, contractors have tested the noise levels of various appliances. Although it sounds strange to eschew acoustic methods, one technique is to use a laser vibrometer (vibration meter) to measure the origins of the noise. The laser is directed to various parts of the appliance (or other noise sources), and the return beam has a shift in frequency imposed on it by the motion of the part.[118]

Where'd You Get Those Peepers?

Most of us have used the little viewer in the door to see who has come to call. We put one eye at the inside end and get a very wide-angle view of the exterior hallway or porch. The door peeper is essentially a Galilean telescope used backwards.[119] As shown in Fig. 16, the optics start with a plano-concave lens followed by a

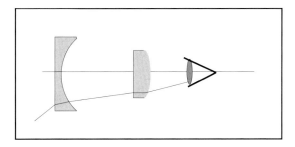

Figure 16 The door peeper.

117 "Dream builders," *Home and Garden TV*, October 8, 1997.
118 Ibid.
119 Goodman, D., "Door peepers," *Optics and Photonics News*, 50, June 1998.

plano-convex lens that provides the wide-angle image to the eye. The telescope and the eye form an equivalent eye that has a longer focal length than the eye alone. The aperture of the equivalent eye is in front of that of the real one. The pupil as seen from the outside is a small virtual image of the aperture on the inside, and there is vignetting so that it is very hard to look in.

The Robo Mower

It's here. A lawn mower that uses radio, sonar, and infrared detection can cut the grass all by itself. Under development at the University of Florida, the mower can cut the grass and miss all the obstacles. A wire is buried around the perimeter and that wire is detected by radio to keep the mower in the yard (to keep your neighbor jealous). I assume that there is some sort of program to make the mower go back and forth in an appropriate pattern, though it could be random.

The Robo Vacuum

For sale during the 2004 Christmas shopping season, this robotic vacuum cleaner was a hit. It is based on the same principles as the robotic mower, but it is less challenging. About a foot in diameter and six inches high, it moves about a room in a random pattern. Clearly it is limited in power because it runs on a battery. It is not clear that it is optical in nature, since it could just use impact sensors and go on its way. However, it was reported that the Florida group was working on a vacuum, and would probably use the same techniques.

The Robo Dog

In 1999, Sony Corporation introduced Aibo, a robotic dog. He sees with an 180,000 pixel CCD sensor and can recognize a ball, sleep, …and bark and piddle. Although this is purely fun, it is related to the robotic lawn mower, autonomous vehicles, and the robotic vacuum cleaner.[120] Although Aibo has been retired, there are other robotic pets available.

Fire Detection

One proposed scheme uses an infrared detector to sense the flickering of a flame or even the reflection of such a flame off walls and the like. The advantages seem to be that just smoke, like that from burning toast, will not set it off.

Another way to detect fire is to monitor the temperature of different parts of the house. This can be done by calibrated infrared detectors. The main problem with

---

120 "Aibo, the Robopooch," *Photonics Spectra*, August 1999.

both of these schemes is that one has to monitor all over the house, and that surely requires more than one sensor.

Firefighting

Forest fires as small as about five feet in diameter are being located now with infrared cameras that are flown in aircraft at altitudes up to 10,000 feet. The modern cameras use electronics to get an immediate image that can be relayed to a central station.[121]

Hydrophilic Mirrors

Researchers at Tokyo University have discovered that when a titanium dioxide film is illuminated with ultraviolet light, the film becomes hydrophilic, that is, the water wets the surface. It therefore flows off the glass in sheets and does not leave little droplets. This means that many surfaces that can be coated with this hard film can be self cleaning. The property wears off gradually when there is a lack of light, but this is easily remedied by exposure to sunlight or light from an ultraviolet lamp. It certainly would continue its effectiveness on windshields. However, in my home, it would increase the time between window washings considerably.

Get the Lead Out

There are techniques for determining whether old coats of paint contain lead, an undesirable situation. However, these techniques, which are essentially spectroscopic, cannot determine the lead content in sublayers of paint.

A simple technique for doing this has been developed at the University of South Carolina.[122] The system consists of two fiberoptic probes. The first is used to point the light from a pulsed neodymium YAG laser. This pulse of light is sufficient to create a plasma, i.e., vaporize a 1-mm diameter area of the layers of paint. The other probe directs the atomic emissions to a spectrometer. It takes about ten seconds for each measurement, so an entire house can be sampled in a reasonable time.

Gotcha!

The now-ubiquitous intrusion detector and door opener was introduced more than ten years ago.[123]

---

121 "Airborne system locates fires," *Photonics Spectra*, June 1991.
122 "Laser technique detects lead in paint," *Photonics Spectra*, October 1997.
123 Eisinger, L., "Sensor switch can detect movement or body heat," *The Arizona Daily Star*, March 15, 1987.

The devices are cheap and clever. A plastic sheet about two inches square has many Fresnel lenses pressed into it. The lenses form images onto one or two pyroelectric detectors that sense a change in heat. Thus, as any warm-blooded creature or other source of heat, like a car, moves in the field of view, there is a change in the detector/s' output. This change is used to activate something, like a light or an alarm.

Regular Roofs

A major shingle manufacturer has turned to image processing to ensure that its shingles are uniform. A CCD camera with a 1300×1030 pixel camera operated at a frame time of 120 μs and strobe of 20 μs images the shingles as they travel down the conveyor belt. The images are immediately evaluated by a 200 MHz computer. Control is accomplished.[124]

Sewer Pipes

We have all been plagued with clogged sewer pipes. The usual solution is to have them bored out. But trees and other roots can grow back in. So sometimes it is necessary to inspect the pipe to repair cracks or joints to prevent this.

At least one company has used a sonarlike device to plot the route of the pipe. Then an imaging system is sent down the pipe, along with its illumination system, in the same way the rotor is snaked along. The TV-like images show exactly where the root of the problem is (sorry).[125] This is a sewer-pipe endoscope!

Computer Security

Some of us have passwords on our computer so only a select few may get to our data. But hackers can often get to such passwords. One better way to do it is use a small imager that images the whorls of our fingertip and then provides access (or not).[126]

Checking Windows

A clever, but simple, way to examine window glass, in or out of the frame, is to illuminate it at an angle about equal to the angle of total internal reflection. Then the light will be reflected into the inside of the pane every place except where there are

---

124 Mendonsa, R., "Machine vision ensures unifrom sizing in roofing products," *Photonics Spectra*, September 1998.
125 "The house doctor," HGTV, September 10, 1998.
126 Mendonsa, R., "Image sensor helps boost desktop security," *Photonics Spectra*, September 1998.

cracks, pits, dirt, and any other imperfections. The window will appear dark except at these imperfections, which will be bright spots.[127] A fixture to launch the light at just the right angle is a useful feature.

Fireplaces

Reflectors, plane mirrors, can increase the room heat from your fireplace. A metal mirror placed in the back of a fireplace can almost double the effect of the fire.[128]

Flashlights

Flashlights come with LED light sources, and are surprisingly bright. These devices, with white LEDs, can be clicked into three different brightness levels.[129] I have several and they work very well.

On the Level

A normal bubble level is equipped with a little diode laser. The level acts as usual, but the laser beam projects up to 1500 feet away to provide a distant reference at the same height.[130]

Industry

Photonics is big in industrial processes and control. It has been reported by the Automated Imaging Association that $1.356 billion worth of machine-vision products were sold in North America in 1996 and $2.8 billion worldwide. The Laser Systems Product Group of the Association for Manufacturing Technology reported $420 million in laser shipments in 1996, almost 50% more than the year before. And it is still growing rapidly.[131]

Laser-Based Friction Reduction[132]

Surface Technology in Israel has developed a technique that reduces the friction of engine parts by about 20%. Tribologists, those who study friction and rubbing,

---

127 "Illumination device for inspecting window surfaces," *NASA Tech Briefs*, November 1998.
128 *SKYMALL*, American Airlines 2003.
129 Ibid.
130 Ibid.
131 *Photonics Spectra*, August 1997.
132 Kreifeldt, E., "Laser-Based Friction Reduction May Improve Engines," *Optics and Photonics News*, 8, September 1997.

know that parts that are too smooth tend to stick. Perhaps the best example of this is two optical surfaces that are "wrung" together. If these two surfaces are optically smooth with a roughness of about 0.5 μm, they become almost impossible to pull apart or move with respect to each other. It is also true that surfaces that are too rough have relatively high friction. So the trick is to make the parts with just the right roughness.

A pulsed Nd:YAG laser is used to make holes that are tens to hundreds of micrometers in diameter in the surface of parts subject to motion. They become little pockets that can store the lubricants. The systems that make these micro holes can move the part or use galvanometrically driven mirrors to move the beam over the part. The choice seems to be based on the size of the part.

Engine Research

Lasers help determine the profile of temperature, pressure, and the like in the exhausts of gas-turbine or other engines. A laser is shone across the exhaust, i.e., perpendicular to the direction of flow. It causes fluorescence in the exhaust, and this fluorescence can be viewed at right angles with an appropriately filtered CCD camera.[133] The laser beam can be a fan beam or it can be a narrow one that is scanned.

Surface Processing

Lasers are also used for other types of surface processing. For instance, some prostheses can be surface-treated to reduce the tendency to corrode, thereby extending their life in the patient. Some organic-based composites have been laser treated to clean and adjust the roughness to improve their adhesive properties.[134]

Laser Surface Treatment

The high power concentration provided by lasers can be used for treating metallic and other surfaces. The process works one of two ways, either by heating the surface to or near the melting temperature and letting it quench, or by heating the surface to about the same temperature and introducing a different material to alloy the surface. One example is introducing nitrogen at the surface of titanium to create a titanium nitride alloy on the surface. Although titanium is light and strong, it has low wear resistance. This alloying solves that problem.[135]

---

133 Magalith, E., et al., "Laser-induced fluorescence fires up engine research," *Photonics Spectra*, March 1997.

134 Hennink, S., "Laser treatment techniques improve materials," *Photonics Spectra*, December 1997.

135 Roemer, G., et al., "Industrial imaging controls laser surface treatment," *Photonics Spectra*, November 1977.

Crack Detection

Interestingly enough, a technique for finding critical cracks in machine parts is based on friction. A high-frequency (20–40 kHz) sound-wave pulse (50–200 ms) is applied to a convenient place on the part to be tested. The vibrations of the sound wave cause the segments of the cracks to rub and create frictional heat. The heat is detected by a thermal viewer.[136]

Integrated Circuits

The transistor was the first solid state electronic amplifier and diode ever developed. It took us out of the realm of cat's whiskers and vacuum tubes that filled a lot of space, got hot, broke, were slow, and otherwise not good. Some readers know of vacuum tubes only from historical accounts, but others of us actually made radios and hi-fi sets with them. The transistor of Shockley, Brattain, and Bardeen (who received the Nobel prize for its invention) took us away from all that.

Then, in 1958, came the integrated circuit. It was a single piece of material that consisted of many transistors. The integrated circuit was a set of transistor amplifiers and diodes that were integrated on a single wafer that could perform the designed circuit functions. The chip that is in our computers today is an advanced form of an integrated circuit. It is made by microlithography.

The first type of microlithography was contact printing.[137] A pattern was made on a drawing board that outlined the different parts of the circuit. This pattern was made into a mask that covered the material. It consisted of opaque and transparent sections—a black and white transparency. Then it was photographed and demagnified so it would be the right size for the little chip. It was then a very small opaque and transparent pattern, less than an inch on a side. This mask was put on a wafer of silicon about 5 to 8 inches in diameter and 1 to 2 mm thick, and covered with a material called photoresist. The photoresist is a material that darkens upon exposure to light.

The wafer would then be covered for a short time with an acid that would not affect the parts that were exposed and vice versa; so, some of the disk would be eaten away. Then metal or other material could be evaporated on to it until the entire circuit—amplifiers, diodes, resistors, capacitors and leads—would be constructed. The size of the mask and the disk determined the density of circuit elements, the number of elements per square centimeter.

The earliest integrated circuits had characteristic dimensions of 200 μm. Details finer than that could not be attained. Soon, almost-contact printing developed to prevent damage to the wafers. The masks were separated from the wafers by about 25 μm. Continuous improvements occurred until in 1974 the line widths

---

136 "Finding cracks and checking our walnuts," *Photonics Tech Briefs*, March 2000.
137 "An interview with Burn Lin," *OE Reports*, 158, February 1997.

reached about 2 μm. This was the wall until Abe Offner invented the unit magnification all-reflective imaging system. The mask and the wafer could be centimeters apart; the imaging system was all reflective and could therefore work with any wavelength, and it was achromatic.

The next advance was the step-and-repeat process. Instead of making a mask that was the size of the entire wafer, a smaller mask was made, a refractive optical system that reduced the size of the image onto the wafer was used, and the wafer was mechanically stepped so that the mask was repeated in a stepwise manner over the entire wafer.

Since fast refractive systems are easier to make than reflective ones, reduction makes better masks and stepping makes better alignment, this process replaced the old one, but many different masks were required for a single wafer.

Then, and obviously in hindsight, people combined the step-and-repeat technique with the unit magnification reflective system, and even combined the refractive and reflective optics with the step-and-repeat.

Today the characteristic dimension is about 0.2 μm with prospects of halving it. The other techniques under consideration are excimer lasers, x-rays, and electron beams. It should be clear that the smaller the characteristic dimensions of these chips, the smaller will be the final devices.

Steel Mill Predictive Maintenance

Infrared inspections are used for many functions that can be heat sensitive. One application is monitoring bottle cars, those vehicles that hold molten metal in large amounts. They have refractory linings that normally are replaced periodically. Monitoring the cars with infrared sensors allows replacement when they need it. This usually means at longer intervals, but it can also mean the prevention of a major accident. One mill, that uses biweekly inspections estimates the savings at $20,000 to $30,000. One car was found to be about 500°F above the maximum rating, and this prevented a potential rupture, which could have caused damage to equipment, lost production, and solidified steel on the car's wheels.[138]

Stripping

Strip mills make steel in large, long strips. They start with fairly thick rectangles of steel. The rectangle is fed between rollers that squeeze them to about half their initial thickness. In the process they heat up. The steel that is then half as thick is twice as long and hotter.

It passes through a few more of these rollers until it is a long sheet of the correct thickness, and quite hot. The entire process is automated with the operators in a lit-

---

138 *Peak Performance*, a publication of AGEMA, summer 1997.

tle control booth high above the rollers. One problem is asperities—usually holes or maybe just depressions in the sheet.

One possible solution is thermal imaging. I had the opportunity to investigate this years ago with Bethlehem Steel. We designed an infrared scanner that could look down on the hot strips of steel. It detected these asperities, but it also sensed drops of water that danced on top of the steel.

I learned what a real cobble is. These sheets attain speeds of about 50 mph. Sometimes, for some reason, there is a hitch in the git-along, and the sheets start to go all over the place in all sorts of folds and knots. Imagine a 10-ft-wide sheet of hot steel rambling all over the place at 50 mph. Don't be there!

Rapid Prototyping

Selective laser sintering is used by Rocketdyne in Canoga Park for rapid prototyping. A three-dimensional computer-aided design is sent to a Sinterstation, about the size of a delivery truck. In it, a cross section of the object is sketched by a carbon dioxide laser onto a thin layer of heat-fusible powder that covers a small platform. The laser beam melts the powder particles into a solid. The platform then lowers a few thousandths of an inch, a roller spreads a new layer of powder, and the laser sketches the next cross section.

The process is repeated for all vertical planes of the object. Then the part and the loose particles are removed, revealing a three-dimensional object that was represented by the CAD drawing.[139] The process has become competitive with injection molding and similar techniques.[140]

Catalogs

It is interesting to note that optical disks are being introduced as optical catalogs for choosing optical components.

Thermal Wave Inspection

This technique makes use of an infrared imaging device. Typically, a bank of heaters, usually five to ten tungsten lamps of high wattage, is used to illuminate the back of a sample. The infrared sensor images the heat pattern at the other side. The variation in the pattern can portray lack of bonding, voids, and other defects in the sample.

The system has also been used in the echo mode. The lamps and the imager are on the same side of the sample. The thermal wave passes into the sample and returns by reflection from the back side of the voids and delaminations. One applica-

139 Tull, M., "Rapid phototyping," *Boeing News*, August 7, 1998.
140 Ruthstiver, T., "Rapid phototyping," *Boeing News*, August 7, 1998.

tion of the echo technique has been the inspection of aging aircraft, in which delaminations, corrosion around wing fasteners, and the like are found.[141] Other variations include the use of flash lamps, the detection of time changes in the heat pattern, and use of a scanning lamp rather than uniform radiation of the surface.

The technique has also been used on rocket materials, especially aluminum honeycomb covered with a skin, and inspection of radomes, the domes that are placed in front of radar systems to protect them—often in the noses of planes. Others have used it to evaluate ship hulls, fiberglass laminates, two-inch thick foam cores, and Kevlar and graphite composites. When assessing damage to luxury yachts, all furniture is removed and space heaters bring the inside temperature about 25°F above ambient.[142]

Paper Quality

By carefully illuminating the paper being drawn on the web in the manufacturing process, image processing can control and monitor its quality.[143]

On an Even Keel

Fiberboard is made in much the same way as paper. The wood pulp is placed on an endless conveyor belt and formed into flat sheets of a given thickness. One innovation to keep the thickness consistent is the use of an optical sensor at the side of the strip. By using triangulation with two sensors, the thickness of the edge can be measured, and this seems to be adequate for the entire width.[144]

Computer Disks[145]

At least one manufacturer uses machine vision to inspect its wafers for irregularities. A million-pixel digital camera was used to look at each wafer. The system required a large database of both acceptable and unacceptable images, and very complex mathematical modeling to compare them. The images were taken at a rate of 15 frames per second (0.066 second frame time) with some exposures as short as 0.015 second. The system could not only reliably identify the disks, but did it five to ten times more accurately than a human (and with no boredom), and it could also identify repeated imperfections.

---

141 Favro, L. D., et al., "Thermal wave imaging for aging aircraft inspection," *Materials Evaluation*, 1386, December 1993.

142 Elber, G., "Infrared inspection in the field and in the factory," *Advanced Composites*, November/December 1993.

143 "Lighting system helps spot defects in paper," *Photonics Spectra*, October 1997.

144 "Laser sensors help reduce waste at fiberboard plant," *Photonics Spectra*, March 1997.

145 "Digital camera reveals wafer anomalies," *Photonics Spectra*, 137, July 1998.

A different system monitored and read the edges of the discs to keep track of each wafer. This system read the digits rather than barcodes, and did it more reliably.

Machine-Tool Calibration

Machine tools do wear out, wear down, and wear away. They need to be recalibrated and have parts replaced. Many have been calibrated by interferometric techniques that are relatively complex and involved in the setup. A laser technique now exists that can measure five degrees of freedom with a measurement uncertainty of 1 to 0.1 parts per million.

In this technique, the output of a helium-neon laser is divided by a polarizing beamsplitter into two beams. The measurement beam is directed to the part to be measured, where a retroreflector and a beamsplitter are attached; it reflects to the sensor where it is combined (interfered) with the reference beam. An optical phase detector counts the fringes thus generated, and this is an accurate measure of the distance. A quadrant sensor on the part measures lateral movement.[146]

True Grit

As grinding wheels are used in various industrial applications, they build up "stuff" on the wheel in between the abrasives, which are very often diamond grit. The stuff is whatever is being ground. In standard practice, the operation stops and a stick with diamond abrasive is used to clean the stuff out. In a new application, a laser is used to do this task. One example is a doubled Nd:YAG laser that operates at 532 nm. Diamond is transparent at this wavelength, so it is unaffected by the laser, but the material absorbs and is ablated. This can even be done while the processing is going on.[147]

Weldment Locator

Laser welding is described elsewhere. Determining where to weld can also be done accurately and quickly with lasers. In one device, a beam of laser light is shone on the weldment, and the beam is then scattered in many directions. The position-sensitive detectors measure angular positions and a computer performs triangulation.[148]

Cut-Leather

Leather is expensive. It is a costly accessory in many cars and a dollar drain in furnishings. One company, Erpo International, has switched to a laser system to lay out patterns on the hides. This semiautomatic system projects the pattern onto the hide so that workers can do a better job in maximizing the use of the hide. They still have to make human judgments about avoiding imperfections. It appears that cut-

146 Kaplan, H., "Lasers quickly calibrate machine tools," *Photonics Spectra*, 1998.
147 Sheppard, L., "Laser sharpens grinding wheels," *Photonics Spectra*, August 1999.
148 Mendonsa, R., "Laser seam finder outperforms mechanical vision," *Photonics Spectra*, 31, May 1998.

tings are still done with knives on a vacuum table, but lasers could be used to do that, too. Between 80 and 120 hides are cut in eight hours.[149]

Smoothies

An example of surface treatment without alloying comes from the semiconductor industry. In the search for larger and larger disks of silicon from which to fabricate chips, the snag is imperfections in the crystal. One way to cure this is by a surface remelt operation using lasers. The laser that has been used is a xenon-chloride (XeCl) excimer laser, operating at 308 nm, with 1-J pulses lasting 100 ns at a repetition rate of 30 Hz. The remelt and refreeze "cures" the imperfections.

With Polish

Lasers have also been used to polish glass lenses. The lenses are first heated to 580°C, about 100°C below their softening point, to avoid thermal stress when the laser is used. A vibrating mirror evenly moves the light from a carbon dioxide laser over the surface. The surface roughness was reduced from 500-nm root mean square (rms) to about 1-nm rms (a really good number and hard to measure).[150]

Micromachining

Micromachining is another form of surface treatment. Some applications are microlens and microcylinder arrays, diffractive optics, and solar cells. Typically, a laser beam is focused onto a photoresist material and scanned over it in a raster pattern. The pattern can be either rectangular or circular. The resist is not always used, but if not, higher laser power is needed. The pattern is controlled by computer.[151]

Peening

For some time metals have been stressed by bombardment with small (0.01 inch) grains to improve both their resistance to fatigue and corrosion. The use of a neodymium-glass laser of some 600 W average power accomplishes this better, with better depth penetration.[152]

Laser Welding

Laser beams can be focused to rather small spots, 1-mm diameter for instance. A modest carbon-dioxide laser emits 10 to 100 W in a beam that is about 1 cm in diameter. So,

---

149 Hennink, S., "Lasers cut time and cost in leather furniture industry," *Photonics Spectra*, May 1998.

150 Hardin, R., "Laser technique polishes glass lenses," *Photonics Spectra*, May 1998.

151 Raguin, D., et al., "Laser pattern generation," *Optics and Photonics News*, 36, October 1997.

152 "Laser bursts strengthen metal parts," *Photonics Spectra*, February 1998.

with such a system, a power of 100 W can be concentrated into 1 square millimeter for a power density of 10,000 W per square centimeter. That's a lot. I have used a 10-W laser to bore through refractory brick. It is no wonder then that lasers can be used to weld metals by melting them in complicated patterns and with exquisite control.

Other lasers, like neodymium-yttrium-aluminum-garnet, are also used in a pulsed mode with equal effectiveness. Most commercial lasers have outputs in the 200 to 300 kW range. Researchers in Haifa have combined plasma welding with laser welding to obtain greater efficiency and speed. They have, for instance, used a 1-kW laser with a 0.67-mm spot size with an electric plasma arc to obtain the performance of a 2-kW stand-alone laser.[153]

Vauxhall Motors uses a laser welder in making wheel arches. Engineers found that they needed a good, three-dimensional representation of the weldment area. So they used a red-diode laser to measure both the width and height of the gap. The sensor helped them reduce the number of reworked parts from 40% to 2%, resulting in a marked increase in throughput—2 or 3 seconds more time per part, but with far fewer mistakes. The application requires positional accuracy of 0.2–0.3 mm.[154]

A modest but effective welding application is used with reed switches. As you might imagine, two reedlike contacts are hermetically sealed inside a glass capsule. This prolongs their life by eliminating dust and other contaminants. The switches are set up on an assembly line, and after assembly the glass cover is welded to the lead frame. A 250 W Nd:YAG laser is aimed through a beam expander and a dichroic mirror and cylindrical lens. The resultant spot is 2.5 inches long and welds several switches at once.[155]

Alloying

Lasers are very convenient devices for creating surface alloys on a variety of parts. One example is cladding the edge of a diesel-engine outlet valve with cobalt to increase its wear resistance. Another is alloying titanium surfaces with nitrogen (to get titanium nitride) to get a much harder surface for increased abrasion resistance.

In this case, a 1.5-kW carbon dioxide laser was used to create a small melt pool. A copper tube supplied the nitrogen. A CCD camera with 128×128, 16-μm elements monitored the process. The stage moves at 90 mm per second. Of course, this can be adjusted for different materials that melt at different temperatures. This nice technique can alloy materials just where it's needed.[156]

153 Normie, L., "Marriage of laser/arc welding promises more for less," *Photonics Spectra*, September 1997.
154 "Optical sensor bridges gap for robotic welders," *Photonics Spectra*, June 2000.
155 "Nd:YAG gets a bead on reed switches," *Photonics Spectra*, July 2000.
156 "Laser alloying," *Photonics Spectra*, November 1997.

Make Your Mark

In this day of knock-offs, it can be important to have a nonerasable means of marking various parts. This is more important in industry than knowing you bought a real Rolex, because it can affect the operation of the entire instrument of which the part is a part. Some applications are catheters, circuit boards, and food packages.[157]

Early systems used carbon-dioxide lasers and lamp-pumped Nd:YAG lasers.[158] More modern devices now use diode-pumped Nd:YAGs. Diode pumping is more efficient since the right pumping wavelength means light is not wasted and there is less heating. The laser shines on the part via an x-y scanner, controlled by a computer. It writes (prints) the appropriate identification code on the part. Any code can be programmed. There is still a trade-off between the use of carbon-dioxide lasers and diode-pumped solid lasers. The gas system (CO_2) is more difficult to replace but lasts longer.

Some parts are marked with excimer lasers that operate at 308 or 351 nm in the ultraviolet. This enables better definition (because of the shorter wavelength) and is a chemical rather than an ablation process, so it is better for some parts.

The usual arrangement is an appropriate laser, one or more mirrors that direct the laser in a programmed direction, and sometimes a lens to focus the laser.[159] A variety of lasers are used—carbon dioxide, Nd:YAG, and others with average powers ranging from about 1 W to 1 kW. If the laser is pulsed, arrangements are made so that just enough pulses are generated on a given spot. If the laser is continuous, the dwell time is adjusted to obtain the proper energy.

A Hole in One—or One in a Hole

The oil industry drills a lot of holes; some have oil and some are dry and some have some kind of liquid in the bottom. Optics help analyze these liquids.

The most successful tools are simple spectrometers, which analyze the composition of the liquids. One is designed to operate at temperatures up to 175°F and pressures as high as 20,000 psi. The analysis is straightforward, near-infrared spectroscopy in the range from the visible to about 2 μm. A two-beam technique is used; one for reference, one for measurement. The liquid to be tested flows through a metal tube with thick sapphire windows to withstand the temperatures and pressures at these depths. An optical refractometer analyzes the gases. It shines an LED beam onto a cube in the side of the pipe and senses the angle of total internal reflection. This is different for gases with different refractive indices at this particular wavelength.[160]

157 Ibid.
158 Wheeler, M. D., "Chip makers weigh benefits and cost of laser marking systems," *Photonics Spectra*, December 1998.
159 Derzy, J., "Pen-type laser: new life for an old system," *Photonics Spectra*, April 1998.
160 Schroeder, R., "Slick engineering," *OE Magazine*, May 2003.

Jewels and Gems

Gemstones, and especially diamonds, are characterized by the four c's–color, carat weight, clarity, and cut. The least understood of these is cut. Cut determines the brilliance (brightness), fire (dispersion), and scintillation (sparkle).

Until now, cuts were based on trial and error (for ancient jewelers) and then the empirical investigations of Tolkowsky, who reviewed and organized their results. The optical and gem industries are combining to bring design tools to gem analysis. The techniques are complicated because of the many facets involved, but real progress is being made using of computer-aided design for the configuration and one of the many different optical design programs.[161]

Uranium Enrichment

Nuclear reactors in power plants use enriched uranium containing 3 to 5% of the U-235 isotope, extracted from uranium oxide that contains about 0.7%. The traditional techniques of gas centrifuge and gas diffusion are fairly expensive, inefficient, and use a lot of U-235. Atomic-vapor laser isotope separation is newer and better (like many detergents).

A uranium vapor is created, and a laser tuned between 550 nm and 650 nm is aimed at the vapor to ionize the atoms, which are then collected by an ion extractor (essentially a charge collector). Each of the production units will contain more than 40,000 optical elements ranging from 1 to 8 inches in diameter to focus and aim the beams. This new system should require less initial capital investment, use 5% of the power, and 20 to 30% less uranium for an equivalent amount of enriched fuel compared to current systems.[162]

Polish It Off

Lasers can be used to polish lenses. A group in Spain has done the first exploratory steps. Using a carbon dioxide laser, they polished 50 square centimeters of a quartz lens, reducing the average surface deviation from 500 nm to 1 nm. The power of the laser softens the glass so that it is sufficiently viscous to flow a little. The laser is scanned over the surface of the lens so that the dwell time and therefore the viscosity can be programmed.[163]

161 Sasian, J., Yantzer P., and Tivol, T., "The optical design of gemstones," *Optics and Photonics News*, April 2003.

162 Grant, B., "Lasers improve uranium enrichment," *Photonics Spectra*, October 1997.

163 Hardin, W., "Laser technique polishes glass lenses," *Photonics Spectra*, May 1998.

Optics Make Optics

Lasers can generate three-dimensional patterns of very small dimensions. These patterns can be microlens arrays, fiber optical couplers, microcylinder arrays and even artistic carvings. In one scheme, the focused laser beam is directed to a material covered with photoresist. The laser is guided in any prescribed x-y pattern on the photoresist. It uses submicrometer spots in areas up to 10-inch diameters. After the laser has exposed the pattern, an acid etch can eat away material to obtain the vertical profile.[164] Although the article does not discuss it, the laser systems can be used to generate the vertical profile as well by ablating the surface differentially with different dwell times.

How It Gets There

It is amazing how our millions of packages get to where they are supposed to go! FedEx has installed 50 very intelligent readers to speed the process along. The system takes 3D measurements of each parcel, locates the barcode, scans it, and records it. It can handle parcels up to $3 \times 5 \times 8$ ft even if they are on the edge of the conveyor belt, and it warns if they are stacked. These large parcels move along the belt at 80 to 200 ft per second (standard ones move at 500 ft per minute).[165]

How does this work? The article did not say, but we can imagine. A laser scans each package. The return is recorded and image processing calculates the irregular figure and converts it to a rectangular, three-dimensional box. It then scans over the exposed surface for a bar code. Since the bar code may be on any side, at least three systems must be used, and I wonder what they do about the surfaces right next to the box in front, or on the bottom?

More Trussful

A laser projection system has greatly increased productivity for a company that makes trusses for buildings. The traditional process is to translate a blueprint into a set of measurements on the lumber, check and recheck the measurements, and make the cuts.

The new process takes the information from a computer design and translates the blueprint into a series of lines projected by a laser onto the material, usually wood. The computer also sets the saw blade angles for the various cuts. It is then a matter of pushing a button to get the perfect cut—with no human error. The com-

---

164 Raguin, D., G. Morris, "Laser pattern generation for the fabrication of micro-optical elements," *Optics and Photonics News*, October 1997.
165 Mendonsa, R., "Mass screening system expedites freight transport," *Photonics Spectra*, March 1998.

pany has increased production about 30% with about half the labor force, and no one needs to be trained to read blueprints or even to measure.[166]

Ninety-Nine Bottles of Beer...

One application of infrared thermal imagers is monitoring the production of beer bottles (without the beer). As the bottles move on the assembly line and are cooling down, they are imaged by the infrared device. This image provides information about configuration and integrity. Cracks and imperfections will show up as differences in temperature.[167]

It's a Hard Life

A laser technique has bean developed that can deposit diamondlike coatings on other materials. These coatings make the materials stronger and harder, and sometimes smoother.

The alternative technique has been chemical-vapor deposition. Three lasers are used: KrF or XeCl at 308 nm, Nd:YAG at 1064 nm, and carbon dioxide at 10.6 μm. A similar technique works to generate a titanium carbide surface. Such surfaces can be ten times harder than the substrate.[168] Nothing is harder than diamond!

It's a Dirty Job

Optics are big in pollution monitoring because so many pollutants have characteristic absorption bands in the infrared. A system with a 1550-nm InGaAs diode laser and a multiple-pass sample cell has been mounted in a smokestack to monitor ammonia, which is sometimes used to reduce nitrous oxides. A PIN diode is used to detect the light. The current to the laser is varied so that the output wavelength is varied. The detector then measures the change, or modulation, in the signal.

Another system, with variations on the theme, uses a collection of diodes and corresponding detectors from the near-infrared out to 12 μm. These are used either with a fiber optic system in the chimney or with a remote telescope system.[169]

166 Mendonsa, R., "Photonics accelerates truss-building," *Photonics Spectra*, August 1998.
167 "CCDs rule, but spectral detectors have their place," *Photonics Spectra*, February 1998.
168 Wheeler, M., "Three-laser method goes beyond diamond films," *Photonics Spectra*, March 1998.
169 Hardin, R., "Diode lasers pinpoint pollutants," *Photonics Spectra*, April 1998.

Perfect Buns

Machine-vision systems are in use in some bakeries to monitor sandwich buns. They show and ensure proper color, uniformity, seed distribution, and shape. I assume that some preliminary work is done to get the proper distribution of the heaters, the buns, and the walls. Then small adjustments can be made, and the system can be optimized.[170]

Packaging

Several innovations have come about in the packaging industry as a result of optics. A simple but effective one is checking for very small holes in materials used in Frito-Lay snack packages. They are metallized polypropylene that need to be air tight to preserve freshness. The tiny holes are found by surface topography with a vertical resolution of 0.1 nm using a Wycko phase-shifting interferometer.

Another application uses ultraviolet light to sterilize milk cartons. One requirement is that all parts of the interior of the carton have sufficient radiation to accomplish sterilization. Breault Research Organization analyzed the situation with their scattering software to determine the geometry of the irradiation.[171]

Little Holes

Vias, small holes in circuit boards, have long been drilled mechanically, but only as small as 0.1 mm. Lasers can make them smaller, and that is the trend. One solution has used tripled Nd:YAG lasers operating at 355 nm. Carbon dioxide lasers are fine for drilling in dielectrics, but they are ineffective for drilling metals. Excimer lasers are relatively slow, so the Nd:YAG was chosen to drill holes as small as 0.025 mm.[172]

Three-Dimensional Imaging

Single-point systems and others that obtain a full three-dimensional representation almost instantaneously already exist. One version of the latter system uses a grating to split a laser beam into as many as 100 lines that illuminate the sample. Three cameras form images of the stripes, and triangulation is accomplished on all the pixels on all the stripes. (Thank goodness for the computational power of today's chips). In its present configuration, the system has a range of fields of view from

---

170 Burgess, D., "Machine vision system scans baked goods," *Photonics Spectra*, January 2004; Douglass, K., "The perfect sandwich bun," *Optics and Photonics News*, March 2004.

171 Kaplan, H., "Photonics advances packaging design," *Photonics Spectra*, March 1997.

172 McCarthy, D., "Tripled Nd:YAG fills gap by drilling holes," *Photonics Spectra*, March 1999.

smaller than an inch to several feet, and the accuracy is one thousandth of the field of view.[173]

Houston Harbors Ships

The Port of Houston has 10 digital cameras between Houston and Galveston that continuously monitor ships. The cameras cost about one-tenth as much as the previous analog versions. The system also has to and does compress the data.[174] I hope they still have them after Hurricanes Katrina and Rita.

I'm Always Blowing Bubbles

A Nd:YAG laser can deliver its 8-ns pulses at 1064 nm to a jar of distilled water through a focusing lens, thereby forming a rapidly expanding plasma, a shockwave, a bright light, and a bubble, ranging in size from 1.6 to 3.0 mm in diameter. The bubble expands and pops, and emits a short light flash (called, logically enough, bubble luminescence). The article says the team that accomplished this is just beginning to reap the benefits.[175] But the benefits are definitely not clear!

Barcode Scanning

We have all seen barcode scanning in the last decade. Perhaps the most ubiquitous use is at the grocery store check-out counter. A clerk takes our purchase and scans it with some kind of barcode reader. Some are mounted in the counter; some are hand-held devices. They all work on the same principle.

A laser beam (it does not have to be a laser, but they are very convenient and bright) scans across a series of bars. The sequence of bars is a code that provides the price and can give inventory information as

Figure 17 Barcode.

well. A detector senses the returns in terms of bar width and spacings. There are even bars on the ends to indicate whether it has been read correctly. One very popular design is a laser beam moved by a rotating multifaceted mirror. Another is a fixed laser beam across which the barcode must be scanned.

173 Benayad-Cherif F., and W. Wilson, "Optical sensor inspects parts with 3-D imaging," *Laser Focus World*, November 1996.
174 McCarthy, D., "Digital cameras improve surveillance in port of houston," *Photonics Spectra*, October 1998.
175 Tatterson, K. G., "Scientists bubble with excitement," *Photonics Spectra*, March 1998.

A recent innovation, not yet on the market, is a scanner with no moving parts.[176] This has been a research project at the University of Central Florida. A tunable laser shines light through a beamsplitter to a collimator that sends light to a diffraction grating. The grating sends a beam of light of a single wavelength in one direction. The laser is then tuned to another color; that light goes in a different direction when it exits the beamsplitter. In this way, the beam is scanned angularly as the laser is tuned in wavelength. The light returns from the barcode and is sent to a detector by the beamsplitter. The arrows show the direction of the light in Fig. 18. Only one color is shown with arrows.

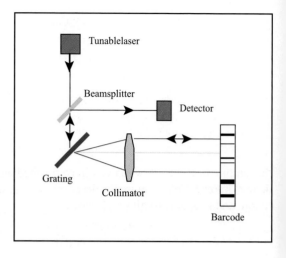

Figure 18 Advanced barcode reader.

Micromachining

Lasers are used for many machining tasks. Perhaps the most demanding are those that require great precision and smooth surfaces. It has been found that if the pulses are too slow and their energy too large, they ablate material by heating it. This can cause microcracks, burrs, and resolidified debris.

Excimer lasers avoid this by breaking chemical bonds with high-energy photons. Femtosecond lasers are so fast that they immediately ablate the material and do not cause heating. A third alternative, generally less expensive, is the use of picosecond lasers that use a variety of solid state materials. These seem to work as well as their expensive counterparts and are easier to use.[177]

Geology

Multispectral cameras from satellites have shown great promise in identifying soils. The TIMS system has been used by Daedalus Enterprises in Ann Arbor, Michigan, in a Learjet. The system has six spectral bands covering the region from

176 "No moving-parts optical setups scan barcodes," *Photonics News*, May 2004.
177 Hermann, T., B. Klimt and F. Siegel, "Slashing the costs of high-precision machining," *Photonics Spectra*, June 2004.

about 8 to about 12 μm. The results provided reasonable identification of the different minerals, like limestone, dolomite, olivine, and latite.[178]

Optics in Everyday Life

The Toilet Flusher[179]

Any one who reads this has probably encountered the more modern toilets, those that automatically flush when you have finished and move away from them. How do they know? Well, because the description is in this book it must be an optical solution, and it is, at least all that I know.

The device is something like the television remote used by couch potatoes. A small infrared light beam shines from the little black bulb on top of the toilet, which is transparent in the infrared. The reflection of the beam from the person is sensed by a small silicon detector next to the laser, the operation being at about 1 μm. Before some one approaches, there is no reflection; then while they do their business, there is a sensed reflection; when they leave, the signal disappears and the toilet flushes. The source can be a light-emitting diode that is modulated to distinguish it from other sources of light in the room.

Some units use passive infrared, involving the detection of transient heat from the human body. This is very similar to the popular motion detectors used for automatic driveway illumination and intrusion detection. They sense heat as the person approaches. Then they sense the lack of heat when he or she leaves. If you are curious about which type you have just used, try this. Put a credit card in front of the bulb, and then pull it away. If it flushes, it is the active system; if not, the passive type. But make sure the card is not warm!

Environmental Planning

Remote sensing from an aircraft by NASA engineers provided information about the microclimates of a number of cities. These images provided information on "hot spots" in the cities. Then urban planners could evaluate the environment for building density, pavement, parks, and the like.

Figure 19 shows a typical output. The colors, from green to red, indicate increasing temperatures.

---

178 Stanich, C., "Thermal IR imaging, a new geologic tool," *Photonics Spectra*, 93, July 1986.
179 *Optics and Photonics Spectra*, 43, September 1997.

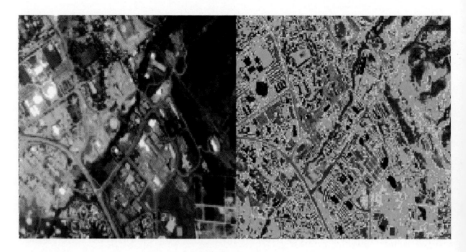

Figure 19 Multispectral image.[180]

Tans

The lure of the golden skin by way of suntanning has waned some with all the additional knowledge about skin cancer. It might be noted that my home, Tucson, Arizona is known as the skin cancer center of the world. There are two regions in the ultraviolet spectrum that give rise to skin cancer, called UVA and UVB, 320–400 and 280–20 nm, respectively. UVB is generally considered the harmful region; small amounts can cause considerable damage, while UVA provides the suntan. Thus, many sun lamps are restricted in their output of UVB while providing UVA. However, the better the filtering, the more it costs. There is still some opinion that UVA can also cause melanoma, a form of skin cancer.[181]

SPF What?

Those of us concerned about skin cancer rub on our sunscreen for protection, but we do not know how often to refresh it. Stickers exist that measure the accumulation of ultraviolet radiation. The user applies the patch and then applies the sunscreen on the skin and on the patch. The color change of the patch tells the user when to reapply or go inside. The patch is truly cumulative. If you go inside and come out later, it still adds it up.[182]

---

180 Image courtesy of NASA (1998).
181 "Handheld spectroradiometer tests sunlamps," *Photonics Spectra*, December 1998.
182 Rowell, N. D., *Biophotonics International*, September/October, 2000.

Tax Returns Made Less Taxing

The IRS is using optical scanners to scan more and more returns. The IRS processes almost $1.5 trillion worth of tax receipts every year (and yet they always find something wrong with mine). Nearly 200 million forms are on paper, keeping almost 30,000 employees busy keying in the data.

New York State's taxing authority mounted a study of scanning these paper returns; 10 million returns were scanned by some 13 high-volume scanners. The results were that labor costs were cut and efficiency improved. About 90% of machine-printed characters and 60% of handwritten characters are read with 99% confidence.[183] The scanners are much like copying machines; the optical character recognition is the difficult part. If you have used a scanner in conjunction with a home computer, you know this is so. We can all expect to have our tax returns scammed...er, scanned in the future.[184] I say, give us a break on our taxes and we will: (a) send an electronic version, (b) send a typed version. Most tax preparers do it with software now, anyway.

Lighting

An extensive area of optics involves lighting and illumination. It ranges from the light we receive from the sun through incandescent bulbs around the home, fluorescents, and so-called daylight bulbs to the vast new area of solid-state lights, principally light-emitting diodes.

Lumens, Luxes, Nits, and Such

No discussion of lighting can be complete, or hardly even started, without some discussion of the units used to describe lighting.

The basic unit is the lumen. It is a light watt, an eyeball watt. That is, it is how much light there is that affects the eye. The lumen is a special kind of power. Our lights are usually specified in both watts and lumens.

Sometimes the information we get is in terms of lux. A lux is a lumen per square meter. It is a power density that is useful to the eye.

A nit is a unit of luminous intensity, a lumen per solid angle. A nit is also a flea egg, but that is irrelevant here. Sometimes luminous efficiency (technically called luminous efficacy) is specified. It is the ratio of the lumens in a source to the watts in the source. A light with more luminous efficiency has more of its output in the spectral region, where the eye is sensitive.

---

183 O'Brien, T., "IRS looks to imaging to tame its paper monster," *Photonics Spectra*, October 1997.
184 Ibid.

Incandescent Lights

Almost all incandescent lights use tungsten wires inside either evacuated or gas-filled enclosures, usually glass. Sir Humphrey Davy first discovered in 1802 that electricity could produce light by incandescence using a carbon arc. Carbon arcs are useful for searchlights, but not for normal lighting, since they generate smoke and are not stable.

Thomas Edison and Joseph Swan in 1879 demonstrated an incandescent bulb using a carbon thread as a filament. It could provide light for only about 40 hours. Lewis Latimer just two years later demonstrated longer-lived carbon filaments.

In 1913 we finally had still longer-lived tungsten filaments. Improvements since then have involved the use of inert gases in the bulbs to improve lifetimes.[185]

Fluorescent Bulbs

In 1852, G. G. Stokes, famous for his work on polarization, discovered that ultraviolet light could be used to generate visible light of different colors, and he gave fluorescence its name. It took until 1924 before he could generate appropriate phosphors for the conversion of ultraviolet light to visible light. Twelve years passed before the demonstration of the first fluorescent lamp, and forty-four more years until the advent of the compact fluorescent bulb. About 60% of the electricity is converted to ultraviolet light in such a bulb, and the overall efficiency is about 25%.[186]

Light-Emitting Diodes (LEDs)

The detailed operation of these is discussed elsewhere. The point to be made here is that they have very high luminous efficacy and also a high rate of conversion of electricity to light. The icing on the cake is that they last a long time.

The Sunlight or Daylight Lamp

This is a form of fluorescent lamp with especially white phosphors. It is claimed that a 27-W bulb of this type gives 50% more visible light than a 100-W incandescent bulb and has a lifetime of 5000 hours. This would make it about eight times as efficient.[187]

---

185 Lister, G., "The drive for energy efficient lighting," *Optics and Photonics News*, January 2004.
186 Ibid.
187 "More lux for less bucks," *Technology Review*, April, 2004.

The Grays

Those of you living in the East and North sometimes suffer depression from the long, gray days of winter. I call these the grays, not the blues. Others have also called it cabin fever. The medical field has labeled it "seasonal affective disorder" (SAD).

A typical office is illuminated at about 700 lux and a home at about 500 lux. It certainly varies from company to company and home to home, even from room to room. The treatment for SAD is light therapy, about an half hour each day in front of a light box that produces 10,000 lux, much greater than typical lighting can provide. This is not a tanning machine; it may even have filters to eliminate the harmful ultraviolet rays that generate tans and skin cancer.[188] The light is intended to be as natural as possible.

My wife and I had a different solution. We lived in the Boston suburbs. It was February. We had two-foot snows once a week for four weeks. The kids were out of school for all this time. I went to interview at The University of Arizona during this period–and we moved to Tucson! Tucson has about 360 days of sunlight every year.

Global Lighting

More than 25% of the electrical use in the world goes to lighting. What an impact it would make if all lighting were much more efficient. In the U.S., about 22% of electricity is used for lighting. Of that, 55% is for commerce; residential is 27%; industrial, 14%; and outdoor, 8%. Commercial lighting includes stores, advertising, and the like. Industrial lighting is in factories and manufacturing plants.[189]

Of the seven billion lamps in commercial buildings in the U.S., 4.4 billion (63%) are incandescent, 2.5 billion (36%) are fluorescent. We surely can replace most of those incandescent bulbs. Residential lighting is almost entirely incandescent. I think this is largely lethargy, but it is also related to the fact that most people are not ready to lay out the larger initial charge for better lighting, even though it will pay off in the long term.

Olympic Lighting

Today, as I type this, March 25, 2004, the Olympic torch has just been lit in Athens, using a mirror to direct the sun's light to the torch.[190] This is surely reminiscent of

---

188 "Dream builders," *Home and Garden TV*, October 8, 1997; Lewis, R., "Unlocking the mysteries of light therapy," *Photonics Spectra*, March 1997.
189 ibid.
190 Paul Harvey News.

the use of mirrors to defend a Greek city from siege, when the soldiers aimed the reflections from their shields to the ships and burned them, it is said (but not proven).

Ginza Lighting

The Japanese have a program to replace as much as 50% of the incandescent bulbs in their country with LEDs. They estimate that this will save almost 38 million barrels of oil per year, since LEDs are about 8 times more efficient than incandescent bulbs. They would save another 25 million barrels if traffic lights and neon signs were also replaced. This is equivalent to almost seven million-kilowatt power plants. A side benefit is the reduction of carbon dioxide in the atmosphere.[191]

Medicine

Because there are so many aspects to the field of medicine, there are many uses of optics in the field. Doctors probe us in so many ways. They look at our eyes with that little light; they look in our ears with an otoscope. And then they pull out all sorts of diabolical instruments to look at our insides. Optics serves medicine not only as a superb diagnostic tool in many different ways, but also, with well-controlled lasers, as tools for repair.

Resetting the Biological Clock

It has been known for some time that our circadian rhythm, or biological clock, is regulated to a large extent by light. What is fairly new is that it is mostly the blue light that sets the clock. So a new technique using only the blue light from an LED can be used, thereby greatly reducing the power requirements, the glare and even sunburn.[192]

Photodynamic Therapy (PDT)

This is a technique that can be used to treat cancerous tissue by use of a photofrin and a laser. Photofrin is a light-sensitive chemical that is preferentially taken up by cancerous cells. A standard dose of the chemical is 2 mg per kilogram of patient weight, 2 parts per million. Then the laser is aimed in the general region of the suspected lesion, but the laser dosage is limited by the need to avoid damage to sur-

---

191 Whipple, C., "LED funding aims to illuminate japan," *Photonics Spectra*, October 1997.
192 Rea, M., "LEDs open new doors," *Photonics Spectra*, January 2004.

rounding healthy tissue. Some experiments have shown that a lower chemical dosage permits a higher radiation dosage. This seems reasonable on the surface.[193]

Another variation of photodynamic therapy is using photofrin and LEDs. This application uses 144 LEDs at the tip of a 9-inch neural probe for the treatment of a variety of cancerous tumors. It can be used for hours at a time, stays cool, and is cheaper than a laser.[194]

Skin Lesions and Cancer

The typical diagnosis for skin cancer is based on visual inspection of an experienced dermatologist, but there are better ways. One group in England used a xenon arc lamp to illuminate the skin via a fiber optic bundle, which also picks up the reflected light and guides it to a commercial spectrophotometer. The light spot was 1.5 mm; the spectrum from 320 to 1100 nm. They investigated 121 patients using three spectra for each location. It was reported that this was at least as accurate as diagnosis by an experienced dermatologist.

I carried out a similar experiment in cooperation with the Storz Company. They obtained fluorescence spectra with an excitation wavelength of about 380 nm and a spectrum from 400 to 800 nm. They provided me with 50 known samples that I used as a learning group and 50 unknowns. I used the ratio of the long-wave to the short-wave part of the spectrum to differentiate benign versus malignant tissue with the knowns. I then found more than 80% of the malignancies with fewer than 15% false alarms in the unknowns. This permitted the design of some simple devices for use in either a dermatologist's or internist's office.[195]

One treatment for basal-cell carcinoma and Bowen's disease is photodynamic therapy, PDT, as mentioned above. One way to do this is to administer a cream that makes the skin sensitive to light, and subsequently illuminate the area with light of an appropriate intensity and spectrum. In one example, a 300-W xenon short-arc lamp provided light that filtered into a 30-μm wide band centered at 630 μm. A dose of 100 to 150 J per square centimeter was delivered on a lesion 2–8 cm in diameter for about 40 minutes. In this study, 88% of the large and 98% of the small patches cleared. There were 88 patches in all. Some did return.[196]

193 Hogan, H., "In photodynamic therapy, less may be more," *Biophotonics International*, July/August 2000.

194 "New LED application promises effective cancer treatment," *OE Reports*, February 1999.

195 Wolfe, W. L., US Patent 6,256,530 B1, 2001.

196 Connolly, Christine, "Photodynamic therapy is recommended for skin lesions," *Biophotonics International*, November 2001.

Telemedicine

Telemedicine involves providing medicine care at a distance. A simple example is to have a good TV at a remote spot. Show the patient and his or her problem on the screen to the experienced medic at "home base." For many applications, this involves recognizing a rash, node, or other pathology.

Surgery at long distance is more complicated. In one application, a doctor at Mississippi Medical Center, which was the home base, worked with doctors in Japan. The screen showed a double image, the general operating room with the patient, and an inset of an MRI screen to show the surgical area. Dr. Sewell in Mississippi could pan and zoom, and send PowerPoint images and illustrations to augment his comments about the operation in real time. Good imagery and a communication line of 512 baud were key to the operation.[197]

A robotically assisted heart operation has also been performed. A robotic surgical system was attached to the operating table. It guided endoscopic surgical instruments. The surgeon sat at a computer console in the operating room, which consisted of a video monitor, computer control system, and two instrument handles. When the handles were moved, the computer scaled the movements for the surgical instruments, smoothed hand tremors and sent signals to the controller on the table and then to the instruments. Voice commands controlled the video camera so that the surgeon could get his preferred view. One year later, all 19 patients were alive and well.[198]

The Maricopa County, Arizona, prison system has introduced remote medicine, using physicians in their home or office locations to help diagnose the ailments of prisoners.[199]

Surrey, England, fitted its motorcycle paramedics with digital cameras that they wear. They speed to the scene and relay images back to the base. A determination is made from the images as to whether an ambulance needs to be dispatched, and the digital images are sent to the hospital emergency room that will receive the patient.

The Netherlands has set up an interactive program for housebound patients. A televison camera, like a camcorder, is set up in the patient's room. It is coupled to the hospital by way of a high-speed (ISDN) line. Then a nurse or doctor can observe the patient and make decisions about medication, visitation, and more. This saves a great deal of time for the medical staff, reduces costs, and provides almost instantaneous medical attention.[200]

---

197 Ott, Dale, "Remotely guided surgery proves successfully," *Photonics Showcase*, September 2002.

198 *Biophotonics International*, September/October, 2001; ibid November/December 1997.

199 "Doctors will treat inmates via cameras," *The Arizona Daily Star*, September 2, 2003.

200 Deutch, A., "TV link may cut health costs," *The Arizona Daily Star*, (via AP) May 12, 2004.

Roust, Louses!

Head lice have long been a problem, if not a scourge. Both lice and their eggs, known as nits, are thought to be a sign of improper hygiene practices, but they have been found on all kinds of people. Two treatments are usual: insecticides and combing. The latter might be called nit picking.

Treatment has been made much more efficient by a professor of pediatrics at Yale. He found that a commercially available fluorescent dye could be added to a shampoo that would bind only to the chitin in the outer shell of the nits and cause it to fluoresce. This makes the combing far more efficient.[201]

Port-Wine Stain

This stain is a birthmark that appears as dark red (the color of port wine). It is caused by dilated capillaries just below the skin's basal layer. It has been treated and removed by application of intense laser light. The birthmark absorbs the laser light and ablates.

The melanin pigment of our skin also absorbs laser light and must be protected. Normally, doctors use a cooling spray for this. It is helpful to know just how deep the stain is to get just the right amount of coolant.

The technique that seems to be best for port-stain removal is a phototacoustic one. Laser light at 532 μm shines onto the skin. It is absorbed by the stain and creates a thermo-elastic response that causes an acoustic wave proportional to the amount of absorption. This wave travels to the surface of the skin, where it can be detected by a piezoelectric sensor. Although still in the development stage, wine stains 570-μm deep have been determined. The technique may also be adaptable to other applications, such as assessing burns.[202]

Liver Spots

These spots, caused by excess melanin and often by sunlight, are brown stains, usually on the back of the hand and forehead; they can be treated by laser irradiation. Several different lasers have been used, but frequency-doubled, pulsed Nd:YAG lasers operating at 532 nm seemed to be the best. The melanin absorbs the light and ablates.[203]

---

201 "Fluorescent shampoo chases lice," *Biophotonics International*, July/August, 2000.
202 Robinson, K., "Photoacoustic probe measures depth of port-wine stain," *Biophotonics International*, May 2002; Manni, J. G., "They're on the way to a billion dollar market," *Biophotonics International*, May/June 1998.
203 Rowell, N. D., "Nd:YAG efficiently treats laser spots," *Bionics International*, December 2000.

Tattoos

Some people have second thoughts about the tattoos they had when they were young and foolish. These can be removed by Nd:YAG lasers, usually operated in a pulsed mode. The mechanism seems to be that shock waves, caused by the high-temperature short pulses, break up the pigment particles as well as alter their chemical makeup. The technique can be applied to a variety of skin pigmentation problems, such as port-wine stains and liver spots.[204] These generally work better on light-skinned people. The lighter skin reflects the laser light; the darker stains or tattoos absorb it.

Skin Resurfacing

This is an alternative to chemical peels and dermabrasion to produce younger-looking, smoother skin. The patient is first treated with alpha-hydroxy acids as a superficial, chemical peel to expose new skin. Then a deep moisturizer is applied just before laser scanning. Wrinkles are treated with a single pass of a carbon dioxide laser emitting about 300 mJ pulses. An entire face might take two such passes, while the area around the eyes was treated with 200 mJ pulses. Of 258 patients, 92% were deemed to have had excellent or very good results.[205]

Skull Replacement

The University of Chicago is pioneering a new technique of partial skull replacement (cranioplasty) for areas too large for titanium mesh and cement—greater than three square centimeters. A three-dimensional profile of the skull is obtained through computed tomography (CT). This mathematical model is then used to program a laser that fashions the new skull part by tracing cross sections on a polymer that the energy of the beam solidifies from a liquid. A prosthetic designer then completes the job with medical-grade methyl methacrylate.

Clearing Stuffy Noses

In some people the linings of the nose, the inferior turbinates, become enlarged, and breathing through the nose becomes either difficult or impossible. Shining laser light of 930 nm on the affected area at least temporarily corrects this. The turbinates shrink.

The application is with a diode laser using a fiber optic to apply the light to several different places. The application takes about 5 minutes. The patient must irrigate the nose with saline solution for four weeks. No bleeding was observed, but there was some temporary swelling (for a few days). After a year, 43% reported that

---

204 Hennick, S., "Q-switched Nd:YAGs remove traumatic tattoos," *Biophotonics International*, May/June 1998.
205 Henry, B., "Laser's magical way," *The Arizona Daily Star*, June 1997.

they had improved air flow. The procedure is better for those with nonallergic rhinitis.[206]

Hair Removal

Although I have accomplished this all by myself on my head, passively, there are those who would like to remove hair from other parts of their anatomy. This has long been done with a razor, although that solution is highly temporary, and with electrolysis, creams, and waxes, which are less temporary but not permanent either.

Recently, lasers have been used. They may not get to every follicle, but they do cover a large enough area to treat a man's entire back in a single session.

It is believed that the laser light is absorbed by the melanin in the subcutaneous hair in its growing phase (hairs alternately grow and rest), and this prevents regrowth, although this is not

Figure 20 What hair?

effective during the resting phase. The treatment must be given at least three times.

The treatment becomes more effective when the laser illumination is coupled with a cooling plate on the skin. The day after the treatment, there is often reddening and sometimes even blistering. This goes away in a few days, but then hair seems to come back very rapidly, but it is actually the dead hair being exfoliated. In a few weeks, when the hair reappears sort of in clumps, it is time for the next treatment.[207]

A single treatment removed about half the hair, while multiple treatments removed about 65%. There was no later regrowth.[208]

Hair Improvement

The other side of this coin is using light to improve hair growth. The idea is that the use of a comb with a little laser improves growth and can even fill in bald spots. Now, this came from an advertisement in my local paper, so it must be salted, especially since some of the print says it works in part like photosynthesis. We know

206 "Diode lasers unclog stuffy noses," *Biophotonics International*, January/February 2001.

207 Manni, J. G., "They're on the way to a billion-dollar market," *Biophotonics International*, May/June 1998.

208 "Study shows hair removal lasts," *Biophotonics International*, July/August, 1999.

that hair is not a plant, and I think we must assume the ad was only drawing an analogy. No detailed, independent tests were cited.[209]

Cardiology

A technique that is still in its infancy and subject to argument is transmyocardial revascularization. It may replace angioplasty or bypass surgery by drilling holes in the heart with a laser. The holes are actually channels that allow the flow of blood in the heart. The technique is minimally invasive, using a laser at the end of a fiber optic, and early studies have shown that patients require less medication and live longer than those receiving the other treatments.[210]

Lung Cancer

A new technique is being investigated for lung-cancer screening. A sputum sample is taken, processed on a microscope slide, and stained with a special porphorin chemical (tetrakis carboxyphenyl porphine, if you care). This chemical selectively stains cancerous cells, which then glow red under fluorescent illumination.[211] Another approach is the use of a fluorescent endoscope that images the lung from the inside and detects differences in the fluorescence spectra of benign tissue and either cancerous tissue or dysplasic (precancerous) tissue.[212]

Breast Cancer

Another test based on a sputum sample is for breast cancer. The technique is called enzyme-linked immunoabsorbent assay and can detect very minute concentrations. A plate is covered with an antibody specific to one of the cancer markers. Another antibody with a chromophore (color marker) is added. It binds and goes through a color change. The intensity of the color, recorded with a spectrophotometer, indicates the concentration of the cancer marker. The study so far has tested 36 women, 12 with malignancies, 12 with benign tumors, and 12 control subjects. All tumors were detected. The number of false positives was not reported.[213]

As early as 1953, infrared imaging was proposed for breast-cancer screening. As we all know, any sort of trauma generates heat. Consider hitting your thumb

209 *The Arizona Daily Star*, March 2004.
210 Morey, J., Cardiology, "When hope hails, photonics finds a way," *Photonics Spectra*, August 1997.
211 "Fluorescent drug screens smokers for cancer," *Biophotonics International*, July/ August 1998.
212 Holzman, D., "Autofluorescence detects lung cancer earlier," *Biophotonics International*, July/August, 1998.
213 Leggett, K., "Spit may identify breast cancer," *Biophotonics International*, May/June 1998.

with a hammer. It throbs and feels hot for a long time. Lesions in the breast, both cancerous and benign, have an increased temperature, the malignant ones a few degrees higher. This has led to imaging patients much as with x-ray mammography.[214]

Early instruments could take as much as 15 minutes to generate the images, but soon better devices were available that could take an image as fast as a TV with good resolution and temperature sensitivity of about 0.1°C.

The University of Arizona did a comprehensive study of the screening technique for the NIH, and found that infrared mammography should not replace x-ray mammography. There were basically three reasons for this: doctors were familiar with x-ray images, less invasive x-ray systems became available, and the infrared systems found too many false alarms that were actually benign lesions.

In recent times, infrared systems have improved, to the point where real-time systems have temperature sensitivity of 0.01°C, and are reasonably convenient and affordable. One system that takes 2048 images in 20 seconds claims the ability to differentiate benign from malignant tumors, but clinical data were not available.[215]

I had the opportunity at University of Michigan in the mid-'60s to investigate the use of infrared imaging for whole-body scanning. We designed what was then state-of-the-art equipment that was held on a structure above an examining table. The equipment did scan the entire body, but the two pictures in Fig. 21 are not quite full-body. The one on the left shows heat patterns, completely white eyes (since the aqueous humor is opaque in the infrared), and patterns between the subject's fingers and

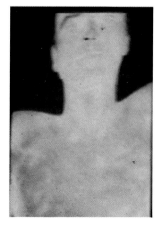

Figure 21 Thermal image.

214 New York Academy of Sciences.
215 Sheppard, L. M., "Star wars technology helps detect breast cancer," *Biophotonic International*, July/August, 2000.

body. The picture on the right shows that we could get resolution about the size of a hair, and it also shows the man has a breathing problem in one nostril. This kind of imagery is useful in analyzing circulation, defining burn areas and even in assessing the effects of smoking, since circulation is drastically changed with one drag of a cigarette.

Methinks He Prostateth Too Much

Enlarged prostates can be decreased with the use of optics. Surgical methods are very bloody, require a catheter in the urethra, and 20% of patients require repeat surgery.

Either a Nd:YAG or other laser can be used to vaporize and coagulate or ablate prostate tissue. The light reaches the prostate via a fiber optic probe. The procedure is virtually bloodless so that recovery is much faster.[216] A stated improvement is the use of 830-nm diode laser and a fused silica fiber that is more flexible than the former quartz fiber.[217]

The results are equivocal. Compared to removal with a scalpel, patients had shorter hospital stays and fewer complications but had to use catheters longer. Over the longer term, patients with laser surgery had to have repeat surgery more often than those with standard surgery.[218]

Ouch!

Radiation is one treatment for prostate cancer. Ionizing radiation is aimed at the prostate from several guns. As with all radiation treatments, it is important to have a sufficient dosage but not too much.

One help for this is a new optical radiation monitor. Fused quartz or silica glass, doped with ions such as copper, fluoresce when the proper light is shone on them. This dosimeter uses a 800 nm 100 mW laser to cause fluorescence at about 500 nm. It shines the light down a fiber, which directs the fluorescent signal back to a photomultiplier. The fiber is small enough to fit in a standard medical catheter. Two are used, one up the urethra, the other up the rectum. I didn't say this wouldn't hurt. The device is ready and approved for clinical trials.[219]

216 Leggett, K., "Lasers in urological practice," *Biophotonics International*, March/April 1998.
217 "Changing laser improves prostate surgery outcome," *Biophotonics International*, March/April 1998.
218 Rowell, N. D., "Laser treatment of prostate enlargement gives mixed results," *Biophotonics International*, November 2000.
219 Leggett, K., "Dosimeter helps monitor prostate cancer treatment," *Biophotonics International*, January/February 1998.

Cervical Cancer

This nasty disease is a threat to many women. The standard diagnostic technique is the Pap smear. Based on this result, the doctor may view the cervix using a colposcope and perhaps direct several biopsies.

A very promising technique is fluorescence detection with the colposcope. A short-wavelength light illuminates the cervix, which fluoresces. A detector senses the fluorescent light that is emitted.

Several approaches have been taken, but none is yet established. One is to examine the fluorescence spectroscopically. The spectra of normal tissue and cancerous and even precancerous tissue are different. Another method is to take each wavelength and process all of them to see the differences.[220,221] Another is to use just a few bands and ratio them.[222]

Another technique we have investigated (a little) is thermal imagery. There is a difference in circulation and therefore temperatures between normal and cancerous tissue. Our simple, exploratory experiment used three women with different degrees of precancer and cancer. We obtained 100% agreement with the evaluation of an experienced obstetrician and fluorescence detection. It would have been good to do more, but we could not find the funds.

The Lighter Side of Lung Cancer

Lung cancer is a killer; we all know that. The five-year survival rate is 14%.

But photodynamic therapy may change that. A selective, light-sensitive drug is injected into the patient; it concentrates in tumor cells, but steers clear of other cells. Two to three days later, a 630-nm light is shone on the cells, which generate free radicals that kill the tissue. Later, a bronchoscope is used to gather the detritus. About 75% had a complete response and 50% were cancer-free in a long-term follow-up.[223]

Colon Cancer

Fluorescence has also been tried at MIT, where researchers found large differences in the emission spectra of normal cells and adenoma cells of the colon.[224] Although the title indicates the biopsy will be painless, it is still necessary to get the spectrometer into the colon!

---

220 Rowell, N. D., "Fiber optic probe simplifies cervical cancer detection," *Biophotonics International*, November 2000.

221 Lok, Corie, "Shining light on cancer diagnosis," *Technology Review*, April 2004.

222 Wolfe, W. L., US Patent 6,256,530 B1, 2001.

223 Lewis, R., "PDT approved for early-stage lung cancer," *Biophotonics International*, March/April 1998.

224 Weiss, R., "New approach offers possibility of painless biopsy," *OE Reports*, April 1998.

Ear Ventilation

Some children have undeveloped or poorly developed eustachian tubes, and resultant infections. The usual procedure to remedy this defect has been the insertion of tubes.

Lately, laser drilling and tunneling have been tried with some success. A small HeNe laser is used as an aiming device; a carbon-dioxide laser is used for removal. An otoscope is used to watch the procedure, which involves the spiral maneuvering of a 140-µm spot to open up a passageway about 3 mm in diameter. The procedure can be performed in a doctor's office in about 5 minutes without anesthetic, although a topical anesthetic makes things easier. The tunnels remain open for about four weeks, enough to take care of 75% of the cases.[225]

Let Him Throw the First Stone

Kidney stones range from small (1 mm) to large (2 lbs), and can be composed of uric acid salts from gout or gallstones of cholesterol and bile. Lasers are ideal for destroying these pains. The fiber optic cable is threaded through the urethra to the kidney, and the tip is put near to a stone. A dye laser sends a pulse to the water next to the stone, where it creates a small vapor bubble. The bubble expands, makes a shock wave, and the stone is shattered. Studies are underway to identify the optimum laser.[226]

Another technique, the ablation of kidney stones or lithotripsy has been used for some time with different lasers. One particular system uses a holmium YAG laser to "zap" the stone, but it also has a mechanism for determining whether the target is a stone or perhaps the wall of the urinary tract. It looks for the photoemission from the stone (or the wall). It differentiates the two. If it turns out to be the wall, a Pockels cell shutters the laser beam within 50 µsec to prevent any damage. The system can be used in reverse if the application is, for instance, the ablation of bone to perform hip replacement.

Another Tissue, Please

A new technique shows potential for the creation of human tissue that could be used to replace damaged organs. Researchers arranged nerve cells from embryonic chicks on a glass slide. Then, with a needle and an 800-nm laser, they were able to coax the cells to make connections and therefore form tissue.[227]

---

225 Robinson, K., "CO_2 laser makes ear ventilation easier," *Biophotonics International,* November/December 1998.
226 Ibid.
227 "Laser-based method could create living tissue," *Biophotonics International,* January/February 1999.

Chronic Bladder Syndrome

This disease, also known as trigonitis, affects women's bladders. The bladder is painful to the touch, and in urination and intercourse. The cause is unknown, but the symptom is that the triangular lining of the base of the bladder becomes granular. Again, Nd:YAG and KTF lasers have been used with a fiber optic probe to coagulate the trigone. The KTF laser is more controllable since it has a shorter penetrating depth in the tissue.[228]

Blood Analysis

For patients in the intensive care unit (ICU), the measurement of arterial blood gases (ABGs), is critical. The measurements are for pH and partial pressures of carbon dioxide and oxygen. Traditional methods have been the extraction of a sample from the patient either with a needle or out of a tube.

The modern, optical technique is performed on the arm, in place, immediately. Typically these use fiber optics and a disposable sensor. This can be either absorption or fluorescence. A specific narrow band of light, determined by an appropriate filter, is transmitted down the fiber to the sensor. The sensor absorbs the light and responds. Different dyes are used for the three different gases.

The read-outs are almost instantaneous so constant monitoring and display of these critical gases can be accomplished.[229] As I write this, my son-in-law is in a neural ICU recovering from a stroke. It is meaningful to me. (As I edit this, he has fully recovered!)

Another approach to this is to embed a special dye (seminampthorhodamine-1) at the tapered tip of a fiber optic probe. The dye fluoresces differently with different values of pH. A tungsten-halogen lamp with a 535-nm filter shines light down the fiber. The fluorescent light goes back up the fiber to a dichroic beamsplitter that separates shorter wavelengths, around 587 nm, and longer wavelengths, around 635 nm, indicating basic and acidic conditions, respectively.

A similar approach is used to measure the effect of thrombolytic drugs to break down blood clots that cause ischemic strokes. The drugs, when effective, break the clots down, the immune system generates D-dimer antigens, and these are detected by a fluorescence technique with another special dye.[230]

---

228 Ibid.
229 Gifford, R., and Bartnik, D., "Using optical sensors to measure arterial blood gases," *Optics and Photonics News*, March 1998.
230 "Fiber optic sensors guide brain attack," *Biophotonics International*, January/February 1998.

A Blood's Eye View

It has been proposed, and partially substantiated, that blood can sense light. Researchers at Cornell University shone light via fibers onto the backs of the knees of subjects in experiments to show it could affect circadian rhythms. It did.[231] The experiment used a halogen lamp in a vented metal housing with a fan to disperse the heat. Light from the lamp traveled through 2400 optical fibers encased in a 1-m-long, flexible plastic tube to a 0.64-mm thick woven pad behind the knees. Since the lamp was remote, there was no sensible heat at the legs. The pads were attached with knee braces. The patients were in reclining chairs with tables over them that had black cloths on them draped to the floor. The control group had the same setup, but the lamps were not turned on. It was reported that the subjects experienced advances or retardations in their biological clocks of up to three hours.[232]

Blood Analysis

When we were first married, my wife operated as a medical technologist. In this capacity, she performed many chemical tests on blood and other fluids.

Today, many of the tests she did by hand are done automatically. The blood, drawn by the technician, is entered into a machine about the size of a grand piano, where it is divided into about 20 different channels; in each a test, such as colorimetry, is performed. This is essentially a test of the amount of absorption at a given wavelength.

The next step is the extraction process, involving noninvasive measurements.

In the offing is a device like the character Bones of *Star Trek* had. Hold a simple instrument against the skin and get a measurement of one or another aspect of the blood. This was done more than ten years ago with a little toe clip to test for blood oxygen.

Recent investigations indicate that blood glucose, jaundice, cholesterol, carbon dioxide, etc. can be measured, also. The process is to illuminate the skin, perhaps with fiber optics, at appropriate wavelengths, measure the reflection, and compare it to a reference. No needles, but an instant reading, simple, accurate, and cheap.[233] This same technique can be used by diabetics to test their blood sugar each day without all the needles.[234]

Drugs can also be delivered without needles. At the top of the skin is a thin (20 μm) layer called the stratum corneum; it is the primary barrier to topically ap-

231 Lewis, R., "Does blood 'see' light?," *Biophotonics International*, March/April 1998.

232 Tatterson, K., "Fiber optic blanket rocks internal clocks," *Photnics Spectra*, April 1998.

233 Robinson, K., "Blood analysis: noninvasive methods hover on horizon," *Biophotonics International*, May/June 1998; Wheeler, M. D., "An end to bloodletting?," *Photonics Spectra*, August 1999.

234 "FDA approves laser-based diabetic test for home use," *Biophotonics International*, January/February 1999.

plied drugs. An "injection" can be made with an 800 mJ pulse from an erbium YAG laser at 2.94 μm in a small package (12×14×38 cm). This device not only bypasses needle phobia, but also eliminates the need for needles, their disposal, and accidental injections of medical personnel.[235]

How Big is the Owie?

For some patients, the healing of a wound is a long and sometimes questionable process. Is it really healing?

A measurement technique has been developed that shines a grid onto the wound. The image of the distorted lines can be analyzed for both area and volume. So a time-series of such images will tell whether the wound is really getting smaller (healing). This device is in the investigative stage, and it later could incorporate the use of color as a diagnostic tool using a color video camera and temperature as an indicator of vascularity, with an infrared camera.[236] We shall see.

Sunscreen Screen?

There are questions as to whether sunscreen really protects against skin cancer. Sunburn is mostly due to UV-B ultraviolet radiation, whereas melanoma (a highly malignant skin cancer) mostly result from UV-A. The latter ultraviolet band is not filtered by either the ozone layer or most suncreens.[237] Although this is still an area of controversy, the message is clear: if you are at all at risk (redheads, blondes, albinos), make sure your sunscreen filters out both A and B and wear a hat and clothes. There should be no nudes in Tucson!

A Skin Game

An interesting polarization imager allows doctors to get a good view of the skin 0.2-mm deep. This provides information about skin cancers. A white light source shines through a linear polarizer obliquely onto the skin area. A small, flat, glass plate on the skin provides optical coupling and reflects the specular beam away. The spot is viewed from directly above with a polarizer that can be rotated to be parallel or perpendicular to the illumination polarizer.[238]

235 Lewotsky, K., "Laser assists transdermal drug delivery," *Laser Focus World*, March 1997.
236 Hennink, S., "Noncontact device measures wounds with light," *Biopotonics International*, March/April 1998.
237 "Sunscreen may not prevent skin cancer," *Biophotonics International*, March/April 1998.
238 "New opportunities for optics," *Photonics Spectra*, March 1998.

The Hole Truth

Catheters require hole diameters as small as 50 μm, and angioplasty balloons require even smaller ones—8 to 25 μm. These can be "drilled" with ultraviolet lasers.[239]

Stroke while the Iron Is Hot

With stroke patients, the quicker the treatment the better. It is important to either relieve the pressure on the brain in the case of an aneurism or get circulation to the brain in the case of a clot. Maryland has introduced telemedicine in its emergency vehicles to improve the timeliness of treatment. The paramedic connects the patient to the necessary monitors, which include electrocardiograms, blood pressure cuppo, heart monitors, respirators, and blood oxygenators. These data along with images, are sent to the hospital, where a specialist can give instructions and prepare the emergency room,[240] and maybe tell the difference between an aneurism and a clot.

Some strokes are caused by blockages in the arteries. These can be solved with a laser that produces photoacoustic shock waves and breaks up the blockage.[241] Others are caused by breakages in either veins or arteries. In either case, time is of the absolute essence.

Brainy Techniques

Researchers at the Weizmann Institute in Rehovot, Israel, have applied optics to investigating brain functions in animals. The camera is mounted above the animal's head, with an opening cut in the cranium. A CCD camera obtains resolution of about 50 μm; alternatively, a video camera does about the same. Changes in oxygenation are identified by illuminating with light at 605 nm; near-infrared light is used to watch the activity of sodium and potassium ions. As the electrical charges caused by brain activity activate the cells, the chemical composition and metabolism change. An activated group of neurons reduces reflectivity by as much as 10,000 times. Thus, the researchers can excite different responses and see which parts of the brain are active.[242]

An infrared device now competes with, or complements, MRI and CAT scans for viewing the brain. Brain tissue and skin are quite transparent in the 750- to 1000-nm region. A fiber can be used to illuminate a portion of the brain, and an-

239 Gitin, M., "UV Lasers: state of the art I: all solid state," *Photonics Spectra*, September 1998.

240 Robinson, K., "Telemedicine can save stroke victims' lives," *Biophotonics International*, March/April 1998.

241 "Lasers blast brain blockages," *Biophotonics International*, July/August 1998.

242 "Optical imaging maps brain's visual functions," *Biophotonics International*, January/February 1998.

other fiber can pick up the signal and transmit it to a photomultiplier or CCD camera. The fibers are placed 2 to 7 cm apart. Although the imagery is limited, a number of things can be detected: blood flow with Doppler, nerve impulses, oxyhemoglobin, and deoxyhemoglobin.[243]

A Real Brain Trust

An experimental technique for removing brain tumors from children involves the use of the drug Potfrin II in the bloodstream. It attaches to and permeates the tumors, leaving the healthy surrounding tissue alone. The tumor is then irradiated with light from 144 light-emitting diodes, and the tumors are destroyed, leaving the viable tissue virtually untouched.[244]

Bottoms Up!

Investigators at The University of Michigan have confirmed, with *in vivo* experiments, earlier *in vitro* experiments investigating the mechanisms that break down collagen in the skin and cause brown spots, wrinkling, splotches, and leatheration. They exposed the backsides of 59 Caucasian people to ultraviolet light and took biopsies. This single ultraviolet exposure on parts of the anatomy that seldom see the sun increased the rate of collagen degeneration 58%, and further exposure continued the increase. Pretreatment with tretinoin (Retin-A commercially) reduced the rate about 80%.[245]

Keep it Clean and Safe

Ultraviolet light is used as a germicidal agent, to sterilize tools and rooms. In one application, the ultraviolet lamps are mounted on the walls of rooms where tuberculosis can be spread. A dose of 10 W per 200 square feet is required for disinfection, but a dose of 0.2 µW per square centimeter for eight hours is the safety limit, according to the article. These translate into 53 microwatts per square centimeter and 0.2 microwatts per square centimeter for 28,800 seconds or 5.7 mW per square centimeter per second. It is clear that the exposure must be monitored and brief. It is also important to monitor the level of illumination. An ultraviolet radiometer with a range from 0.7 to 70 mW per square centimeter can do the job.[246]

---

243 "The promise of near-IR spectroscopy," *Biophotonics International*, January/February 1998.

244 "NASA shines light on tumor treatment," *NASA Tech Briefs*, March 1998.

245 "Getting to the bottom of photoaging," ibid.

246 "Portable UV radiometer helps minimize TB risk," *Biophotonics International*, January/February 1998.

Nd:YAG lasers have also been used to destroy bacteria on an investigative level.[247]

Are You Hip?

Hip replacements are very successful, but some 10% of them need to be replaced again after years of use. These replacements are called euphemistically *revisions*, and are complicated. One difficulty is the removal of the old cement, which is normally done with a surgical chisel. A better technique has been developed, but it requires consideration during the first replacement. The cement is treated with an appropriate dye. Then, upon replacement, a laser is used to vaporize the cement, with the dye acting as an absorber of the laser radiation.[248]

The CyberKnife

The increased use of flat-panel displays in radiography allows real-time imagery, convenient manipulation and, if necessary, repeat imaging. One very important application is the CyberKnife from Accuray. It delivers precisely focused and aimed x-ray doses to a targeted tumor from a number of different directions.[249]

Diabetic Relief

Many diabetics put their health at risk by not testing their blood sugar on a daily basis. Who wants to jab himself with a needle every day? Now, a laser-based device can take this sample without the jab. It is about the size of a videotape cassette; it includes an erbium:YAG, battery-powered laser that vaporizes a portion of the skin and generates a drop of blood. All you do is put your finger in a slot and push a button.[250]

Bless the Beasts...

Veterinarians are also tuning into optics, seeing the light, so to speak. One vet removed a tumor from a champion goldfish stud (the concept was new to me, too) by squirting anesthetic into the aquarium, dipping out the fish and removing the tumor with a carbon-dioxide laser. She wanted to keep it out of water as short a time as possible and to preserve the slime and the scales on the fish. The laser was fast, bloodless, and the cut self-healing.

247 Weiss, S., "Lasers aid in bacteria destruction," *Photonics Spectra*, February 1998.
248 Lewis, R., "Laser shows promise in re-mending hips," *Biophotonics International*, July/August 1997.
249 Quad, R., M. Gauer, B. Giambista, "Digital radiography gains ground," *Photonics Spectra*, January 2004.
250 "NFDA approves laser-based diabetic test for home use," *Biophotonics International*, January/February, 1999.

Another vet has declawed more than 250 cats with a 12-W carbon-dioxide laser. The use of clippers can cause pain in the cats near the claw itself, an area rich with nerve endings.[251]

Up to Snuff

A system that uses a laser source and collimating optics along with a camera is used to analyze the properties of nasal sprayers. The laser beam is collimated to a plane, and this illumination plane is moved across the spray area. The camera takes 500 successive shots per second, and can thereby obtain the geometric and uniformity properties of the spray.[252] A similar system that analyzes fuel injection is described in the section on automobiles.

The Skinny

Under development is a patch-and-sew kit for replacing skin and covering wounds. Made of a reconstituted form of natural animal protein, elastin, the material can be fused to the surrounding skin by a series of laser pulses.[253]

Lyme Disease

The use of a computerized microscope has proven useful in the detection of the spirochete bacterium that causes Lyme disease. Replacing arduous visual examination, a series of algorithms and different modalities allows rapid, automatic determination.[254]

Helping the Vampires

Drawing blood from the tiny veins of infants can be a daunting task, and one that can even endanger life. In one case, it took about 45 minutes to insert an IV into an infant.

A head-mounted infrared camera can be of great help. The skin is quite transparent at wavelengths from 1 to 2 μm, but veins and blood are not. Thus, a low-power laser can illuminate the area where the needle is to be inserted. The

251 Drolette, D., "More veterinarians see the light," *Biophotonics International*, July/August 2000.

252 "Imaging system keeps nasal sprays up to snuff," *Photonics Spectra*, February 1999.

253 "Laser-fused patch could mend wounds," *Biophotonics International*, July/August 1997.

254 Waggoner, J., "Digital microscopy used in early detection of Lyme disease," *Photonics Spectra*, June 1991.

veins show up nice and dark, whereas the skin is invisible.[255] It can be viewed with a Snooperscope. Why not use it for all of us?

Eye Relief

Although there are many forms of glaucoma, they all result in an increase in pressure between the lens and the cornea. In one form, the iris jams against the lens and blocks the flow of fluid to the mesh below, which is the outlet. This is called acute-angle glaucoma.

The simple (and it is simple, and painless, and noninvasive) solution is to drill a hole in the iris with a laser.

In another application, the membrane that separates the front and rear parts of the eye, right behind the lens, becomes occluded. Again the simple procedure, after removing the lens, is to "zap" the membrane with a laser. This pops the membrane that is under tension and clears the way to the retina.

This is better than the previous procedure which was to jab a needle into the eye!

Another form of glaucoma is called open-angle glaucoma, caused by clogging of the outlet mesh, the trabecular mesh of cilia. In this case either a doubled Nd:YAG or an argon laser at 514 nm is used to break up the mesh.[256] This is a simple enough procedure that optometrists have been doing it in their offices.[257]

Glaucoma is usually detected by examining the quality of peripheral imaging, since glaucoma sneaks in from the sides. A more modern version is the use of polarized laser light. The fibers that radiate from the optic nerve are birefringent; that is, they separate the incident polarized light into two polarizations and directions. The instrument then measures the phase shift between these two beams. This in turn is a measure of the thickness of the fibers.

The return imagery shows both the thickness of the fibers and the fiber density. This information is enough for the diagnostician to assess whether and how much glaucoma exists, long before pressure increases can be observed.[258]

A detached retina used to mean blindness, but now the surgeon can weld it back into place with a laser if it is caught quickly enough. Generally, the surgeon reattaches the retina surgically and spot welds it with the laser.

255 "Head-mounted IR scope locates tiny veins," *Biophotonics International*, March/April 1999.

256 Robinson, K., "Opthalmic technology update, lasers go where scalpels rarely tread," *Biophotonics International*, January/February 1998.

257 Robinson, K., "Optometrists one step from becoming laser surgeons," *Biophotonics International*, March/April 1998.

258 Callendar, O., "Diagnosing glaucoma with laser precision," *Optics and Photonics News*, May 2004.

Do You See What I Say?

Although computed tomography (CT) is a very valuable tool for diagnosis, some patients get rather claustrophobic when they are in the tube. The optical microphone is not affected by and does not affect the electromagnetic field of the MRI or x-ray machine. This provides a means for patients to communicate and, it is hoped, relieve their anxiety.[259]

Military

Optical systems perform a wide variety of functions for military applications. They are useful in strategic and tactical applications used by carriers, ranging from geosynchronous satellites to the GI in the foxhole. The applications include air-to-air missile guidance, detection and annihilation of ICBMs, communication (largely with fiber optics), imaging in the visible and the infrared, and more.[260]

Biological-War Gas Detectors

Saddam Hussein threatened to and maybe did use biological weapons in the Gulf War. There are devices that can detect such agents. One of them uses the characteristic spectra of the fluoresence of these chemicals. The Naval Research Center has developed a hand-held sensor about the size of a brick. It consists of a violet source that illuminates a 100-μm diameter glass fiber. The resulting fluorescent output is detected by an array of 500-μm diameter fibers that transmit the light to small detectors, which surround the illuminating fiber. Fluorescence is generated in the waveguide when a toxin comes into contact with the coating on the fiber, an antibody. The system can detect anthrax, botulism, and ricin.

Other devices that have been developed to detect these deadly gases are all based on spectroscopy. They sense the signatures of the germicidal-bacteriological (GB) agents. Some have been designed to protect airfields and other installations. They can be relatively large, but must have a good range. They usually scan an area, sometimes 360 deg around. Others are for company or platoon areas. These need to be carried by a man or two, or a Hummer. Fortunately, the range requirement is then reduced.

Air-to-Air Missile-Guidance Systems

Infrared missile-guidance systems were in the news during the first Gulf War. One TV clip showed such a guided missile go right down the chimney of a bunker.

259 Schwartz, J., *Biophotonics International*, November/December 1999.
260 Hardin, R., "Photonics in military," *Photonics Spectra*, September 1997.

Other footage shows the individual Scud missile shacks, and soldiers being picked off one by one by Hellfire missiles of this type.

The Sidewinder missile is the granddaddy of these devices, which have become more sophisticated since their early introduction in the 1950s. A schematic of the missile head is shown in Fig. 22.[261] A window, called an Irdome or infrared dome, is shown on the left. It protects the innards from dirt and hail and other debris. The infrared radiation from the target passes through the Irdome to the mirror of the simple (Cassegrain) telescope system and focuses onto a reticle.

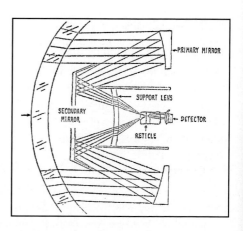

Figure 22 Sidewinder schematic.[261]

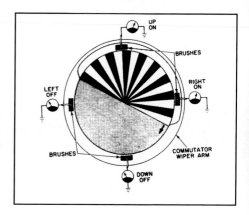

The reticle is shown in Fig. 23; it spins about the axis in its center. The position of the target image, a small spot, provides information about how far off boresight it is. The control system of the missile drives the missile in the direction that moves the image to the center. The reticle[262] has electrical pickoffs in several places. The reticle spins. The 50% transmission part gives an electrical reference and the magnetic pickups provide the mechanical reference.

Figure 23 Reticle.

Thus, the electronics "know" the angular direction of the spot, the target.

The target was not just the enemy aircraft, it was usually the jet engine of the enemy aircraft, a very vulnerable spot!

If there is a spot on the reticle, the electrical output will be as shown in Fig. 24. There is a square wave when the blades are moving over the spot. Then a long, constant output at about half the value. This allows the orientation of the target to be determined.

261 Fender, J., "An investigation of computer-assisted stray radiation analysis programs," dissertation, The University of Arizona, 1981. (Image courtesy of J. Fender.)
262 Holter, M., S. Nudelman, G. Suits, W. Wolfe, and G. Zissis, "Fundamentals of infrared technology," Macmillan, 1962.

These devices are sometimes fooled by clouds, but the multiple-bar design tends to smooth out a cloud signal, since the cloud is usually on more than one bar or space and provides little or no modulation. Cloud edges were sometimes a problem, and other reticle patterns were developed to compensate for this.

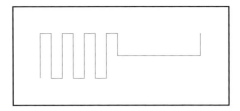

Figure 24 Electrical output.

Countermeasures were developed that usually took the form of some kind of flare. The counter-countermeasure techniques are probably still classified. One could be the use of two-color reticles.

It is interesting to note that the guidance systems were usually tested with unmanned aircraft that had flares on their wingtips. The Sidewinders almost always took off the flares!

Air-to-Ground Missiles

There are two major optical types air-to-ground missiles. The famous ARMs (antiradiation missiles) home in on the radar beacons emitted by the enemy on the ground. The two major optical types are the laser-designated missile and the map matcher. The former is used in tactical situations.

In a laser designator, a laser shines on the target via a modern artillery spotter, often in an aircraft of some kind. The missile tracks the laser spot. False alarms are avoided to a large extent because the laser beam is almost monochromatic and is modulated, that is, pulse coded. Things in nature are just not like that.

Map-matching guidance has been used for some time in long-range missiles, such as the Tomahawks fired from aircraft carriers. A map of the area to be hit was inserted into the memory of the missile head. It was guided by conventional means to the area of the target, generated imagery of the territory below, and compared it to its memory. When it finally had a good enough match, it would finish its job. This, of course, involved rotations and magnifications, but it did work. This technique has been largely replaced by GPS techniques, which are more accurate, reliable, and not optical.

Air-to-Air Missiles

The optical versions of these, the Stinger and the Chapparal, for instance, are essentially Sidewinders. At least they work on the same principles. Modern versions also use infrared imagers and process the imagery. One way this can be done is to move the head to keep the brightest part of the infrared image in the center.

Antiballistic Missile Detection

During the Cold War the most important threat to our security was intercontinental ballistic missiles, or ICBMs. We had infrared devices that could detect and probably defeat them, but we will never know that, thank goodness. The detection was done in one or more of three stages: launch, midcourse, and re-entry.

Launch detection seems very simple. These rockets give off copious amounts of energy, much of it in the form of infrared radiation. Just detect where it comes from. But from where and in what part of the spectrum and how do you eliminate all the false alarms?

An obvious place from which to do the detection is in geosynchronous orbit, because then the satellite remains over the part of the Earth that you wish to monitor. The spectral region to use should include the wavelengths where the rocket plume emits most, and these will be the water bands at about 2.5 μm and 5 μm and the carbon-dioxide bands at 4.3 and 14 μm. It may be enough to pick just one or two of them.

Then, several looks must be taken to determine a trajectory, with the later looks, just before it goes ballistic, being the most important. False alarms can be reduced by the proper choice of spectrum and the determination of trajectory from multiple examinations. Of course, the trajectory cannot be predicted until the missile goes ballistic.

Midcourse detection occurs after the rocket has shut down and the payload ejected: the trajectory is then ballistic and predictable with a few looks. There is no plume, so the payload body must be detected. The missile is at about room temperature, 300 K, because it interacts radiatively with the cold of outer space and the heat of the Earth. It is a reasonable target for the infrared, and the background is essentially nonexistent. The background can be characterized as a blackbody of about 60 K—very, very cold. So these devices have to be very sensitive, and they have to work rapidly; midcourse lasts about 20 minutes. Part of the threat during the Cold War was very many warheads, multiple independent re-entry vehicles (MIRVS), all to be detected and defeated in a time frame of about 20 minutes.

The final stage, re-entry, presents a different set of problems. The payload vehicle now becomes very hot from the friction of the atmosphere, but the time frame is just a few minutes. So the infrared device can be in the shorter wavelengths and less sensitive, but the interceptor must travel at very great speeds, much greater than that of sound. This puts the onus on the window that must withstand very high temperatures and pressures.

Designs exist for all of these. Some of the early warning devices (launch detectors) have been in place and operated for years. Recent tests have shown that the kinetic energy vehicles (KEVs) have had several successful tests (and some failures), and deployment is under discussion. The KEV shoots down the incoming missile by smashing into it. This is almost the equivalent of shooting down a bullet with a bullet, but it has been shown to be feasible. Our country has avoided using atomic weapons to explode incoming missiles in space in order to comply with nonproliferation treaties. I think the fact that we did it at all is amazing. Most of the failures had to do with the rocketry, not the guidance.

Better Drops

The Air Force is developing a LIDAR system (essentially a radar that uses laser light) that measures three-dimensional winds. This is to improve the accuracy of aerial deliveries. The system provides three-dimensional maps of wind velocity with an uncertainty of 0.5 m per second every 100 meters of altitude. It uses a diode-excited laser with 12 mJ at 100 Hz repetition rate.

Attack Laser

Almost from the first day of the invention of the laser, people considered its use as a weapon: aim a very high-power laser at a target and vaporize the target. It is not that simple. Depending upon the wavelength of operation, the atmosphere can absorb the light. Even in an atmospheric window, turbulence can distort the nice, tight laser beam and spread the energy. Even in a nonturbulent, transparent atmosphere, the laser itself can heat the air and form a negative lens that spreads the energy.

The beam is more intense in its center than at its edges. So the air, which always absorbs a little, heats up more in the center than at the edges. The refractive index of air decreases with an increase in temperature. Thus, a negative-gradient-index lens is produced.

The beam must also be trained on the target as the target moves, and most of the power will be reflected from most targets.

In spite of all these difficulties, the Air Force is proceeding with an oxygen-iodine chemical laser that produces hundreds of kilowatts of power in a package that weighs 373 kg and fits in a Boeing 747. It was to see final testing in 2002, having passed two preliminary tests on turbulence and beam spread. A tracking device was to be used to train the beam on theater missiles, like Scuds, that are hundreds of miles away. The laser should be able to weaken the structure of the missile enough that it will self destruct.[263]

The well-known Strategic Defense Initiative (SDI), promoted by Ronald Reagan, also known as Star Wars, envisioned the use of lasers as weapons. The basic idea was that a high-powered laser could burn through a critical area of a plane, missile tank, or other weapon. Another thought involved blinding soldiers as well as guidance systems. For the first of these applications, a high-powered, in fact, high-average-power laser was necessary.

The first of these that made any sense was the MIRACL (Mid Infrared Advanced Chemical Laser), a large chemical laser that could attain an average power

---

263 "Air Force's attack laser makes the grade," *Optics and Photonics News*, September 1998.

of 10 kW in 10-second bursts.[264] Unfortunately, such lasers often used a jet engine or equivalent to generate enough power and provide the metastable energy situation required for both lasing action and sufficient power. If you are to obtain 10 kW output, you need more than that as input, usually something like ten times as much.

The largest chemical laser (prototype) weapon is the Airborne Laser in a Boeing 747, a chemical oxygen iodine laser capable of megawatt outputs. It is intended for an antiballistic missile application.

The Tactical High Energy Laser (THEL) under development by Israel and the U.S. is based on a deuterium fluoride laser. When used at tests at White Sands Proving Grounds in New Mexico, this laser system occupied five trailers. It is hoped it will be squeezed into one trailer, a C-130, or a large helicopter. The THEL was successful in shooting down missiles.

A recent test with the MIRACL system has destroyed artillery shells, cruise missiles, Katayusha missiles, and a faster, longer-range missile as well.[265,266]

Solid state lasers have made significant advances so that they now are competitive in output and smaller. One such device is in the engineering development phase, but provides 100 kW output from a system that is on a hybrid-electric Humvee. Part of the success of these improvements in solid state high-energy lasers is the use of diode pumping. When ordinary lamps are used, much of the light is not of the correct wavelength to cause pumping. This means that the laser is only about 1% efficient and there is much heat to dissipate. At 1% efficiency, we need a megawatt of lamp power to get 10 kW. The development of these solid state high-energy laser weapons was ongoing in 2003 and expected to provide results in about five years.

Nonlethal lasers are the real version of the phasers of *Star Trek*. They are meant not to blind permanently but to obscure vision temporarily. One approach is a visible diode laser that is bright enough to flash-blind, disorient, and frighten. Just bright light, but the chance for permanent damage is still in doubt. Another approach is the use of an ultraviolet laser that would induce fluorescence in the eye of the receiver. This makes it hard to see!

Know It All; See It All

The new battlefield is visual and computerized. Spy satellites hover overhead. Unmanned drones fly overhead with both visible and infrared cameras. The Global Positioning System (GPS) keeps track of where things are. All of this is displayed in Humvees, tanks, and troop transports, as well as at headquarters. The battlefield

264 Hecht, J., "Solid state high-energy laser weapons," *Optics and Photonics News*, January 2003.

265 "Antimissile laser downs large-caliber rocket, *Photonics Spectra*, June 2004.

266 Hardin, W., "Weapons of war: laser offense offers best defense," *Photonics Spectra*, September 1997.

contains far less confusion as different units move into position, back up others, and keep in contact with cell phones as well as portable radios.[267] The prototype is teens in the mall with their cell phones.

Search and Rescue

One proposed search-and-rescue scheme applies to downed aircraft. It is a small laser scanner on a rescue plane that senses a return signal from a retroreflector. The catch is that the plane must have the reflector, and it must be oriented reasonably well.[268]

Nautical Fibers

The Navy has plans to replace much of its copper cabling with fiber optics.[269] This suggestion was made in a summer study in 1970 that I chaired in Monterey at the Naval Post Graduate School. Things take time and technology has to catch up. Fiber optics were experimental then.

The Sniperscope

The Snooperscope and the Sniperscope were World War II devices for seeing in the dark. A beam of invisible, infrared light is projected on to the battlefield by an individual soldier. This small searchlight, about six inches in diameter, is an ordinary searchlight with an infrared filter over it. A telescopic sight with an image converter tube is used for sighting. The tube is a phototube that is sensitive to the light of the searchlight. The image is portrayed on the screen in shades of green. The Snooperscope is a Sniperscope without the searchlight. It uses someone else's light! These have been largely replaced by two types of night-vision devices—thermal infrared devices and nightscopes.

Nightscopes

The heart of these devices is an image-intensifier tube that takes very low levels of ambient light and amplifies them greatly. They allow the soldier to see in very low ambient light levels, but there must be some light.

---

267 Keyser, J., "Digital warfare tool helping 4th Infantry hunt Iraqi guerillas," *Arizona Daily Star*, January 2, 2004.
268 Hand, A., "Laser searches for downed aircraft," *Photonics Spectra*, May 1998.
269 Hardin, W., "Weapons of war: laser offense offers best defense," *Photonics Spectra*, September 1997.

Most of our military vehicles have infrared imaging devices for driving at night. Tanks have these and viewers for the tank commanders and gunners. I saw a tape of part of the first Iraqi war. It was night. At about ten miles distance was an Iraqi Scud missile complex. It consisted of a power station, the missile launcher, communication shack, and several other small structures. The infrared viewers on the tanks showed clearly all these features without revealing they were there and viewing.

They targeted first the communications shack, and fired a Hellfire infrared-guided missile. It was a direct hit. The next target was the power shack. Ditto. It was a very impressive display of the use of optics in warfare!

Transportation

Many optical applications occur in the transportation industry. The rear-view mirror, its dimmer mode, and the convex side-mirror are discussed in the chapter on mirrors. Here I cover many other applications involving cars, trucks, RVs, trains, and traffic control, as well as some of the manufacturing techniques that provide better and cheaper vehicles.

It has been said by a member of the Aeronautics and Space Engineering Board that airline delays cost $9 billion a year, and that some 40,000 automobile accidents occur each year in the approximately 3 trillion miles driven during that time. Photonics is being applied to help alleviate these problems.

Optical sensors have been used to monitor road temperature to alert crews to salt them. Interferometers sense the deflection of large, heavy, metal plates that trucks drive on to be weighed. This is much faster than standard scales. The uses of LEDs for panel display, signal lights, and even headlights are discussed elsewhere in this chapter.

Inspecting ship ballasts for harmful organisms using a spectrometer, can substantially reduce the spread of disease (ships dump their ballasts in their new ports of call). Fiber optic hydrophones can be used to encircle ships in port to warn of unauthorized intrusions that may be security risks. Shipping containers can be closed with special seals that change their spectral characteristics when tampered with. The seals need to be affixed at the source and checked at the destination.[270]

Laser Positioning in Automotive Manufacture

Laser positioning systems have been used in both the automotive and aircraft industries. Early applications were the installation of windshields in trucks. Then rear

---

270 Hitz, B., "Photonic solutions for transportation," *Photonics Spectra*, January 2004.

windows, seam sealant, and stud welding were adapted to the system.[271] Now hundreds of such systems are used in both industries.

The systems are of basically two types, one employing several cameras and lasers and using stereo or triangulation techniques. The other is a single module. Both provide three-dimensional information, as they must, for these assembly operations.

The Perceptron system shines a precise laser line on a surface, where it becomes a contour line. The x, y, z coordinates of some 500 points on the line are then determined by triangulation with their Tricam camera.

Banks of Tricams are used in a Lincoln plant to place the windshield precisely into place. Doors are installed in a similar way, but in this case six degrees of freedom, three position coordinates, and three angular coordinates are needed to guide the door accurately into the door frame. Boeing has used similar techniques, but obviously on a much larger scale. The tail-to-tip centerline of the first 777 was "off" by only 0.023 inch (0.58 mm). As many as fifteen 20-ton jacks are used in the assembly of the fuselage, and they are all guided by laser alignment techniques.

High-Speed Cameras in Crash Testing

High-speed cameras have also contributed to improvements in the transportation industry. One major and obvious use is in the testing lab, where high-speed photography of crash events is highly desirable. Two types of cameras are used for this application: the standard film camera and the electronic camera that uses an array of silicon detectors. Each has its advantages and disadvantages that will be discussed after the application is described in more detail.

We have all heard of the crash tests and heard the dummies discuss their adventures on advertisements. A car is propelled toward a wall at a specified speed, depending upon the requirements of the specific test. For a car traveling at 30 mph, the time from crash to crush is about 100 ms. The airbag opens at a rate of about 200 mph (293 feet per second), i.e., the surface of the bag moves that fast. It moves the two feet from the steering wheel to the driver's head in 6.8 ms. A standard video camera records a frame every 1/30 of a second, 33 ms. At this speed, the edge of the bag would be a blur, and there would be only one shot of it, with no information about how it expands. Similar calculations apply to the crumpling of bumpers and doors and other parts.

If we wish, say, ten images of the bag as it expands, the frame time must be less than one millisecond, 0.68 ms, actually. This leads to camera requirements that take in excess of 1000 frames per second. Engineers at SRI International in Menlo Park, California, have used multiple cameras at different frame rates from about 1000 to 5000 frames per second, and at different angles.

---

271 Kaplan, H., "Laser alignment helps appearance, safety, efficiency," *Photonics Spectra*, 96, July 1998.

Those employing these techniques use high-speed film or electronic cameras and as much as a million watts of tungsten-bulb lighting to get sufficient sensitivity. Both film and CCD cameras depend on the number of photons they absorb, and this is proportional to the rate of the photons, times the time of an exposure. These exposures must be very short to get the very fast frame rates, so the photon rate must be increased.

The film cameras are generally less costly, $10,000 compared to $60,000. The CCD cameras reduce the size of the field of view in order to decrease the frame time, but they have images that are immediately available. Even with a darkroom on site, the film systems have about an hour delay from picture taking to picture viewing. This can be especially frustrating if the testing is of the trial-and-error type.

High-speed cameras are also used to analyze engine combustion. Combustion is rapid. Fuel injection takes about 5 ms while the flame propagates in fractions of a millisecond. Although visible cameras are valuable in flame and ignition investigation, infrared and ultraviolet cameras are also important, as flames emit in those regions of the spectrum as well. The flames of normal mixture ratios are amenable to visible analysis, but emissions in extremely lean-burning fuels are dim.

Infrared Cameras in Brake Testing

Infrared cameras are used at Oak Ridge National Laboratory to inspect the performance of brakes. Rotors are mounted on dynamometers and spun at 120 mph. Pads are pressed against the rotors to simulate extended braking action, as may occur on long downhill roads. After just a few minutes, the heat patterns on the rotors are evident in a good infrared camera with frame times of about 15 μs. Each test produces about one hundred 12-bit, 256×256 element pictures to be analyzed. These images enable manufacturers to redesign pads and rotors to eliminate or reduce the hot spots.

Laser Speed Detectors

Laser systems are an alternative to radar speed detectors. As is common knowledge, radar detectors can be both avoided and spoofed by relatively low-cost systems mounted on the dash or in the window. The radar system sends out a series of pulses, which bounce off the potential speeding car and are reflected back to the radar receiver. The receiver in the car can detect the pulses at a greater distance than the policeman, because the policeman's radar system has a two-way trip to make. The laser works the same way, but the potential that either a laser or a radar system, or both, may be in use ups the ante for the would-be speeder.

Laser speed detectors are called rangers. They determine the range at a given instant, and another, and another. Since the changes in distance and time are known, the rate can be determined. Light and radar travel at 186,000 miles per second, or 9.8×10^8 feet per second or 6.7×10^8 mph. So the round-trip time for a laser pulse to a car that is one mile away is 2 ns (two billionths of a second). A train of coded pulses can measure the time of flight and, since it is encoded, is not subject to extraneous pulses.

Laser Bump Avoiders

Lasers can also be used to prevent colli-sions. Figure 25 shows how a laser mounted on the front of a car can see the return beam from the rear end of the car in front.[272] The system uses a pulsed laser and a filter. The filter blocks most of the ambient light, passing only the laser light (and the small amount of ambient light of the same wavelength). A diode detector measures the flight time of a pulse, and therefore determines the range. The clos-ing rate can also be calculated, and brakes applied if need be.

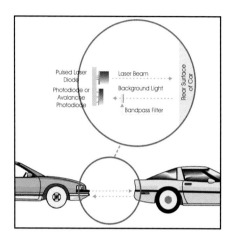

Figure 25 Laser collision preventer.[272]

Speeder Identification

In California, prototype identification systems are in use. A laser speed detector is mounted in an appropriate place, like an overpass, a tower, or a tree crotch on the side of the road. When a speeder is detected, a high-resolution camera takes a pic-ture of the license plate. The owner receives a citation several days later in the mail!

Traffic Control

Many communities are now installing cameras at important intersections to moni-tor traffic. Tucson has recently equipped several sections of I-10 with these cam-eras. The information is sent to a central station and can then be distributed to those with the proper equipment. Drivers can make decisions about routes based on real-time information on traffic density and speed.[273]

The cameras do not have to be camcorders. In fact, sequential still shots at in-tervals of about half a minute can provide enough information without data over-load. Note that traffic moves about a mile in a minute at 60 mph. The cameras cover about two miles.

272 Rainbow, P., "High-powered pulsed laser diodes take on new industrial and commercial applications," *Photonics Spectra*, October 2004. (Image courtesy of Laser Components, Inc.)
273 *Arizona Daily Star*, March 25, 2004.

Israel is testing a prototype travel monitor. An infrared video camera with associated computer capability is mounted between a pair of 20-foot high poles on the side of the road. It monitors the traffic, recording a photograph of a car, its speed, and the distances to the next cars.[274]

The critical aspects of this application are storage and the subsequent readout. It is not practical for someone to sit and watch a full day's tape of traffic. However, image-processing techniques and/or sampling techniques are available. Regular video cameras can also be used in the daytime. We were told, when we were in Israel, that it is the only place where sound travels faster than light; you can hear the horns behind you honk before you see the light turn green!

The Golden Eagle system in Moscow reads license plates in real time. It also determines speed and checks for a valid registration and current payments.[275]

Watching the Bridges

Laser vibrometers (vibration meters) are used to measure the health of bridges. A laser shines on the wire support of a bridge, and the wire motion is measured by the Doppler effect in the return beam. The speed of change in position provides a measure of the frequency of vibration. Changes in the frequencies indicate changes in the wire and possible flaws.[276]

The University of Vermont has embedded fiber optics in the concrete deck of a steel truss bridge over the Winooski River to monitor chemical and structural changes. They monitor strain with a Bragg grating and chloride with a chloride sensor in the fiber. The Bragg gratings change spacing when strained and therefore the wavelength of the light reflected from them. The chloride sensor uses a perforated tube that allows chloride ions to migrate to a reagent. The reagent changes color and this is sensed by a spectrometer. The chloride ions are mainly a result of salting the bridge for snow and ice, and they cause corrosion.[277]

The I-10 bridge in Las Cruces, N.M., is equipped with an instrument having a fiber optic strain gauge that senses overweight or just heavy trucks that pass, the structural health of the bridge, and the resonances caused by the loads.[278]

274 "IR to monitor israel's roads," *Photonics Spectra*, December 1986.
275 Chernushich, A. P., "Preview of I10 traffic flow now on web," *Photonics Spectra*, December 1999.
276 Naiman, J., "Laser vibrometers simplifying bridge condition evaluation," *OE Reports*, May 1998.
277 "Fiber optic sensors assess the health of bridges," *Optics and Photonic News*, February 1998.
278 Friebele, E., "Fiber Bragg grating strain gauges," *Optics and Photonics News*, August 1998.

The Horseshoe Falls Bridge of the Columbia Gorge Highway contains a series of fiber optic strain gauges in its structure. In this way, a continuous record of the strain introduced by the vehicles that cross it.[279]

The Taylor Bridge over the Assiniboine River in Manitoba, Canada, has a similar structure.[280]

Lighting the Roads and Cars

The United Kingdom plans to install LEDs for their traffic signals, replacing tungsten bulbs.[281] The design, by Nottingham University and Signal House, consists of some 100 LEDs in each light, each with its own lens. Although this sounds much more complicated and expensive than the standard lights, the tungstens last about six weeks while the LEDs are expected to endure for 14 years, a ratio of more than 1:20. This not only saves material cost, but also the time and expense of replacement.

Diode lasers, close relatives to light-emitting diodes, are replacing tungsten bulbs in modern cars.[282] The incredibly bright diode lasers shine on fiber optics or thin-sheet transparent plates. The very unusual problem in these designs is decreasing the brightness to a level that is eye-safe. This is generally accomplished by spreading the light. The increased brightness, however, allows for more electrical efficiency and more efficient use of space. As the ad once said—wider on the inside, narrower on the outside.

One version shines the light from a diode laser into the end of a glass plate using a fiber. Once inside the plate, the light is contained by total internal reflection, except where it should come out. This is often accomplished with a cylindrical lens on the surface of the plate. These can make very thin, efficient tail lights with many cylindrical lenses on them.[283] Further into the future, headlights may also be made in this fashion.

279 McCarthy, D. C., "Fiber sensors safely convey traffic data," *Photonics Spectra*, March 2001.

280 "Multiplexed sensors monitor bridge structure, materials," *Photonics Spectra*, February 1999.

281 Glaskin, M., "LEDs put railroad lighting on more efficient track," *Photonics Spectra*, July 1998.

282 Marinelli, M., and J. Remillard, "Diode lasers light the way for automotive signal lamps," *Photonics Spectra*, November 1997.

283 Remillard, J., M. Marinelli, and T. Fohl, "Automotive exterior lighting, from filaments to lasers," *Optics and Photonics News*, August, 1999.

Engine Deposits

Spectroscopy has been used for evaluating engine deposits, using the residues on the pistons of diesel engines as a function of position.[284]

License-Plate Reader

Video imaging can be used in various ways to monitor traffic flow, both legal and illegal. The United Kingdom used some 50 imagers placed at strategic locations to obtain statistics on traffic flow in a proposed expansion of a road system.[285] (The technique is termed "destination analysis." The anticipated flow is predicted by where the traffic went from and to in the area).

Boulder, Colorado, has introduced, on a limited basis, a series of such imagers to nab speeders and red-light violators.[286]

Better Night Driving

Cadillac announced in 2000 that it would offer infrared imaging vision enhancement as an option.[287] This system was under development for about ten years. It incorporates an array of thermal detectors, about 240×340 elements in size. Tests showed that appreciable improvement in vision was available during fogs and mists, and at night using this system. Oncoming headlights can be seen, but they do not glare. People and animals are detected by their own thermal emissions at ranges greater than possible with reflected light from headlights.

The image was projected on the windshield by means of a head-up display.

Ford also planned a night driving system with an image intensifier. It was to enhance existing visible images, not the infrared ones.[288]

These pictures[289] (Figs. 26 and 27), taken with what appears to be experimental devices, show the advantages of thermal imaging in night driving. The left-hand picture is a visible shot of the interior with a view through the windshield. Note the headlights of the car on the left and the barely perceptible taillights of the car on the right. The people are not visible. In the infrared picture all these are quite plain; the infrared radiation from the heat of the taillights and from the people provide a good image.

---

284 "FTIR examines engine deposits," *Photonics Spectra*, October 1997.
285 "License-plate reader to model traffic flow," *Photonics Spectra*, March 1991.
286 Wolfe, W., personal observation.
287 Eaton, J., "Cadillac will offer option to help night vision," *The Denver Post*, August 23, 1998.
288 Hand, A. J., "IR in your (luxury) car," *Photonics Spectra*, August 1999.
289 Dean, S., "Intelligent vehicles increase safety," *Optics and Photonic News*, December 2004. (Image courtesy OSA, copyright 2004.)

Figure 26 Visible scene.[289]   **Figure 27** Infrared image.[289]

In 1997, more than 3000 animal car accidents occured in Colorado.[289] Cadillac engineers claim that objects can be seen five times further with this system than with standard headlights.

The Other Side

One of the main traffic hazards that the night-vision devices help avoid is collision with deer and other large animals. In fact, Cadillac showed deer on the screens of their devices in their ads. Another approach to this is to let the deer give the alert. In addition to fences, heat sensors can be used to detect these animals and trigger warning lights. Radios on herd leaders are also being tried.[290]

Trunk Safety

General Motors plans to introduce infrared sensors in automobile trunks to sense animals or people.

Such a detection would automatically pop the lid for safety's sake.[291] The article does not mention whether it pops the trunk when the vehicle is in motion. One option is to warn the driver.

290 "Engineering for deer life," *Photonics Spectra*, June 2004.
291 Eaton, J., "Cadillac will offer option to help night vision," *The Denver Post*, August 23,1998.

Detection of Ice on Aircraft Surfaces

An imaging spectrometer is being developed to detect ice on aircraft surfaces.[292] A white light shines onto a surface that may or may not have ice on it. The spectrum of the reflection then indicates whether there is ice on the surface. The shape of the spectrum determines this and the depth of absorption bands indicates the ice thickness. This could be a simple spectrometer or even use just a few wavelengths. An imaging polarimeter has also been used. The light-polarization characteristics of ice are different from those of water, paint, or aluminum, and these differences are used as a discriminant.[293]

Analyzing Surface Flows

Infrared cameras can be used to analyze air flow patterns on airplane control surfaces.[294] This is normally done in a wind tunnel, but can also be performed in flight tests. Turbulent flow creates a higher temperature on the underlying surface than does laminar flow. Thus, this differentiation can be made.

Fire Away

General Motors has been using both visible and infrared imagers to analyze the spread of fires in cars. Visible imagers are hampered by smoke and soot, whereas infrared devices are sometimes saturated so that temperature measurements were sometimes limited. Fires were started in various positions—at the rear, the sides, and near the gas tank. The information is used to improve fire retardation techniques.[295] The techniques used to extend dynamic range in firefighting imagers could be applied here.

A Downer

Downed aircraft have used lasers and other beacons to signal their distress. Unfortunately these generate many false alarms. A system that might be considered the inverse of this has been developed by Daedalus in Ann Arbor, Michigan. It uses a laser scanner on the search aircraft and retroreflectors on downed aircraft.[296]

---

292 "Optical remote detection of ice on aircraft surfaces," *NASA Tech Briefs*, September 1998.

293 *Optics and Photonics News*, August 1998.

294 "Remote in-flight infrared imaging for analyzing surface flows," *NASA Tech Briefs*, September 1998.

295 Kaplan, H., "Let it burn," *Photonics Spectra*, June 1999.

296 Hand, A., "Laser searches for downed aircraft," *Photonics Spectra*, May 1998.

Boat Hulls

One technique for examining the integrity of ship hulls uses infrared imagers. The process is to strip the boat down to basics, just the hull. Then the hull is heated from the inside to 30–40°F above ambient. The hull is then viewed from the outside by the infrared imagers. Discontinuities and asperities in the uniform heating indicate possible delaminations, cracks, and the like.[297]

On a Clear Day

Clear-air turbulence can sometimes be very disturbing and even deadly, but it is mostly just disturbing. However, an optical approach is being tried to warn pilots in enough time. An infrared Doppler system such as radar sends a pulse ahead of the aircraft. It bounces off the particles in the air, and the intensity of the return indicates the density of particles. The Doppler shift indicates the speed of the particles, and these two measurements are indications of turbulence. The range is 15 to 30 km, enough to give a 30-second warning. The current system has created a situation in which the warning is no longer heeded, probably because of too many false alarms.[298]

The system sends out a single-frequency pulse at 2 μm that strikes the airborne particles and scatters back to the receiver. A base frequency shift occurs because of the relative velocity between the atmospheric particles and the plane. The additional frequency shifts result from the motions of the particles. If there are a lot of shifts because of lots of particle motions, then there is turbulence.[299]

Rescue Operations

After the crash of Swissair 111 just off Nova Scotia, the usual sonar investigations of debris for clues to the reasons for the crash, there was still much to do. Investigators called in a laser line-scan imager that was towed submerged behind the investigatory ship. The line scanner used a doubled Nd:YAG that operated at 532 nm to illuminate the ocean floor. This is the ideal wavelength where the water is most transparent. Four mirrors scan a line transverse to the direction of the ship's motion. A photomultiplier tube detects the reflected signal. The result of the search for clues was not reported.[300]

297 Robinson, K., "IR cameras save the ship," *Photonics Spectra*, January 1998.
298 "Making your skies friendlier," *NASA Tech Briefs*, March 1990.
299 Tatterson, K., "Avionics looks to photonics to watch turbulent skies," *Photonics Spectra*, February 1998.
300 Weiss, S. A., "Detector helps crash investigation," *Photonics Spectra*, December 1998.

Welding Aluminum

The automobile industry has been making cars more fuel efficient, in part by making cars and trucks lighter with the use of aluminum rather than steel. One such device is a $1.6-million, 4-kW Nd:YAG laser system. It was chosen in preference to a carbon-dioxide laser because it created a higher-viscosity liquid at the weldment, and this was more stable. The laser welder saves money two ways compared to the former method using rivets: no rivets are needed, and the laser system works about four times as fast as the equivalent riveters. So long, Rosie.[301]

Autonomous Vehicles

These are cars, trucks, and airplanes that can travel by themselves or almost by themselves.[302] I have always thought how nice it would be to play bridge on the way to see my kids in California. These vehicles are possible through the use of optical imagers, optical rangefinders, and telemetry.

Two Houston Metropolitan Transit buses and three passenger cars were specially outfitted and tried in San Diego. They used a 640×480 CCD as the imaging sensor. In earlier tests, the center line was used as reference to orient the vehicle to the correct lane. But California roads do not all have center-line stripes. Therefore, additional cues were incorporated into the software to orient the vehicles.

Tests on I-15 north of San Diego showed promise. A Lancia was modified by the University of Parma and successfully completed a 2000 km trip 95% autonomously. A Humvee has been instrumented with an infrared camera, laser ranging device and ranging visible imager.

Although this is an expensive approach, it proved to work rather well in the unfriendly environment of the battleground. These problems are different—traveling on a highway versus going across country in a war zone. Proper markings can make autonomous operation feasible and relatively cheap. A rear-mounted laser ranger can warn against rear-enders. More sophisticated and expensive equipment can enable the military to operate Humvees, tanks, and reconnaissance vehicles without a driver. They can be programmed for a certain course or operated from a remote position.

Similar technology can be used to remotely pilot helicopters and small airplanes. The cues are now three-dimensional and can be augmented with a GPS system. Such vehicles can be used for army recon, for protecting our borders, and in escapee chases.

---

301 "Laser welds aluminum truck cabs faster, cheaper," *Photonics Spectra*, December 1998.

302 Wheeler, M. D., "One eye on the road," *Photonics Spectra*, June 1999.

Don't Snow Me

An article describes three prototype "smart" snowplows that have high-intensity fiber optic warning lights and GPS and infrared sensors for measuring air and pavement temperature.[303] The temperature determinations help to determine how much salt or calcium to use. The article ends with the plea for a plow that will start itself in the middle of the night and plow the streets and sidewalks remotely. It could be done. Design a sensor that senses snow accumulation, perhaps a sensitive balance (scale). When enough snow has accumulated, send a signal to the ignition and the door opener. Guide the plow with GPS or equip it like the remote vacuum cleaner!

Skin Check

Perhaps the simplest, yet very effective, optical technique used for inspecting aircraft is the digital camera. Mechanics take pictures of parts in question. The digital images can be sent to the home base where engineers can evaluate them, if necessary. They can also be sent on to the manufacturer if the problem is too complex. Surely the best imagery and good zoom capability are desirable.

Go with the Flow

NASA has been using an infrared camera to monitor flow patterns on the wings of test aircraft. An observing aircraft flies with the test aircraft and takes infrared pictures. Since the mixing in a turbulent flow is greater than in a laminar flow, more heat is transferred. Therefore, a surface that is initially warmer than the freestream air exhibits a higher temperature where there is laminar flow than where there is turbulent flow. Thus, to some extent the flow pattern can be imaged, even if indirectly.[304]

Cool it

NASA is experimenting with a spectral technique to measure ice and water on aircraft surfaces, such as aluminum. The reflection spectrum of ice is different from the very flat spectrum of aluminum and even somewhat different from water. So an imaging spectrometer can do the job. The spectrometer used had 21 wavelength bands each about 10-nm wide, operating from 850 to 1050 nm.[305]

---

303 "Plowing with photonics," *Photonic Spectra*, February 1998.
304 "Remote in-flight infrared imaging for analyzing surface flows," *NASA Tech Briefs*, September 1998.
305 "Optical remote detection of ice on aircraft surfaces," *NASA Tech Briefs*, September 1998.

Rails

Railroad rails have problems with subsurface cracks, usually in the direction of travel and especially at bends and junctions. The rails have to be rough enough to create good friction between themselves and the train wheels, but roughness on the sides is particularly bad. Oils and grease have been used with some success, but they are temporary and not always environmentally friendly.

Laser glazing is effective, permanent, and environmentally friendly. The process generates a smooth, thin melt layer that rapidly solidifies. This generates a surface that is smooth, with higher yield strength and more elastic compliance. It took about 1 kW of power to treat a six foot length of rail with a Nd:YAG laser. After 30,000 cycles, the rails still had 40% less friction than untreated ones.[306]

Lighting the Rails

Light-emitting diode signals are under testing by the United Kingdom's Railtrack. The signals must be visible from all angles (in front) a mile away to trains traveling up to 140 mph. Therefore, the system uses some 114 LEDs with lenses canted at appropriate angles. Although the new lights cost about 60% more than existing incandescent systems, they have an estimated life of 14 years instead of about six weeks. This represents an enormous economy in manpower for replacement of bulbs.[307]

Optics Takes its Toll

The Golden Gate Bridge in San Francisco uses a 1280×1024 CCD camera to photograph cars at the toll booth. The cars are illuminated by a bank of 120 infrared LEDs so pictures can be taken day and night. The vehicle's size and speed as well as its license plate, are recorded. The scofflaws are sent a bill shortly after they run the toll.[308]

Utilities

Optics plays a role in various aspects of the utility industry. Infrared devices inspect power lines for imperfections, lasers confine huge energy densities for the establishment of fusion power (we hope), and waste products of fission reactions are located.

---

306 Whitney, M., "Lasers make rails safer for travel," *Photonics Spectra*, April 1999.
307 Glaskin, M., "LEDs put railroad lighting on more efficient track," *Photonics Spectra*, July 1998.
308 McCarthy, D., "High-speed camera system takes its toll on violators," *Photonics Spectra*, September 1999.

Pipe Down

The People's Republic of China is mapping some underground pipelines. In the Liaohe oil fields are many pipelines for which there are no decent records. Nobody knows where they are, exactly. Some infrared airborne instrumentation, by Daedalus in Ann Arbor, Michigan, has been used to map these underground lines. The project, begun in 1989, uses an aircraft flown at an altitude of 600 m and a commercial infrared sensor. Most of the site consists of harvested rice fields (at the right time) with no vegetation cover. Some 360 pipelines have been discovered and mapped in the 70-square-mile area.[309] The thermal signature shows up as the heat difference between the pipes and the surround diffuses to the surface.

The Inside Story

Chinese researchers have developed a technique for inspecting the insides of pipes. A laser shines into a device that sends its beam out in a circular pattern. This is known as an *axicon*, and it is simply a cone or a truncated cone. The light reflected from the inner wall of the tube enters a wide-angle lens and is focused on a CCD camera. It can operate in pipes from 8- to 14-cm diameters and has a resolution of 100 µm using a 691 nm, 10 mW laser, and a 524×580 pixel camera.[310]

There is less to this than meets the eye. The largest wall diameter is 140 mm; the circumference is almost 450 mm. The 580 pixels in one dimension would generate a resolution about 750 µm. It is also not trivial to collect the light from 360 deg to shine on the CCD. There are certainly ways to do this, but this sounds a little mysterious.

The New York Version

New York City has had similar problems with its underground pipes. Actually, Consolidated Edison has been using robotic inspection of gas pipes in Yonkers, New York, my hometown, which is just north of the Big Apple. The robot is a train of seven modules, two for locomotion, two for batteries, and one for a central computer. The front and back drive modules each have a 640×480 CCD camera with bright white LEDs and a fisheye lens that gives a 190-deg field of view. Thus the robot can see forward, backward, and to the sides to check out the interiors of the pipes. The modules are connected to each other with articulations so that the entire unit can wiggle through curves and bends. The length of pipe that can be examined is determined by the battery life and the range of the transmitter. This device should be more versatile and cover more territory in a shorter time than previous tethered

---

309 Waggoner, J., "Mapping buried pipe systems with thermal IR," *Photonics Spectra*, 18, March 1991.
310 Hand, A., "Sensor quickly inspects inner pipe walls," *Photonic Spectra*, September 1998.

versions.[311] The picture (Fig. 28) shows both a typical eight-inch main and the robot.

Solar Energy Systems

Different types of solar energy systems exist. Some are large mirror systems that reflect sunlight to a central point; others consist of panels of silicon solar cells. There are different geometries for the mirror systems.

Paraboloidal Solar Collectors

Figure 28 Pipe robot.[311]

A large paraboloidal mirror is controlled so that it faces the sun throughout the day. Depending on its size, it can collect considerable power and energy.

The sun deposits approximately 1500 W of power on every square meter. So a paraboloid that is two meters in diameter collects about 4700 W. That is enough to run most residences most of the time. The solar power, however, must be absorbed and transformed into electrical power.

One scheme[312] for the absorption is to use a cylinder or sphere with a small hole, about the size of the parabolic image of the sun. The sunlight that enters the hole will bounce around inside and eventually be almost totally absorbed. The heat so generated can then be transformed into electrical energy in a number of ways. One example is a steam-turbine generator.

Solar Panels

Solar panels are large arrays of detectors that turn photons from the sun into current-providing electrons in the material. This can then be converted into power.

Ten thousand square miles of these panels can generate, in about six hours of sunlight, a day's worth of electric energy for the entire U.S.[313] A patch 100 miles square in the western deserts could do this.

This is a renewable power source that is underused to a great degree in the United States. There are two reasons for this. One is cost; the other is convenience of a sort. The cost of a home unit is still high enough that it takes more than ten years to amortize its installation, but the panels can provide power that is independent of the grid. As I write this, the Eastern United States is recovering from a mas-

---

311 Fischer, A. L., "Robot explores gas mains in New York," *Photonics Spectra*, October 2004. (Image courtesy Hagen Schempf.)

312 "Blackbody evaporator unit for point-focus solar collector," *NASA Tech Briefs*, January 1998.

313 "Device turns water, sunlight to fuel," *Photonics Spectra*, August 1998.

sive grid breakdown, and California is on the back end of an electric power crisis that was caused in part by agreements with electrical power companies. We need to view the promotion of solar power with individual, roof-mounted units compared to modernizing the grid.

One complication is that the sun does not always shine, but it does 360 days a year in many of the states in the southwest and much of California. The sun also does not shine at night, locally; but it does shine someplace. In many cases, a storage mechanism is in order to play the evening shows on TV, but even without storage, a major load would be taken off the current means of power generation.

The solar cells generate about 100 W per square meter. A normal household operates on an average of about 1000 W. So a roof with a 5-m by 5-m array will supply the energy needed, but may not store it. One solution is to feed it back to the grid rather than having an autonomous system.

For the manufacture of solar cells, the material of choice right now is polycrystalline silicon, rather than crystalline silicon, since it is considerably cheaper, a few hundred dollars per square meter. So, even without the costs of labor and the like, a household installation must cost several thousand dollars.[314]

It really does cost about $10,000 for the household unit, all told. Since a typical annual electricity bill is $1000, it would take 10 years to pay off the investment. I have suggested that the government subsidize this so that payoff would take only five years. People would line up to do it. Energy would be saved and the grid would be safer. The economy would improve, and there would be more tax income to help pay for it.

More people in Kenya have these systems than systems that are on the grid, and the Dutch have recently built a 5000-home development with all its 1-MW power needs supplied by solar cells.[315] Japan has plans for subsidization to reach to the point at which 3% of its energy will come from solar panels. We are at about 0.01%.

At least one application has used Fresnel lenses to increase the energy on a given photocell and thereby improve the efficiency of the panel. The lenses are made of plastic 3.3 inches wide and hundreds of feet long—mass produced because they do not have to be high quality.[316]

Wasted

The Hanford nuclear plant in Washington state has 177 tanks of underground nuclear waste that need to be disposed of somehow. Radiation chemists are using a complicated optical system to assess the types of reactions and nuclear active chemicals in these tanks. They use a 9-MeV electron gun accelerator that incorporates a 5-W pumped laser to excite the species and another to analyze them.

314 Lerner, E., "Solar cells expand their niche," *Laser Focus World*, November 1996.
315 Drolette, D., "Photovoltaics grows up," *Photonics Spectra*, December 1999.
316 Gaughan, R., "Lenses boost solar cell's power," *Photonics Spectra*, October 1998.

The U.S. Department of Energy (DoE) stores more than 700,000 metric tons of radioactive depleted uranium hexafluoride in about 57,700 steel cylinders. A technique has been developed to check these cylinders for leakage using fluorescence. I do not know why a Geiger counter is not viable, but they have developed a technique that sends pulses of excitation light and uses time- and wavelength-resolved luminescent detection.[317]

Hanford also uses a DIAL system to measure the gaseous effluent from nuclear waste in underground or aboveground tanks. The beam is sent over a path near these tanks, strikes a retroreflector and returns. The differential absorption is a spectroscopic measurement of the pollutant gases.[318]

Nuclear Robotics

A robot is soon to be used to investigate the interior of the Chernobyl reactor. Three CCD cameras, well-protected from nuclear radiation, are the eyes of the robot. The images they obtain are sent out by way of a 1000-m fiber optic umbilical cord.[319]

Uranium Enrichment

Nuclear reactors in power plants use enriched uranium containing 3–5% of the U-235 isotope that is extracted from uranium oxide, contains about 0.7%. The traditional techniques of gas centrifuge and diffusion are fairly expensive, inefficient, and use a lot of U-235. Atomic vapor laser isotope separation is newer and better (like many detergents). A uranium vapor is created, and a laser tuned between 550 nm and 650 nm is aimed at the vapor to ionize the atoms, which are then collected by an ion extractor (essentially a charge collector). Each production unit will contain more than 40,000 optical elements ranging from 1 to 8 inches in diameter to focus and aim the beams. This new system should require less initial capital investment, use 5% of the power and 20 to 30% less uranium for an equivalent amount of enriched fuel compared with current systems.[320]

317 Hand, A. J., "Luminescence aids detection of toxic leaks," *Photonics Spectra*, December 1999.
318 Grant, B., "LIDAR helps unravel environmental mysteries," *Photonics Spectra*, April 1998.
319 Wheeler, M., "Robotic 3-D imager to brave chernobyl," *Photonics Spectra*, August 1998.
320 Grant, B., "Lasers improve uranium enrichment," *Photonics Spectra*, October 1997.

The National Ignition Facility (NIF)

Fusion reactors provide the hope for almost unlimited power with no radioactive waste and comparatively little danger. But they are still just a hope. In order to start a fusion chain reaction, incredible heat and temperature must be generated.

One way to do this is with lasers. The idea is to illuminate the fusion target with a very small spot of very high energy at wavelengths that are efficient for absorbing the power. The National Ignition Facility is one place where this is being attempted. The following brief description should be enough to convince any reader how incredibly complicated this is, and why some scientists think it will never happen. I hope it does. One of the prime needs for a good society is an economical, clean source of energy.

The NIF has 192 laser beam systems. Each starts with a Nd-glass laser that is pumped by a flashlamp. The 10-J pulse is fed to a pinhole for beam shaping. A Galilean telescope passes the beam through another pinhole and expands it to a 40-cm square beam. Then it goes to an amplification cell (much like a laser, but just amplification), with four passes; then through a Pockels cell, which adjusts the timing of the pulse, both how long and when. It is frequency doubled twice, from 1065 nm to 520 nm to 350 nm. The pulse has a low-power pedestal 15 to 20 ns wide. On top of it is the high-power pulse that is 3 ns in duration.

The 192 beams must fit in a 600 μm spot, where they generate as much as 2.2 million joules and a peak power of many billion watts. Part of the optics train includes adaptive optics that are used to refine the wave fronts so that the beams can be combined in this small spot. These are only some of the optical components, and all of them are on the cutting edge of producibility.[321]

Pollution Monitoring

One technique for monitoring, and therefore controlling, smokestack pollution from power plants is Raman spectroscopy.[322] The technique, using a laser emitter, can monitor the amounts of carbon dioxide, carbon monoxide, and nitric oxide.

Water Detection

At a critical place in New Mexico, which will not be revealed, six natural gas lines converge, lines that serve California. El Paso Natural Gas has introduced new, faster water detectors. Water in gas may cause pilot lights to fluctuate or go out and may even freeze and clog a pipe.

---

321 Hogan, W., Atherton, L., Paisner, J., "National Ignition Facility design focuses on optics," *Laser Focus World*, November 1996.
322 "Raman spectroscopy could simplify pollution monitoring," *Photonics Spectra*, October 1997.

The optical sensor is a laser absorption spectrometer about the size of a breadbox. I have worked on similar problems in several different guises. I suggest that they replace the spectrometer, which is relatively large and expensive, with a two- or three-band instrument. The spectra of methane, the main constituent in natural gas, and that of water are sufficiently different that a few bands can be used. Choose a water-absorption band, say 2.7 μm, a band that does not absorb water, and a band independent of methane, take the ratio, and the job is done—with a couple of filters, a detector, and a simple source of radiation.[323]

Japanese Lights

MITI, the Ministry of International Trade and Industry in Japan, is organizing the development of LEDs for all sorts of lighting to save energy. The project is to cost some ¥ 5 billion, starting with LEDs for ordinary room lighting. They should save 37.74 million barrels of oil and last 50 to 100 times longer than conventional incandescent bulbs. [324]

The Oil Industry

Oil refineries need to be able to get fast, reliable results on such properties of the oil as octane, cetane, percentages of paraffins, olefins, haphthalenes, aromatics, benzene, and oxygenates. They have, over the years, used multiple, dedicated analyzers to make such assessments. At least some of them are switching to an infrared Fourier transform spectrometer.[325]

Weather and Climate

Weather is what happens to us now or maybe yesterday and tomorrow. Climate is weather over years and centuries. Optics has quite an effect on weather and climate, and it has much to do with how we monitor and even affect it.

Beach Erosion

An airborne laser system measures beach erosion. A laser system is mounted in the bay of an airplane. The laser shoots a pulse to the ground and measures the total

---

323 "Laser-based detector puts the freeze on water," *Photonics Spectra*, September 2000.
324 Whipple, C., "LED funding aims to illuminate Japan," *Photonics Spectra*, October 1997.
325 Mendonsa, R., "Oil refinery finds FTIR Spectrometer is slick," *Photonics Spectra*, September 1977.

time of flight. A Global Positioning System on board records where the plane is. The height records can then be compared in the laboratory with historical records. The sampling rate is 2000–5000 pulses per second, essentially continuous. The plane flies at 135 mph and the uncertainty in the measurement is 15 cm.[326]

It's Greek to me

Athens has a pollution problem, and it has been measured by a DIAL system—differential absorption LIDAR. The main problem occurs in the summer, when smog is mostly ozone formed from such things as toluene, benzene, and nitrogenous gases.

Researchers used the DIAL as an analytic tool to investigate the meteorology and atmospheric constituents on both micro (meters) and meso (kilometers) scales. The DIAL emits two short laser pulses of slightly different frequencies (wavelengths). One is a reference beam in an in active part of the atmosphere; the other is tuned to a characteristic reflection of the gas under investigation.

Both the intensity of the returns and the time of flight are recorded. A ratio is taken of the sensor beam and the reference beam returns. This gives a measure of the amount of the pollutant. The time of flight gives the range. Measurements are repeated in different directions to get a volumetric sampling of the atmosphere. The DIAL wavelengths are 282.4, 286.9, and 398.3 nm for measuring ozone, sulfur dioxide, and nitrogen dioxide, respectively. The corresponding reference wavelengths are 286.3, 286.3, and 397.0 nm.

The titanium-sapphire laser emits a relatively wide spectrum of light from about 750 to 870 nm at a few hundred millijoules. This is then selected by prisms and frequency doubled and tripled in nonlinear crystals, yielding pulses of about 25 and 5 millijoules at 375 to 400 nm and 250 to 290 nm, respectively.[327]

Optics in Depth

The Swedes use a combination of DIAL and laser ranging to map their Fjords and coastal regions. The depth finder agrees with acoustic (sonar) measurements to within about 15 cm. This obviously improves navigational safety. At the same time, they measure ozone, carbon dioxide, and various pollutants with the DIAL technique.[328]

326 Mendonsa, R., "Airborne lasers map beach erosion," *Photonics Spectra*, December 1997.

327 Bourson, A., "Laser technique sniffs out pollutants," *Photonics Spectra*, March 1997.

328 Grant, B., "LIDAR helps unravel environmental mysteries," *Photonics Spectra*, April 1998.

It's a Dirty Job

Optics is big in pollution monitoring because so many pollutants have characteristic absorption bands in the infrared. A system with a 1550-nm InGaAs-diode laser and a multiple-pass sample cell has been mounted in a smokestack to monitor ammonia, which is sometimes used to reduce nitrous oxides. A PIN diode detects the light. The current to the laser is varied so that the output wavelength is varied. The detector then measures the change or modulation in the signal.

Another system, with variations on the theme, uses a collection of diodes and corresponding detectors from the near-infrared out to 12 μm. These are used either with a fiber optic system in the chimney or with a remote telescope system.[329]

Weather Prediction

The weather satellite is described elsewhere. It maps clouds and their movements. Another approach is the use of a LIDAR that can measure the range to clouds from an aircraft, and therefore, with repeated measurements, the direction and velocity of clouds. The system uses a carbon-dioxide laser that generates 1-J pulses at 1 to 30 times a second in the 9–11-μm region of the spectrum. The return from the clouds is detected by an appropriate infrared detector. The beam is about 1 m in diameter at a 10-km range, providing a detailed, relatively high-resolution, three-dimensional map in real time.[330]

A similar instrument is used as an altimeter to measure the topography of the Greenland and Arctic ice fields. A pulsed Nd:YAG laser is used to send a beam of light at 1064 nm to the surface. The time to get a return to a 1-m mirror and detector is recorded and translated into a distance. The laser pulses repeat at 40 times per second, thereby producing spots on the ground 70 m in diameter with 175 meters center-to-center distance.[331] This provides an adequately sampled topographic map. Since light travels about one meter in a nanosecond, a time accuracy of one-hundredth of a nanosecond (easy) gives a vertical resolution of one centimeter. This is more than adequate.

It's a Rough Job...

Sea-surface roughness can be measured by optical glints from the waves. Large waves, with meter wavelengths, are easily measured by a number of techniques. Smaller waves, on the order of centimeters, can be measured by monitoring the retroreflective returns from a laser. The system, in a plane or platform, scans in an-

---

329 Hardin, R., "Diode lasers pinpoint pollutants," *Photonics Spectra*, April 1998.

330 Whitney, M., "Sky-bound LIDAR offers tool for weather projections," *Photonics Spectra*, May 1999.

331 Van Belle, M., "Laser altimeter measures ice sheets," *Photonics Spectra*, May 1999.

gle from perpendicular to almost horizontal. Each glint is a reflection back from a wave surface perpendicular to the laser beam. Since the angles are all different through the scan, this produces statistics for the wave slopes. That information, in turn, gives information about winds, an essential part of weather prediction and reporting.[332]

Round and Round

A group in New Zealand uses a large ring laser to measure the variations in the rotation rate of the Earth. It is made of a 1.2-m slab of Zerodur glass (glass with almost no thermal expansion). The counter-rotating laser beams are helium neon. The device is located in a large coastal cave to further minimize thermal changes. The device is accurate to one part in ten million in order to detect the millisecond fluctuations in the rotation rate.[333]

332 Shaw, J., interview, "Laser-glint sensor measures sea surface roughness," *OE Reports*, June 1998.
333 Hardin, R., "Ring laser measures earth's rotation," *Photonics Spectra*, December 1997.

Chapter 5

Critical Steps in Physics Involving Light

I think there are several really critical aspects in the development of physics. These include the origin of the universe, the establishment of a heliocentric world, the origin of quantum mechanics, the laws of relativity, and spectroscopy. There are others, but these are certainly momentous, and they are all intimately involved with light.

The Origin of the Universe

Most scientists now believe that the universe began in a giant explosion called the Big Bang. All the matter of the universe was in a lump smaller than a golf ball. It then expanded as a giant plasma. As the Bible says, the universe began with light. Calculations show that as a result of 15-billion years of expansion, the radiation of that initial explosion has gradually cooled to 3 K, three degrees above absolute zero. That is the theory.

About 20 years ago my friend John Mather headed a team from NASA to measure this. It was called the COBE DIRBE experiment. Radiometric and spectrometric devices were put in a satellite and kept at a temperature below 3 K with liquid helium. Sure enough, they found that the background radiation looks like a 3 K blackbody radiation.

The Heliocentric World

The theological approach to the nature of the world led us to the Ptolemaic arrangement of the planets, sun, and moon. The Earth was at the center. The sun, moon, and five planets rotated around it. In fact, Dante's descriptions of Paradise were believed accurate in terms of all the spheres.

Copernicus argued vehemently against this model of the universe. His book describing it was placed on the Index in 1616. Even informed scientists doubted Copernicus' theory on the grounds that there should be parallax among the stars and a rotating Earth would surely pull itself apart.

This theory survived until the observations of Galileo with his optical telescope. He found four moons circling Jupiter, a miniature solar system. The rotation of the sun was observed through the motion of sunspots. The phases of Venus were observed to be the same as Copernicus had calculated.

Galileo made these observations around 1610 and published his results that year. Even then, some who should have known better argued that there had to be seven planets (including the sun and moon) because there were seven openings in the head, seven days in the week, and seven metals of alchemy.

Galileo was warned by the Church in 1616 to lay off. (They surely did not say it that way.) He did until 1632, when Pope Urban VII took the See. He had long been a friend of Galileo, and Galileo then published Dialogues on the Great World Systems. He was later forced to retract it after house arrest, jail, and many disabilities.

The real success came somewhat later after Kepler had codified the calculations into a simple set of rules that really worked.

Quantization

The Origin of Quantum Mechanics–Quantization of Emission and Absorption

During the latter years of the 18th century and the beginning of the next, scientists were very concerned about the nature of blackbody radiation. A blackbody radiator is ideal; it radiates everything allowed by its temperature. It was the subject of intense theoretical and experimental investigation because the results depended on only inherent properties of radiation. The density of states function predicted how many different wavelengths of light could be in this ideal cavity. It was

$$\frac{2\pi c^2 h}{\lambda^5},$$

where c is the speed of light, h is Plancks constant, and λ is the wavelength of light.

The wavelengths allowed in the cavity are determined by the fact that there must be nodes at the walls; the electric field in a metal has to be zero (because metals are conductors and cannot support differences in field strengths). Notice that the density of states function involves only the fundamental constants c and h, the constant π and the wavelength λ. That is part of what made this so intriguing to the people who first studied them. The theoretical developments were made by Lord Rayleigh, one of the most prolific investigators of all kinds of wave motion, and by James Jeans, a highly reputed English theoretician.

The second part of the derivation was to calculate the probability that these states existed, or were occupied. How is the energy E distributed among all these different waves? The classical calculation was the Boltzmann factor $e^{-E/kT}$, the exponential raised to a negative factor: the energy divided by Boltzmann's constant k and the temperature T. Again, fundamental things. This would give the equation

$$\frac{2\pi c^2 h}{\lambda^5} e^{-E/kT} = \frac{2\pi c^2 h}{\lambda^5 e^{E/kT}}.$$

This equation did not agree with some very careful measurements made by a number of investigators, including O. Lummer and E. Pringsheim, H. Rubens and F. Kurlbaum. There was even a problem in the theory. As the wavelengths get shorter and shorter, the radiation gets larger and larger, tending toward infinity as the wavelength goes to zero. This was known as the *ultraviolet catastrophe.*

Planck, with some desperation, assumed that the energy was discontinuous. It is hard to say just what led him to this, but it did lead to the right answer:

$$\frac{2\pi c^2 h}{\lambda^5 \left(e^{E/kT} - 1\right)}.$$

In this formulation, the energy of the vibrations of the matter that gives rise to the radiation was quantized. The energy E was identified as the energy of a photon, but that did not come until later. It was the quantum of energy. This was the beginning of quantum mechanics, and it was a shaky one. Planck was not very happy with the idea of discontinuous energy steps, and no one yet had the idea that the radiation was quantized.

This investigation into the nature of blackbody radiation was the birth of quantum mechanics.[1]

It is interesting that Planck thought that both emission and absorption were quantized. Then he changed his mind to believe that only emission was quantized. Finally, he concluded correctly that both emission and absorption are quantized.

The Photoelectric Effect—Quantization of Light

This was the experiment that nailed down the quantum nature of light. Planck quantized the emission and absorption, but not the light itself. Einstein, in a very busy year for him,[2] contemplated this situation: the emission of light is quantized; the absorption of light is quantized; what happens in between? Of course, we now know that light is quantized and it was proven by the two aspects of the photoelectric effect—photoemission and photoabsorption.

The Compton effect was one experimental proof of the quantized nature of light. A. H. Compton found that x rays (a form of very high-frequency light) scattered from a material have lower frequencies than the rays shone on the material. He reasoned that quanta of the incoming radiation collided with free electrons in the material. As a result it gave up some of its energy and momentum, and therefore

---

1   Cajori, F., "A History of Physics," Dover, 1928.
2   This was the same year he proposed the special theory of relativity and described Brownian motion accurately.

had a longer wavelength. There is no way to explain this with just the wave theory of light.

The photoelectric effect is a second experiment that confirms the ideas of Einstein. As light is incident upon a photoelectric cell, the resulting current is measured. In the experiment, electrons were emitted from the cathode and their energy was measured. It was found that the energy of these electrons was independent of the intensity of the light. The current, the number of electrons per second, would increase, but the electron energy stays the same as the intensity changes. But if the wavelength of the light changes, so does the electronic energy. Einstein's equation is

$$E = h\nu - W,$$

where h is Planck's constant, ν is the light frequency, and W is the work function of the material (kind of a barrier to letting the photons out). This shows clearly that the electron energy is proportional to the photon energy and the frequency.

In a vacuum tube, the opposite of the photoelectric effect can be demonstrated. A beam of electrons is fired at an electrode and light is emitted. As expected from the direct photoelectric effect, the light has frequencies up to a limit, when the photon energy $h\nu$ is higher than the electron energy $\frac{1}{2}mv^2$. Again, this cannot be explained by wave theory.

Relativity

The laws of relativity, for they are no longer theories, are intimately related to optics. The law of special relativity deals with bodies that move in inertial frames of reference. That is, there are no forces or accelerations involved. The frames move with uniform motion, constant velocity, and no turns.

What is a frame of reference? It is the place you are moving, the way it moves. One frame of reference is the Earth. Others are an airplane, a train, a car, rocket ship, satellite, etc. These frames, in general, move with respect to each other. Einstein postulated that there can be no preferred frame of reference—who would choose and how?

Imagine you are on a train. You observe another train that is moving with respect to you. Which one is moving? If there are no forces, and the tracks are incredibly smooth, you cannot tell whether you are moving or not. So you could be still and the other train moving. It could be still and you moving, or you could both be moving. Therefore there is no preferred frame of reference. Since that is so, all the rules of physics must apply equally well in all frames.

That is relativity: all motion with respect to various frames of reference is relative. Next, Einstein assumed that nothing travels faster than the speed of light and that information can travel at the speed of light.

Now we can carry out a simple thought experiment. Imagine that you are stationary at a high altitude observing an aircraft that is about to fly directly away from you. If you have to ask questions about how that can be, change it to a train and a low altitude. As the plane (or train) leaves you, a passenger drops a stone. We can go back to basic physics or ask a friend to calculate how long it takes

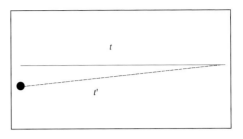

Figure 1 Illustrating special relativity.

the stone to drop. The passenger will observe that time, but you will not.

As the stone dropped, the plane or train moved away from you, so the time you observe is the time the passenger observes plus the time it takes the light signal to get back to you from the plane's new position.

You observe that it takes longer. The diagram (Fig. 1) illustrates a plane traveling from left to right as the horizontal line. It takes a time t for the stone to drop. The line will be vt long, where v is the velocity of the plane.

The stationary observer, indicated by the circle, observes that the time is $t + t'$, where t' is the time it takes light to get back to the observer. This would be vt/c.

Note that for a standard airliner traveling at about 500 mph, this value is about $7.5 \times 10^{-7} t$. This is not observable by any ordinary means. In this example it will be a very small amount longer, but it will be longer, and it gets much more significant if the vehicle travels much faster so that it is farther away.

This means that the physics observed in the vehicle is different from that of the observer. This is contrary to Einstein's theory. How can this apparent dilemma be resolved? What is the answer to the riddle?

The answer is that time slows down in frames that move, have a velocity, and the higher the velocity, the slower the time. This has been proven in a number of ways. One was the use of atomic clocks on the ground and in a transcontinental aircraft. The time it took for the flight across the country was recorded on both clocks. The traveling clock showed that it took less time; time on the plane slowed down. The difference between the times recorded by the two clocks was significant and larger than the uncertainty in the measurements.

Time also slows down in regions of high gravity as a consequence of the law of general relativity. This is too complicated to try to explain. Einstein himself needed two years to learn (from his wife) the proper mathematics to make the calculations.

One of the experiments that proved him correct occurred during a solar eclipse. The famous theoretical physicist, Sir Arthur Eddington, was asked by reporters at that event whether it was true that only three people in the world understood general relativity. He paused, wrinkled his brow and thought. The reporters urged him not to be modest. He replied, "On the contrary, I am trying to think of the third." So I will not even try. But let me cite two experiments.

The experiment observed by Eddington and colleagues was a measurement of the bending of light rays from different stars by the gravity of the sun. Again, experiment and theory were in agreement. Finally, the duration of a full orbit of the planet Mercury was measured. It differed from classical calculations of orbital mechanics, but not from relativistic calculations. The difference is small and not seen with other planets because they are not as much influenced by the sun's gravity.

Spectroscopy

Spectroscopy is the science of measuring optical spectra in order to determine the structure of different forms of matter. It was an extremely important tool for determining the nature of the atom, and it is used in chemistry, medical, forensic, and other labs to identify various materials. It probably started with Grimaldi.

In the middle of the 17th century, Marci, Grimaldi, Hooke, Descartes, and most notably Newton were investigating colors. At that time, they did not understand colors, although they had been observed as coming from white light by Seneca during the first century A.D. In fact, before the work of Newton with prisms, it was thought that a prism actually produced colors, not just separated them.

Newton used the sun as a source shining through a small hole in a dark shade. It went from there through the prism and onto the opposite wall. There was a spectrum, an array of colors. Newton, of course, believed avidly in the corpuscular theory of light. Therefore it was not so surprising, but rather interesting, that his first explanation was the same as a curve in baseball: the globs of light were spinning and following curved paths of different curvatures. This conjecture would not stand the test of his own investigations, and he finally came to the conclusion that light was not homogeneous, but consists of "difform rays, some of which are more refrangible than others." In modern English this is "different rays, some of which refract more than others."

It was almost a century later before spectral lines were observed by Thomas Melvill. He used a flame, a pinhole, and his eye. He dropped various chemicals into the flame and saw "all sorts of rays, … but not in equal quantities; the yellow being vastly more copious than all the rest put together." We know today that what he saw mostly was the sodium d lines, which are yellow. Then Wollaston observed lines at the base of a flame and Fraunhofer observed the lines from the sun that are named after him.

The next step was made by J. W. F. Herschel, who stated that the bright spectral lines were a means of detecting small quantities of materials. We were almost at recognizing spectroscopy as an identifier. It was William H. Fox who stated that every spectral line indicates a specific chemical compound.

Then came photography and diffraction gratings and more and more identification of what the spectra really are. Spectroscopy was then used to measure and identify the composition of the sun, unravel the structure of the atom, identify chemical compounds, and some of the many applications described elsewhere in this book.

The Michelson-Morley Experiment

In 1864, J. Clerk Maxwell presented his famous four equations describing electromagnetic fields and waves: they describe
light. It was one of the highlights of physics, a uniform theory of electromagnetism.
As they were studied and applied, it seemed
that they had an inherent asymmetry. That
is, they predicted different things in different frames of reference.

For example, a person traveling toward
a light source should measure light at a
higher velocity than one at rest or traveling
from the source. This implies an absolute
frame of reference. Michelson, the first

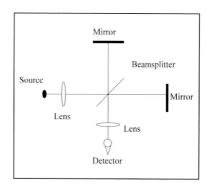

Figure 2 Michelson interferometer.

American to win a Nobel prize, and his colleague, Morley, set up an experiment to
find this frame. It consisted of a Michelson interferometer, which he invented for
the purpose. They started their experiments in 1885 and had them refined by 1900.
The instrument is shown schematically in Fig. 2 for convenience, and is described
in more detail in Chapter 2. Simply, light comes from a source and is collimated by
a lens. It is divided into two beams by the beamsplitter. Each beam goes to its re-
spective mirror and is returned to the beamsplitter. The beamsplitter then operates
as a beam combiner and sends the two overlapping collimated beams to the detector
lens, which focuses the light to a spot on the detector. The two mirrors can then be
set so there is complete destructive interference on the detector, and there will be no
light sensed. This means that the two paths are identical, and light takes exactly the
same time to travel each path.

Michelson put the interferometer on a large concrete slab and mounted it on a
pool of mercury. Assume that the interferometer moves parallel to the line from the
source to the beamsplitter because of the motion of the Earth. Then the time difference for the two paths can be found to be

$$\delta t = \frac{Lv^2}{c^3}.$$

There is a difference! Note that the Earth travels about the sun at 3×10^4 m per
second, so this difference is about 3×10^{-17} for a path of one meter. The experiment
was repeated many times over a period of more than six months, with the apparatus
in different orientations. They found absolutley no shift, and they were disap-
pointed. But this surely helped set the stage for Einstein's remarkable theory of
relativity.

Appendix A

Sizes of Things

The reader needs to know some fundamental ideas about optics to understand some of the instruments and phenomena described in this book. It is not necessary to read through them all now, but reference can be made as each individual instrument or phenomenon is described.

Numbers

This book is about devices and phenomena, about technology. Technology cannot exist without numbers, and numbers are described in all sorts of ways. In everyday life, a large number such as 1,234,567,899 is written as a string of numbers, usually with commas separating every three numbers for ease of reading.

In scientific notation that number is written as 1.234567899×10^9, where 10^9 means one billion, 1,000,000,000. So if 1.234567899 is multiplied by 1,000,000,000, the result is 1,234,567,899. This notation allows the precision of values to be indicated.

For instance, the speed of light is 2.99792458×10^5 km per second. The number given this way means that all those digits are significant. If it were known less accurately, the number would be specified, for instance, as 2.99×10^5 km per second. And, to put the icing on the cake, if the value were specified as 2.990×10^5 it means that it is known more accurately than if it is specified as 2.99×10^5. The zero is significant in the enumeration.

Scientific notation also uses prefixes like "milli" and "kilo" to modify numbers and units. Table 1 provides a list of useful prefixes.

Our national budget is now up over a trillion dollars, that is tera (terror?) dollars, or T\$. We also can see now what an attoboy is worth, 10^{-18} boy. That's not much of a compliment!

The Sizes of Things

Optics deals with very small dimensions as well as very large dimensions. This section gives some ideas of these different dimensions and the units that are used to describe them.

The wavelengths of visible light range from 0.3 μm for violet light to 0.8 μm for red light. How small is this? Well, 1 μm (micrometer) is a millionth of a meter, and a meter is a little larger than a yard—39 inches actually.

Table 1 Numerical prefixes.

Symbol	Name	Common Name	Exponent of 10
E	exa		18
P	peta		15
T	tera	trillion	12
G	giga	billion	9
M	mega	million	6
k	kilo	thousand	3
h	hecto	hundred	2
da	deca	ten	1
d	deci	tenth	−1
c	centi	hundredth	−2
m	milli	thousandth	−3
μ	micro	millionth	−6
n	nano	billionth	−9
p	pico	trillionth	−12
f	femto		−15
a	atto		−18

Yellow light at 0.5 μm is much smaller than a human hair and the fibers in the web of a black widow spider. In fact, there are about 100 waves of yellow light in an average human hair. Yellow light is also described as having a wavelength of 500 nm.

A nanometer, nm, is one-thousandth of a micrometer, that is, one billionth of a meter. A typical atom is about 5 nm in diameter. These are small dimensions.

In the midrange of dimensions are the meter, used in the metric system of units, and the kilometer, which is one thousand meters. A kilometer, km, is approximately one-half a mile, actually 0.6113 mile, and a mile is 1.609344 km. Clearly, the approximations of 0.6 km per mile and 1.6 mile per km are pretty good. The meter is actually 39.3700 inches, but the approximation of 39 inches is less than 1% in error. The centimeter, one one-hundredth of a meter, is 1/2.54 (0.3937) inch; there are 2.54 centimeters in an inch. There are 25.4 millimeters, one thousandth of a meter, in an inch. There are 30.48 centimeters in a foot. A nautical mile is 1.852 km.

Astronomy deals with large dimensions. These distances are often described in terms of light years and parsecs. A light year is the distance that light travels in a year. The speed of light is described below and is approximately 300,000 km per second or 186,000 miles per second. There are 365 days in a year, 24 hours in a day, 60 minutes in an hour and 60 seconds in a minute, or $365 \times 24 \times 60 \times 60 = 31,536,000$ seconds in a year. So a light year is 9,460,800,000,000 km (= 9.4608×10^{12} km) or

5,865,696,000,000 miles = (5.865696×10^{12} mi.). That is a long way! Note that the sun is only 8 light minutes away, 46.9×10^{12} miles. An astronomical unit is 1,495,978,70×10^8 kilometers. A parsec is 206.265 AU = 3.0857×10^{13} km.

Speed and Velocity

Speed is a measure of how fast something moves, and velocity adds to speed a direction. That is, velocity is speed in a specific direction. The English system of units typically uses feet per second and miles per hour. The metric system most frequently uses meters per second and kilometers per hour. Since there are 5280 feet in a mile and 3600 seconds in an hour, one mile per hour is equal to 1.467 feet per second. The common speed of 60 mph converts to 88 feet per second. Since there are 1.6 km in a mile, 60 mph is equal to 96 kilometer per hour, or almost 100 kilometers per hour (with 4% error).

Angular Measure

Angles are measured in a number of ways. Perhaps the most common is a degree, but it is not always the most convenient. There are 360 degrees in a circle, there are 60 arcminutes in a degree and there are 60 arcseconds in an arcminute. So we find that there are 21,600 arcminutes in a circle and 1,296,000 arcseconds in the same circle.

Angles are also measured in terms of radians. There are 2π (6.283185307) radians in a circle. Smaller angles are described in terms of milliradians (one-thousandth of a radian) and microradians (one millionth of a radian).

Temperature

Some of the devices described in this book depend upon the temperature of a body. Temperature is a measure of the average kinetic energy of a material. The temperature scale used most often in the U.S. is the Fahrenheit scale. In this scale, water freezes at 32°F and boils at 212°F.

In most of the rest of the world, the Centigrade or Celsius scale is used. In it, water freezes at 0°C and boils at 100°C. Since there are 180° between freezing and boiling in the Fahrenheit scale and only 100 in the Celsius scale, a Fahrenheit degree is only 5/9 of a Celsius degree.

Absolute zero, the state at which there is absolutely no molecular motion, no temperature, so to speak, is –459°F and –273°C, but it is also measured in the Reaumer and Kelvin scales. Each defines absolute zero to be 0 R and 0 K, respectively. Thus, a Fahrenheit temperature is 459 degrees smaller than a Reaumur temperature. Water freezes at 459 R and at 273 K.

Table 2 shows some common temperatures on these four scales.

Table 2 Temperature-scale comparisons.

Kelvin	Centigrade	Rankine	Fahrenheit	
373	100	671	212	Boiling Water
310	37	557.6	98.6	Body Temperature
295	22	531	72	Room Temperature
273	0	491	32	Freezing Water
77	−196	139	−320	Liquid nitrogen
				Cold shoulder
0	−273	0	−459	Absolute Zero

Appendix B

Information Sources

The main source for information about the applications was several monthly magazines that are semitechnical. They are sometimes called "throwaways." The information is usually presented without review and by science writers rather than scientists. I found this the proper source for most of these applications for a book intended for nonscientists. I have found some articles in more technical publications, written my own versions of the writeups, and often used the pictures directly. I am indebted to the publishers of these periodicals for permission to use this information and especially the pictures. The other source of information was standard textbooks and monographs. These were the main source for information in the Basics, Instruments, and Nature sections of the book. I list here the details of the publishers for any who would like to get more information.

Magazines

Photonics Spectra
Laurin Publishing Company
PO Box 4949
Berkshire Common
Pittsfield, MA 01202

Biophotonics International
Laurin Publishing Company
PO Box 4949
Berkshire Common
Pittsfield, MA 01202

SPIE
PO Box 10
Bellingham, WA 98227-0010
360-676-3290

Laser Focus World
Pennwell Publishers
1421 S Sheridan Rd
Tulsa, OK 74112

Optics and Photonics News
The Optical Society of America
2010 Massachusetts Avenue, NW
Washington DC 20036-1023
800-762-6960

NASA Tech Briefs
APBI.Net
1466 Broadway, STE 910
New York, NY 10036

The text references are organized below according to the different chapters of the book.

Basics

Two general texts that cover both geometrical and physical optics, with a little bit about photons, are

Jenkins, F. A., and White, H. E., *Fundamentals of Optics*, Third Edition, McGraw Hill, 1957.

Strong, J. D., *Concepts of Classical Optics*, W. H. Freeman and Company, 1958.

The classical and advanced treatment of the electromagnetic theory of optics is

Born, M., and Wolf, E., *Principles of Optics*, Pergamon, 1959.

Three modern texts on the process of optical design, but with descriptions of lenses, binoculars, microscopes, telescopes, and other instruments:

Smith, W. J., *Modern Optical Engineering*, Second Edition, McGraw Hill, 1990.

Shannon, R. R., *The Art and Science of Optical Design*, Cambridge University Press, 1997.

Fischer, R E., and Tadic-Galeb, B., *Optical System Design*, McGraw Hill, 2000.

Two good books on polarization:

Shurcliff, W., *Polarized Light*, Harvard University Press, 1962.

Collet, E., *Polarized Light: Fundamentals and Applications*, Marcel Decker, 1992.

A delightful lay treatment of quantum electrodynamics:

Feynman, R. P., *QED: The Strange Theory of Light and Matter*, Princeton University Press, 1985.

The two best books on scattering:

Van de Hulst, H. C., *Light Scattering by Small Particles*, Dover Publications, 1981.

Bohren, C. F., and Huffman, D. R., *Absorption and Scattering of Light by Small Particles*, John Wiley & Sons.

An old but useful book on photometry, including the response of the eye:

Walsh, J. W. T., *Photometry*, Dover Publications, Third Edition, 1958.

Books on radiometry that also include a little photometry:

Wolfe, W. L., *Introduction to Radiometry*, SPIE Press, 1998.
McCluney, R., *Introduction to Radiometry and Photometry*, Artech House, 1994.
Wyatt, C. L., *Radiometric System Design*, Macmillan, 1987.

Instruments

Probably still the best introduction to spectrometry is:

Sawyer, R. A., *Experimental Spectroscopy*, Dover Publications, 1963.

Three good books on holography:

Collier, R. J., Burckhardt, C. B., and Lin, L. H., *Optical Holography*, Academic Press, 1971.
Hariharan, P., *Optical Holography: Principles, Techniques and Applications*, Cambridge University Press, 1996.
Caulfield, H. J., *Handbook of Optical Holography*, Academic Press, 1979.

Two oldies but goodies on interferometry:

Tolansky, S., *An Introduction to Interferometers*, John Wiley and Sons, 1973.
Candler, C., *Modern Interferometers*, Hilger and Watts, 1950.

This father-and-son book has sections on interferometers, microscopes, and other instruments:

Malacara, D., and Malacara, Z., *Handbook of Lens Design*, Marcel Dekker, 1994.

These two are good on cameras and their lenses:

Grimm, T., and Grimm, M., *The Basic Book of Photography*, Plume, 1997.
Kingslake, R., *A History of the Photographic Lens*, Academic Press, 1989.

This four-volume, foot-thick tome covers almost everything in optics:

Bass, M., Van Stryland, E., Williams, D., Wolfe, W., *Handbook of Optics*, McGraw Hill, 1995.

Nature

Minnaert, M., *The Nature of Light and Colour in the Open Air*, Dover Publications, 1954.

Corliss, W. R., *Rare Halos, Mirages, Anomalous Rainbows, and Related Electromagnetic Phenomena*, Glen Arm Sourcebook Project (definitely not a beginning book).

Critical Experiments in Physics

Brophy, J. D., *The Achievement of Galileo*, Griffon House, 2001.
Galilei, Galileo, *Dialogue Concerning the Two World Systems, Ptolemaic and Copernican*, University of California Press, 1967 (Galileo's own account).
Planck, M., *The Origin and Development of the Quantum Theory*, Clarendon Press, 1922 (his Nobel prize address).
Planck, M., *The Theory of Heat Radiation*, P. Blakiston Son and Company, 1914.

An introductory but, of necessity, a very mathematical treatment:

Resnick, R., *Introduction to Special Relativity*, John Wiley and Son, 1968.

A nice historical treatment of most of physics, that includes descriptions of these experiments and their interpretations:

Ripley, J. P., *The Elements and Structure of the Physical Sciences*, Wiley, 1964.

Two books on the Big Bang:

Fox, K. C., *The Big Bang Theory: What It Is, Where It Came from, and Why It Works*, Wiley, 2002.
Harland, D. M., *The Big Bang: A View from the 21st Century*, Springer, 2003.

A modern source of additional information is the internet. One nice site is of the Large Binocular Telescope Observatory, which can be found by searching on those four words on any search engine. It has pictures of the insides and outside, the staff and more. A similar site can be found by searching on "Palomar Telescope." It describes all of the telescopes on the mountain as well as the Hale, which is described in this book. A search on "optical telescopes" will yield many places to buy them, but also sites like *Wikipedia,* which is a free, online encyclopedia and NAOA, the National Association for Optical Astronomy have articles on many telescopes. Similar results will be found for searches on microscopes, interferometers, and most other optical instruments. Searches for the different applications are more involved. I tried "infrared forensics" and got a list of suppliers of infrared cameras, but also some articles on using infrared techniques for detecting forgeries. Searching on "infrared and police" provided a *Wikipedia* article and several more proclaiming that it was legal to view houses to search for marijuana and to scan license plates. Searching for more sites requires whatever imagination you can muster. If all else fails, ask a teenager!

Glossary

Anamorphic lens: a lens that has different magnifications in different orientations, a cylindrical lens, for example.

Aspheres: circularly symmetric lenses or mirrors that have concave or convex surfaces that are not spherical.

Astigmatism: an image aberration caused by different magnifications in different directions, generally from off-axis sources.

Avalanche diodes: diode detectors with high applied voltages that cause electron multiplication in the diode and thereby increase efficiency.

Baud: a unit of data rate, one byte per second.

Beam combiner: same as a beamsplitter, but combines beams.

Beamsplitter: a device that separates a single beam into two or more beams.

Binary optics: optical elements that control the wavefront by diffraction rather than refraction; also called diffractive optics.

Bit: a single piece of information, a binary digit, a one or a zero.

Blackbody: an idealized radiator that emits all the radiation possible for the temperature of the body.

Byte: eight bits.

CAD: computer-aided design, the modern way to do drafting with a computer.

CAT: computer-analyzed tomography. A technique that obtains three-dimensional imagery by using x rays at a number of different angles and from these different angles mathematically reconstructing the image.

CD: compact disk. One of a variety of circular disks, about 4.5 inches in diameter, that store data.

CD-R: a read-only CD.

CD-RW: a readable and writable CD.

Colposcope: an optical device for inspecting the cervix.

Conduction: the act of moving something in space, often electricity, but also heat and other things.

Conductor: a material that conducts electronic current in its stable state, such as a copper wire, also heat and other conductors.

Dichroic: applied to beamsplitters and lenses, meaning one color is transmitted and a different one is reflected. Also called dichromatic.

Dipoles: a combination of a positive and a negative charge somewhat separated from each other.

Doping: the process of introducing specific impurities into otherwise pure crystals and detectors.

Double-beam spectrometer: a type of spectrometer that automatically corrects for the source spectrum.

Double-pass spectrometer: a type of spectrometer that uses the dispersing element twice.

Double-monochromator: a type of spectrometer that uses two dispersing elements.

Electromagnetic field: a region in which there is influence from an electrical source. A radio wave, from the transmitter to the receiver, is an electromagnetic field.

Electronic conduction: the motion of electrons along a conductor.

Exit pupil: the pupil that is at the output of the optics, as with a pair of binoculars.

Eyepiece: a lens on a telescope, microscope, or binoculars that relays the image to the eye.

Fill factor: the ratio of the sensitive area to the total area of a detector array.

Frame grabber: a device that immediately captures and stores whatever TV frame is being displayed.

Gas: a substance consisting of molecules or atoms free to move about with respect to each other, and rotate and vibrate.

GPS: global positioning system. A system that uses a number of satellites and triangulation to determine the position of objects on the ground.

GRIN: GRadient INdex lens, which controls the wave front by a variation in refractive index rather than shape.

Hydrophone: a device for locating sound underwater.

Insulator: a material that does not conduct electronic current, like salt or cotton.

Incident (on): refers to light impinging on an object, often a plane.

Ionic conduction: the motion of ions along a material.

Ischemic: a restricted blood flow or lack of blood flow.

LED: light-emitting diode, a small emitter of light.

Metal: an example of a conductor.

Monochromatic: describing light of a single color, single wavelength, or a single frequency. Actually, light cannot be of exactly one frequency; there is always a narrow band. It is often called quasi-monochromatic light, but that nuance is not used here.

Monochromator: the part of the spectrometer that separates the colors.

MRI: magnetic resonance imagery. A technique similar to x rays, but one that uses magnetic fields.

Ocular: same as an eyepiece.

Offner relay: a relay with unit magnification, consisting of a concave and a convex mirror. It produces a ring field with almost all aberrations completely corrected.

pH: percent hydrogen ion. A measure of acidity and alkalinity. A pH of 7 is neutral.

Phase plate: a device that shifts the phase of a wave.

Photoresist: a material that can be affected by light. Typically, it is resistant to an appropriate chemical where its has been illuminated, but is dissolved by the chemical where it is not exposed.

Pixel: a picture element, one of many little elementary parts of an image. In an LED display, each LED is a pixel.

Prism: an optical element that may either deflect a beam by refraction or disperse a beam into its component colors.

Pupil: an image of a stop.

Quantum efficiency: a measure of how many electrons are generated in a detector for each incident photon.

RAM: random-access memory. A form of digital memory allowing data to be changed.

Raster scan: a scan pattern that is a series of parallel lines, usually in a rectangular pattern.

Real image: an image formed by the intersection of real rays.

Residual strain: when a force of any kind is applied to an object, it gets strained, and the structure is skewed from its normal state. This can often be relaxed by the application of heat, but some strain may remain, the residual strain.

Ritchey-Chretien: a two-mirror telescope of the Cassegrain type in which both mirrors are aspheric.

ROM: read-only memory. A memory that cannot be overwritten or changed.

Semiconductor: a material that conducts electronic current only if some other energy is applied, materials like silicon or gallium arsenide.

Solid: a material that is not a liquid or gas.

Spatial filter: a device to adjust the cross section or other spatial aspects of a beam of light.

Spectrometer: a device for obtaining the spectrum of a material.

Spectrum: a graph or other indication of how much light there is at each frequency or wavelength.

Stop: a physical object that limits the size of a beam, as in aperture stop.

Thermal expansion: the process by which an object increases its size as it is heated.

Tomography: the process of inferring a three-dimensional image by the use of many images taken at different angles.

Uncertainty principle: a principle enunciated by Werner Heisenberg that no two special variables can be known to an accuracy better than a certain value. For instance, the uncertainty in time multiplied by the uncertainty in energy cannot be less than about the value of Planck's constant. The same for the uncertainties in momentum and position.

Valence: a measure of the number of extra or missing electrons in an outer orbit from the stable number of 8 or 2.

Vignetting: partial masking of the optical field of view by some of the optical elements.

Virtual image: an image formed where real rays do not intersect. An example is shown in Fig. 1, where S shows the real image at the convergence of rays; S' is the virtual image. It cannot be real, because it isn't there.

Voltage divider network: a common circuit used for infrared detectors. Voltage is applied by a battery or equivalent at the left, and that voltage is then divided proportionally to the two resistors, one of which is usually the detector (Fig. 2).

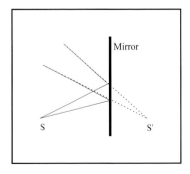

Figure 1 Virtual image.

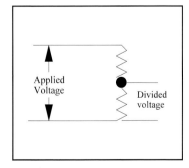

Figure 2 Voltage divider.

William (Bill) L. Wolfe was born in Yonkers, NY, at a very early age. He attended Bucknell University in Lewisburg, PA, where he recently attended his 50th reunion. He graduated cum laude with a B.S. in physics. He went on to The University of Michigan, where he worked bull time at The Institute of Science and Technology, taught at the university's Dearborn campus, and earned an M.S. in physics and an M.S.E. in electrical engineering. In 1966, he went to Honeywell's Radiation Center in Lexington, MA, where he was Chief Engineer and Department Manager of the Electro-optics Department; he also taught at Northeastern University. In 1969, he moved to Tucson, where he became Professor of Optical Science in the Optical Sciences Center of The University of Arizona. He remained in that position until 1996, when he became Professor Meritless (officially). He is a Fellow of both OSA and SPIE, served on many committees for both and was President of SPIE in 1989. In 1999, he was awarded the gold medal of SPIE for his work on handbooks and optical material measurements and for mentoring "a remarkable number of students" in optics. Since his retirement, he has written two books on infrared system design—one on radiometry and one on imaging spectrometers. He has also caught and released an incredible number of gorgeous trout and solved many, but not all, crossword puzzles. He has been wonderfully supported for 50 years by his trophy wife, Mary Lou. They raised three children and are now enjoying six grandchildren.